C000056648

NAOMI JACOB

Gollantz:
London, Paris, Milan

THE GOLLANTZ SAGA 6

Futura

A *Futura* Book

Copyright © Naomi Jacob 1948

First published in Great Britain in 1948

New hardback edition published in 1985
by Judy Piatkus (Publishers) Limited

This edition published in 1985
by Futura Publications, a Division of
Macdonald & Co (Publishers) Ltd
London & Sydney

ISBN 0 7088 2693 8

Printed and bound in Great Britain by
Collins, Glasgow

Futura Publications
A Division of
Macdonald & Co (Publishers) Ltd
Maxwell House
74 Worship Street
London EC2A 2EN

A BPCC plc Company

To
Isabella and Dario
My kind friends
MICKIE

Fasano, 1948

BOOK ONE

CHAPTER ONE

'THAT'S the lot, sir.'

'Very good, S'gt.-Major.' Emmanuel sighed. 'It takes more energy to wind up a camp than to run one, I believe.'

'Very often the way with things, sir.'

'Queer to think that in less than a week this place will be deserted. We've been here a long time, eh, Watkins?'

'Best part o' three years, sir. If I might say so, we've not made too bad a go of it. Plenty of the men wish they weren't goin' home again.'

Emmanuel nodded. 'They say that, possibly they believe it. They'll feel differently when they get back. Poor devils, some of them haven't much to go back to, from what I hear. The whole country was a battle ground.'

'They've nothing much to thank "Musso" for!'

'Oh well, he paid for his idiocy. Thanks, S'gt.-Major, that's really the last of those infernal forms. Good night. You might find Moroni and send him to me, will you?'

'Very good, sir, and good night.'

The door closed, and Emmanuel stretched his long legs and lay back with closed eyes. He was tired ; winding up a P.O.W. camp entailed so much work, so much attention to details which appeared unimportant. His eyes felt weary with the constant scanning of lists, checking equipment, accounting for beds, blankets, cooking-stoves and the like.

Slowly, almost unwillingly, he opened his eyes and surveyed the shabby little room which had been his office for nearly three years. It had been like an oven in summer and filled with the stuffy, heavy heat of an oil stove in the winter. Yet he had come to have an affection for the place, as he had for the whole camp. He had come there wearing a uniform which was almost new ; he glanced at his cuffs bound with leather. It was old enough now, in all conscience !

Then he'd been Lieutenant Gollantz. Last month he had been told that he could put up a major's crown in place of the three 'pips' to which he had attained. How long ago it seemed since that day when he had first worn the uniform and heavy boots of a private soldier! His training lingered only vaguely in his mind, as did the court-martial where, despite everything, he felt that he had been given a particularly square deal.

There had been something strange about that business when he was recalled, because they were being rushed overseas and the telegram which had been sent to him had never been delivered. He had missed the trooper, and that and the fact that he had struck a sergeant who insulted him had resulted in a court-martial.

Remembering it all, Emmanuel frowned, his mouth twisted a little. Had he been right in suspecting that his brother Julian had been involved in the loss of the telegram? Or was it only that his hatred of Julian made him imaginative and biassed?

Anyway, it was all over, and he felt that he had vindicated himself in North Africa. Not that he'd done anything spectacular, or particularly brilliant; chiefly, he felt, because his officer—they'd called him 'Reggie'—had been well disposed towards him, and had been able to write reports which were not only convincing but admirably expressed.

Anyway, he had been given his decoration and his commission. Then the unexpected air raid in Alex when he had been wounded, the long weeks in hospital, weeks filled with pain, weakness and, later, with complete boredom, had faded into a dim memory. The voyage home, medical boards, and finally he had been put in charge of a P.O.W. camp for Italian prisoners.

How nervous he had been, how depressing he had found the camp, and what a godsend Sergeant-Major Watkins had been—what a tower of strength! Together they had worked and planned, and slowly the Italians had become interested in making the camp more attractive; they had shown real ingenuity in building rockeries, making paths, fences, railings and the like. They had scoured the neighbourhood for climbing plants, trails of ivy, violet and primrose roots.

Captain Harshire, who had gone only that morning had disapproved; he had even grumbled openly that the place 'doesn't look like a P.O.W. camp at all!'

Emmanuel had asked, 'How should a P.O.W. camp look?'

Harshire had replied, 'Well, if I may say so, not like Kew Gardens. In my opinion, prisoners should be treated like prisoners, not trained to become amateur gardeners. I may be wrong, but——'

'I think that you *are* wrong,' Emmanuel had said gently, and Harshire, noting the change of tone, had deemed it best to say no more.

Bradley and Francis, the junior officers, had developed tremendous keenness for the camp; they were both energetic youngsters, with ideas and enthusiasm, both full of admiration for Emmanuel's ideas, and possessing respect for his determination that discipline must be maintained.

Not that there had been much difficulty, the Italians had a philosophy which they practised; they were prisoners, they were in a foreign land separated from their families. Moodiness, flashes of insubordination and disobedience only resulted in life being decidedly uncomfortable.

In addition these things did nothing to bring their release nearer. It was obviously better to conform to rules, to obey orders, and to gain such small privileges as might be granted to men of good behaviour.

There had been one or two cases which presented difficulties, such as when Bruno Costa and Dante Cicio were found to be meeting two village girls every time the opportunity offered. They were both young, strapping fellows; they had picked up a little English, which they delighted to speak, and they were—as Emmanuel realized—longing to talk once again to girls of their own age.

He had sent for them both, and had spoken to them at length and with considerable force in their own language. They had been sulky; Costa had been on the defensive, but slowly Emmanuel's complete reasonableness had broken down their antagonism. He had realized that they were both young, well-built, healthy young men with healthy appetites. They had stood before him. Costa a red-haired Italian from Venice. Cicio a more stolid and less good-looking fellow from Livorno. Both had been prisoners for nearly three years, first in Africa, and later they had been transferred to the camp where Emmanuel was in charge.

'How old are you?' Emmanuel had asked Costa.

'Twenty-two, Commandante.'

'And you, Cicio?'

'Twenty-three, Commandante.'

'Married?'

Costa had nodded. 'I was married three months before I was taken prisoner, Commandante.'

Cicio had admitted that he was merely engaged, adding that he had known Maria for five years.

Emmanuel had laid the tips of his long fingers together, in the way which was so like his grandfather's. His face was very grave, but in it neither of the Italians found any anger. When he had spoken his voice was even, and filled with reasonable kindliness.

9

He had said. 'Listen, both of you. You are here living un-natural lives; that is because this life which we lead here is the result, or one of the results, of war, and war in itself is not a natural thing. It is not even a reasonable thing.' He had glanced at the papers which lay at his elbow. 'You, Costa, are a gondo-lier; you, Cicio, I see, a fisherman. Both good free lives, with the open sea—or the lagoon, and it is like a sea, is it not so? But even the sea and the lagoon must be restrained. Kept within bounds, you understand.

'You have imagined that when you were taken prisoner that the war was over for you both. Indeed it was, so far as fighting was concerned. Now you have to fight—yourselves Things which may be natural, which may be right and good outside a prisoner-of-war camp, cannot be allowed inside one. You are both—of this I am certain—men of the world, so it is not neces-sary for me to enlarge on this matter. In Venice, Costa, your wife waits for you, in Livorno there is the Signorina Maria longing for your return, Cicio. For their sakes, it is better that you do not walk and talk with English girls.

'Lonely men are often reckless men, men who act without thought of consequences. Then in this camp there are rules. Everyone must obey those rules. I obey them, your officers obey them, the sergeants obey them—this also applies to you. Rules must be obeyed.

'You are still soldiers, you are still Italian soldiers, and you must be able to return to your wives and sweethearts with clear eyes and clean hearts. This is what you can still do—for the honour of your country.

'In the life of all soldiers there must be restraint. You are still soldiers. There, I have said enough. Believe me that I under-stand, I even sympathize—for I know how you must long for the bright eyes, the kind voices, the gentle hands which belong to the women you love. I say, Costa . . . Cicio . . . be patient. The day will not be long in coming. The lagoon will still be there, your gondola like a black swan will be waiting, and—your wife, too, will be waiting. Cicio, there in poor Livorno there is much to be done, but there is still the blue sea, the saltness on your lips when the wind blows from the sea . . . and there will be also your sweetheart waiting.

'This time, my soldiers, there will be no punishment. And,' he had smiled at them, that charming smile which seemed to light up his whole face, 'there will be no second time! I have great trust in you both.'

When they had gone, Hawkins had said, 'My word, sir, I'd give a lot to be able to patter to them like what you do. Must mike a difference, say what you like. It's a great gift, sir, to have langwidges.'

The matter of Carlo, the big ironworker from Turin, had been more difficult. Carlo longed for strong drink, and a great deal of it. He had been sent to work on a farm, and some teetotal labourer had given him his beer at lunchtime. The craving for more had grown, and he had stolen from a public-house where the prisoners had been sent to build a wall under the direction of a British workman. Carlo staggered home, and when one of the guards noticed his condition and put him under arrest he had grown violent.

He had appeared before Emmanuel looking very much the worse for wear. It was obvious that he believed that he would get off lightly, and the torrent of furious contempt which Emmanuel hurled at him almost caused him to stagger backwards.

He was told that he was a bad soldier, that he had no knowledge of either self-restraint or discipline, and 'what is worst of all, at a time when your nation needs every one of her sons to uphold her dignity and her prestige, you, Carlo Beltoni, betray her. The misfortunes of Italy are not sufficient, another must be added—that you have the right to call yourself an Italian!'

The huge man stared, his mouth agape, and finally burst into tears. Carlo Beltoni fought down his desire for strong drink.

Emmanuel often said of the Italians, 'An old race, but a young people, frequently very *naughty,* rarely actually wicked.'

Emmanuel's thoughts were broken by a knock on the door, and as it opened the voice of Sergeant-Major Watkins said:

'Private Guido Moroni, sir.'

Guido entered and stood to attention before Emmanuel's desk.

Emmanuel looked up and smiled. 'Sit down, Guido. I want to talk to you.'

The little Italian, who had once looked like some round-faced cherub, sat down, his work-worn hands hanging between his knees. His uniform was shabby, his hair was cut very short, the waves which he had once cultivated so carefully had vanished. He looked healthy enough, but thin and hard. There only remained a memory of the one-time exquisite, the look of dog-like devotion in his eyes when they rested on Emmanuel's face.

Emmanuel said, 'Well, Guido, it's almost over, and you're going home. You're glad, aren't you?'

'I have been at home ever since I was admitted to this camp. My home is where Emmanuel Gollantz happens to be,' Guido said. He sat silent for a moment, then asked with anxiety in his voice, 'And you will return to Milano?'

'I don't know—yet. Oh, I shall come back to see how things are. We've got to face it, Guido, there may be little or nothing left. We may not have a gallery any more, no pictures—nothing.'

'Have no fears. Before I left, as I told you, everything that was the most choicest was hidden in the cellars, and a wall built in—which was made to appear old and dirty—to hide them. Oh, you will find very much that is good, Emmanuel.'

He watched the face of the man for whom he had such a complete and wholehearted admiration as he spoke. Emmanuel was silent, twisting a pencil in his long, fine fingers, frowning a little.

Guido thought, 'When I first knew him he was young; his hair was black as the darkest night; he was twenty-seven, I think. Now, at the temples his hair is like snow, the rest is grey. Sometimes his face looks grey also. I have known him when he was filled with misery, when he was poor, when he lost the one woman who has ever filled—completely filled—his heart. I have known him at times of great and wonderful success, when he was acclaimed as being the greatest expert, the most knowing man in the business. Now, how old is he—this man I love so dearly? He is nearly fifty; his son is nearly a grown man. Simeon is more than twenty and as tall as his father.

'He has not enjoyed the war as have some men, he has not enjoyed this camp, but it has been an escape from the world of which he is beginning to be a little afraid. Here he has felt safe, at least. Now he wonders what he will find in the new world which has been made out of all this blood, these dead men and ruined houses. He would have hoped for a "brave new world"—he knows that it will not even be "new", it will be made out of the shreds and ruins of the old. My poor fine Emmanuel!'

Emmanuel put down the pencil and, leaning forward, began to speak.

'You see, Guido, my father is growing old. He is seventy, and for many years he has not been very strong. My mother, too, is no longer young. For a long time the business in Bond Street has been declining. There is that big house to be kept going —Ordingly—and there is also my brother, Julian——'

Guido said with suppressed passion, 'Of this one do not speak, if you do'n mind. The name is offensive to me.'

'And to me, I assure you, but he exists all the same, and he is an expensive luxury! I have always believed, and so does Sir Nathan Bernstein, that he is perfectly able to work if he wishes.

12

True, during the war he has been employed in some capacity—God knows what!—at Whitehall. He looks very well in uniform, he'll be sorry to give up wearing it. He'll retire to Ordingly, levy toll on my father, live extravagantly, indulgently—he and his wife and his son. The money will have to come from somewhere.

'I'm the third generation to be in the antique business, Guido. One day Ordingly will be mine and later Simeon's. The title will come to me, not that I particularly hanker after it, but—there it is! My younger brother, Bill, will be all right. He's clever, he was making a fair income before the war, he'll go far now he's out of the Navy. No need to worry about him.

'I have never wished to remain in London, never enjoyed working at the place in Bond Street—incidentally it's one of the few big places left undamaged in Bond Street—but,' he spoke more slowly, 'I may have to remain there. Oh, I shall come to Milano, I shall do everything in my power to—with your help —get the Gallery into working order again.' With a sudden impulsive movement he stretched out his hand to the Italian. 'I can rely on your co-operation, my dear Guido, can't I?'

'You mean,' Moroni said, 'that you wish me to return to Milano, to see how the business stands, and to work for you until that day, which will be so happy, when you can come and once more take up the work for which you are so fitted. That is, I think, what you are trying to tell me. My dear master, my always friend, my Commandante. I am as ever at your service! This is one of the things which need not be said between us— it is completely part of my nature. I remain, always your devoted and obedient Guido Moroni, as they say in business letters so excellently.'

Emmanuel straightened his shoulders, as a man might who throws off a heavy burden; he smiled, and with the smile years seemed to fall away from him. He looked younger, stronger, filled with confidence for the future. Guido too, in returning the smile, seemed to recapture something of the young man who had worked so wholeheartedly with Emmanuel in the little shop in Milano, long before old Simeon Jaffe had arrived and changed the whole course of Emmanuel's fortunes.

'Then tomorrow,' Emmanuel said, 'you will be a free man again! So far as any man is free; I think sometimes that we all go in chains, Guido.'

'That is no doubt true,' Guido agreed, 'but what is important is the quality of the chains. Heavy, rusted, bloody old chains, these only impel—no, wait!—impede movement. Fine, light, golden chains—these are different; those one will carry

13

with pride and happiness. Gold chains bind me to you, bind you to Simeon, your son—heavy chains bind us both to bloody fine but tedious old British Army. You note how improvement is my English!'

'Undoubtedly, but cut out the use of that word—bloody.'

'But this is the—one moment until I remember—ah! yes—this is the operative word of the British Army.'

'I've pointed out,' Emmanuel said dryly, 'that you are going to be quit of the Army, my dear Guido.' He rose and held out his hand. 'I'll see you before I go, and you go. Good luck, and write to me very fully from Milano. A document will be waiting for you at the British Consulate, appointing you my agent with full powers to direct affairs. I shall know that you will do everything possible, and'—again that smile which never failed to warm Guido's heart—'I shall come to see you as soon as it is humanly possible. Until then, I shall rest completely content that everything is in your hands. *A rivederci*!'

The next morning Emmanuel saw the Italians paraded for the last time. Some of them were excited, inclined to chatter nervously and with a touch of hysteria; others looked apprehensive and oppressed, as if they wondered what the new Italy might hold for them.

Lieutenant Francis, standing at Emmanuel's side, said, 'Taking them all round, sir, they look pretty well cared for, don't they?'

'Most of them have put on weight,' Emmanuel answered. 'I can remember some of them when they got here—they were like men who had completely lost heart. Their self-respect had gone. Well, if you've managed to put back a man's self-respect you've done pretty well by him.'

He spoke to them in their own language, simply and directly. He told them that they were going to find changes—changes which for some of them might seem disastrous.

'For many years you have been children, talking like parrots the words which the Fascists taught you. Now you are going home as men, men who are free. The long night of Fascismo is over, the dawn is here, and after the dawn will come the heat of the day. In the heat you must work, there will be no time for *siesta* if your country is to rise again like the Phœnix from its ashes. Sow and you will reap; forget to till the land, to tend the ground, to sow with care—and there will be no harvest. You are the men of the new Risorgimento—fight well! Here we hope that you have been as happy as men without their freedom can

14

be. We have worked together, many times we have laughed together, and I believe that we have learnt to respect each other. Always I have said that you might be *birichini*—naughty children. I have always held that to find one of you who was *cattivo*—bad and wicked—was very, very rare.'

They glanced at one another and grinned; this was one of the Commandante's stock jokes and it had worn well, but it still gained its quota of smiles.

Emmanuel continued, 'We wish you good luck wherever you may be going, whether it is to the great cities, to Milano, Turin, Genova, Rome or Napoli; to the rich farm lands of Lombardy and Tuscany, to the olive groves, to the wide fruit fields, to the factories of industry. General Eisenhower has told the world that "Italy has earned her passage", President Roosevelt and Winston Churchill have expressed their wish that Italy shall take her honourable place among the free peoples of the New Europe. *Vi auguro tutte le felicità. Andate con Dio!*'

It was over. For a moment they stood staring at the tall spare figure before them; they seemed bewildered, uncertain. The phrase 'as sheep without a shepherd' came to Emmanuel's mind. He sent a quick nod in the direction of Sergeant-Major Watkins, heard the sharp staccato order for dismissal given for the last time, heard the steady tramp of feet, then turned and walked back to his office.

Francis followed him. Emmanuel sat down and indicated to his junior that he should do the same.

'I feel that we can both do with a drink,' he said. 'Ah,' as the door opened, 'Bradley, you're just in time. In that cupboard —as if you didn't know!—you will find what is necessary. You're off this evening, Bradley? You're going to Germany, eh? And you, Francis? I forget for the moment.'

'Me, sir? I believe it's M.E. I've not got much longer to go; wish it could have been Trieste. Still—well, your very good health, sir.'

Bradley said, 'Good luck, sir. Thanks for everything. It's been a pretty good time, taking it all round.'

With that complete seriousness with which Englishmen drink each other's health and good fortune, they drank, and set down their glasses.

Emmanuel said, 'I wanted that! I'm too nervous to make speeches.'

'It was jolly good, sir—I gathered. Watching the chaps faces, they seemed to like it.'

'Their good manners are highly developed,' Emmanuel said.

There was a knock on the door. Bradley opened it, and turning asked, looking over his shoulder, 'Would you allow Moroni to speak to you for a moment, sir?'

'Moroni—yes, of course.'

Guido entered, and in some subtle way Emmanuel felt that he had changed. There was about him an air of assurance and confidence. He held his head high, his dark eyes were very bright, he walked forward with what almost amounted to a strut.

Emmanuel said, 'Ah, Guido,' then turning to the two officers he added, 'Gentlemen, may I introduce my Italian representative, Signor Moroni? Guido—'Tenente Bradley *anche* 'Tenente Francis.'

Guido clicked his heels together, bowed and said, 'Ver' mooch 'appiness for me. 'Ow do you do, very well, I 'ope.'

He turned back to Emmanuel, his eyes were shining with pleasure ; he had ceased to be a prisoner of war, he had become once again Guido, the exquisite of the Galleria, the Guido whose clothes were the admiration of all right-thinking young Milanese. Even his uniform looked suddenly less shabby!

He pulled a small packet from his tunic pocket and began to speak rapidly.

'Commandante, you may remember one Vittorio—he is from Padua, and artist of merit. Last night—for I wish to be prepared for everything—I spik with Vittorio. I tell him that I must have cards. Cards to state clearly my position. He is a good fellow, most of the night he works. I now present the work for your kind inspection! I feel that you will cry as I did . . . "Magnificent! This will be no letting down for the house which I am to represent!" Please—look!'

He handed Emmanuel a card of considerable size, on which was written so carefully that it appeared to be engraved from copperplate, the words:

SIGNOR MORONI GUIDO

Completely representing House of Gollantz.

Works of art, antique materials, china,
old gold and silver, statuary, carpets and
furniture.

Principal: Emmanuel J. Gollantz. M.C.

Headquarters: 70 Bond Street, London.

While Emmanuel studied the card, which in itself was a small work of art, Guido turned to Bradley and Francis and offered them cards, saying as he did so:

'Chentlemen, if you doan mind, the card of Moroni. Honoured to be representing the House of Gollantz, Milano, Eff at any time you weesh to obtain dignified presents for papa, mama, nono—thet is grendfather or grendmuzzer, smaller but ver' delightful gift for ver' beautiful lady, furniture for your splendid 'ome, pictures to present to the Nation's Gallery in London—so you may become great benefactor—I shell 'ave them. Only one class—*primo*! All is damn' good, like the wife of old Julius Caesar of which your Shakespeare wrote—she doan have no air of being suspicious 'anging round her, that dame! 'Appy to see you any old time!'

He drew a deep breath gustily. Emmanuel's eyes twinkled. Guido was enjoying himself.

Bradley said, 'I say, that's very decent of you.'

Guido beamed at him, 'Not a bit! Doan mention eet, my old top 'Tenente!' Conversationally, he added, 'Long time ago, when I was first of all prisoner, there was an officer who always to ozzer officers said, "Right, me old treasure." Ver' much a friendly man. But'—he shrugged his shoulders—'when I made translation, *"Mio vécchio tesoro"* appeared to miss the eye of the bull. I doan use it—I chuck it over the board, you understand?'

Bradley said, 'Perfectly. Well, good luck, Signor Moroni.'

'And now, allow me to make my leavings. Commandante, I have much business in Milano! Ha, how good that sounds, like music in my ears. I am excitable! For reason why not? One English poet writes this, "We know that the end is the best of all."

'This is the end of one chapter—now, we begin another. *Saluti*! I, Guido, go to fight the world, until it falls on its knees and weeps, saying, "This Guido is a terrible man, he has beaten us!" Commandante—come to Milano, see me again wearing my beautiful English clothes!' He indicated his shabby prisoner's uniform. 'My 'eart is still the 'eart of English gentleman, as is my spoken words, but my clothes are only bloody catastrophe!' He seized Emmanuel's hand and wrung it with great intensity, 'Best of all men! I shall work—and work better, for it will be for you. Have no fears. Gentlemen, I veesh you everything you'd like best for yourself.'

He propelled himself through the door as if already he was late for business appointments. As the door closed, Bradley said, 'He's a caution, sir, isn't he?'

Emmanuel sat down and pushed forward his glass. 'I can do with another, Francis. Yes, he's—what I suppose you might call —a caution. He came to me first a rather scruffy, not too clean

17

Milanese to help in a very small shop I had at that time. I remember how he used to clean his nails—and believe me they needed it!—with an old dagger.

'He had a predilection for eating garlic, and in moments of excitement he always breathed heavily. But he watched, he learnt, and presently he blossomed out into what he firmly believed were typical English clothes. He prides himself upon being mistaken frequently for an Englishman! I have never actually seen it happen, but he used to assure me that it was true.

'Yet, for all his little affectations, his preposterous clothes—when he could get them—he has the most loyal heart, he is completely unselfish, and he has proved his devotion to me—and to my family—many, many times. No, that's a fine fellow, believe me. Now, you want to pack and get off. Good luck to you both and thank you for everything. Gollantz, Bond Street, will always find me.'

Emmanuel stood at the door watching them go. Two pleasant lads, going off to other countries, ready for whatever fate might hold for them. In the distance he could see the prisoners—who were prisoners no longer—filing past the Sergeant-Major's office, signing themselves out of the camp, taking the first stage of their journey which should bring them at last to their homes.

The curtain was coming down on another act of his life. Behind him lay the Army, the camp, the men who had worked with him and under his orders ; before him—what was he going to find? A new world, a world with changed ideas and ideals, a world filled with restrictions and limits, a world where the people he knew were growing old. He was no longer 'Young Emmanuel', for 'Old Emmanuel' his grandfather had long since been gathered to his fathers, and he himself was definitely middle-aged.

The last of the prisoners were straggling through the gate, climbing into the truck which would take them to the station. Sergeant-Major Watkins came swinging across the camp towards him.

He saluted smartly. 'The last of them gone, sir. Sergeant Manders in charge of 'em, sir. Some of 'em were quite upset to go. Imagine it! Queer chaps, like children i' lots o' ways. Now there's just me, an' Manders, an' Corporal Harris. We're 'anding over to Ordinance immejetly. Marchin'-out orders all ready. O' course your formal " 'and over" was made yesterday. No need for you to wait, sir, if you want to get away.'

Emmanuel said, 'If I want to get away! Yes, I suppose I do,

like some of the Italians, but I'm not quite sure. Life's a queer business in these days.'

'Just so, sir,' Watkins agreed, 'but I recall an old song, "Somewhere the sun is shining"—hope we both find it, sir.'

'I hope so, too, Watkins.'

'I lay any money we do, sir! Good-bye, sir. All the best.'

CHAPTER TWO

EMMANUEL lay back in the taxi and closed his eyes. London seemed strange, unfamiliar and faintly unreal. The names on the theatre posters were new to him, there were new diversions of traffic, even the people crowding the streets seemed to have changed. He had come to London rarely during the last three years; London meant going out to Ordingly, and going to Ordingly meant the probability that he would be forced to meet his brother Julian. Max and Angela had sensed his reluctance to visit their home, and had come with good grace, and offering no comments, to meet him at one of the big hotels. Angela had always dreaded any sign of friction between her elder son and Julian, and Max seemed too tired to question anything.

'Home' in London meant to Emmanuel his little house which lay off Knightsbridge, where Hannah Rosenfeldt ruled, where there was peace and tranquillity, and a certain sense of being removed from the active, bustling life of a great city.

Emmanuel was driving there now. The taxi had turned into the long straight stretch of Piccadilly, past Hyde Park Corner, and into Knightsbridge, with the Park on the right looking a little dusty after the summer warmth.

'Left,' he said to the driver, 'and left again.'

The roar and hum of the traffic grew indistinct, the little square looked wonderfully quiet; the small old-fashioned houses looked neat and well cared for, as if their owners were determined to preserve them and lavish attention upon them. The taxi stopped.

The dark claret-coloured door at the top of the three stone steps opened and Emmanuel could see the bulky figure of Hannah, her face wreathed in smiles. He was home.

He ran up the steps and took her hands in his. She said in the husky voice he knew so well, 'Welcome, welcome!' then to the driver, 'Leave everything there, in the hall. That is right!'

She led the way into the little white-panelled sitting-room, which Emmanuel had furnished with such care. The good old furniture gleamed softly, there were flowers, the curtains were

20

bright and looked crisp, as if they had been recently ironed. The china and glass in the two tall cabinets threw out bright colours and reflections of light. He stood silent, looking at it all; sensible that here at least was peace and order and a certain satisfying dignity.

'Ah, it looks so very good,' he said. 'Hannah, how shall I ever be able to thank you for keeping this home together for me? For the care you've given to Simeon, for the thousand things which I shall never actually know, but which I can only surmise and be grateful for?'

'Tush! Such a yen!' she replied. 'I have kept it together because it was a roof over my head as well as over Simeon's. Nothing very splendid about that, surely! Now, you will have some tea? I have still some of the China tea which you used to like so much.' She made a grimace. 'Not for me! I like tea to be tea—not pale, wishy-washy stuff that smells of oranges or whatever it is. Sit down; try to look as if you were at home and not paying an afternoon call!'

He sat down in the Chippendale arm-chair, which despite its straight back he always maintained held more actual comfort than any other chair in the world. The thin elderly maid brought in tea.

Emmanuel said, 'Well, Martha, I'm back, you see.'

'I'm very glad to see you, sir. You've done your bit if ever anyone ever did. You've not brought no batman this time, sir?'

'Martha, I'm finished with batmen. I'm not a soldier any longer. Tomorrow I have the right to go to the White City, and get a suit of civilian clothes, shirts, a complete outfit and——'

Hannah said crisply, 'It's to be hoped that you'll do nothing of the kind! Clothes off the peg, indeed! A nice thing! What's the matter with going down to see Mr. Tracy? He's done you very well up to now.'

Emmanuel, pouring out the pale yellow liquid which smelt so delightful, smiled. 'Don't be a snob, Hannah. I've earned a "civvy suit" and I'm going to have it! We have got to readjust our ideas, my dear. This is a new world—an uncharted sea on which we're embarking.' He sipped his tea with appreciation. 'How good this is!'

She sat watching him, her plump hands clasped, her eyes dark and intent. She had known him for years. At the age of fifteen she had entered the firm of Gollantz as a very junior clerk. She had dealt with the post book, later with the petty cash; then she had been promoted to the 'costing' office, and by dint of taking long courses in shorthand and typing, she had finally become private and confidential secretary to Max Gollantz himself.

She had lived sparingly, had saved sufficient money to buy herself a small house at Northwood of which she had been inordinately proud. She had never spoken of the private business of the firm, she had never allowed anyone to realize that she watched with apprehension the ever-widening breach between Emmanuel and his younger brother Julian. She had never permitted Max Gollantz to guess that she noticed his growing preference for his second son, and his inability to judge Emmanuel fairly.

She had known of Emmanuel's engagement to Viva Heriot, she had known when it was broken off, when Emmanuel went abroad and remained to all intents and purposes an exile. More —she knew why he had gone, realized that he had shouldered the blame for what might have been an unpleasant and sinister scandal in order to protect his brother. She had seen him return, marry Viva Heriot—she was now Mrs. 'Toby' Tatten—go abroad again, and when his divorce was over he had married Juliet Forbes, who had died a year after their wedding.

In 1939 he had returned home again, leaving his splendid Gallery in Milano, and bringing his son, Simeon, with him. He and the boy had gone to Ordingly—and it hadn't been a success. That was when she had sold her house and offered to keep house for Emmanuel, to look after Simeon while his father was serving in the Army. . . .

His gratitude had been unbounded; Hannah Rosenfeldt knew that he had never ceased to show his thanks to her in every possible way. All through the war she had kept his home going, with the help of the elderly maid, Martha, who had once been a nursery-maid at Ordingly when Emmanuel was very young.

Hannah's love for young Simeon was great, motherly and infinitely protective; her feeling for Emmanuel Gollantz was barely this side of idolatry. She saw in him the ability, the courtesy and the charm of his grandfather—the first Emmanuel Gollantz; she had seen him as a young man filled with enthusiasm for his work, with ambition and possessing at the same time those ideals with regard to all business dealings which his grandfather always insisted were the foundation of the firm's success.

She watched the change in him, when first he assumed responsibility for his brother's faults and misdemeanours. She had understood why he had allowed himself to be blamed—not actually for any sense of nobility or self-sacrifice, but because

22

of the tremendous love which he had for his mother, who had always loved Julian the best of her three sons.

He had been remarkably handsome—Emmanuel and Julian Gollantz had been regarded as two of the best-looking young men in town—his hair had been very dark and his appearance, which was admittedly in those early days slightly affected, had helped to single him out from other men of his own age.

Now, despite its slight tan, his face looked very thin and desperately tired. His hair at the temples was white, the rest thickly shot with silver. His eyes were rather sunken, the skin below them a little discoloured. His mouth appeared to have lost its fullness and it looked thinner and tighter.

Hannah thought, 'He looks his age. There may be energy, vitality and purpose left, but the last of his youth has gone.'

Aloud she said, 'Simeon comes home the day after tomorrow.'

Emmanuel looked up, and again he smiled. While the smile lasted he looked less than his age ; as it faded the years crept back again and took possession.

'That will be pleasant. We've made—or rather, to be just, you have made—a good job of Simeon. He's a fine boy. I wonder what he wants to do, Hannah?'

'I don't wonder, because I know,' she answered. 'He's been through all the usual ambitions. He wanted to be a soldier, an airman, an engine-driver ; then he thought that he'd like to go into the firm. Lately he's been talking about being a lawyer like Mr. Bill and Mr. Charles Wilmot. I've an idea that he still hankers after the flying, but——'

'Oh no! Not that! It's not possible now that he's lost his foot, Hannah. Of all the many things this war has brought about, I resent that most.' He paused. 'It's natural, I suppose. My son. He was filled with such hopes ; he once confided to me that he hoped to become . . . an air ace. Now, he'll go maimed and halt all his days. It hurts me more than I can tell you. It is something of which I am conscious each time I watch him enter a r-room.'

Hannah said briskly, 'Rubbish, Emmanuel. Rather congratulate yourself that he was spared when so many boys—were not spared. I can assure you that the loss of his foot only makes a regret in Simeon's heart because it means—the end of his life in the Air Force. For the rest he is young, strong, and filled with vitality.' She shrugged her massive shoulders. 'I have no fears for Simeon.'

Emmanuel stared at her, his eyes dark and thoughtful, holding something of resentment. Then they cleared, and he said, 'I suppose you're right. I still r-resent it for him. All so useless. All so wasteful.'

She responded, 'War is always useless, always wasteful. Why should an exception be made for—Simeon Gollantz? *Nu,* you have finished your tea . . . ?'

'And very good it was, Hannah. Thank you.'

'Ah,' her tone was still brisk and matter-of-fact, 'it is nothing. We are glad to have you home again, Emmanuel.'

Emmanuel was driving down to Ordingly. His car had been laid up for some minor ailment in the Knightsbridge garage, now it felt to him as if it was actually pleased to be out and about once more. It was old, elderly at least, but he reflected that there was still a lot of heart in it. He had debated as to whether he should go to the Gollantz Galleries before going to Ordingly, but he decided against it. His father resented anything which seemed to indicate, however unintentionally, that he was trying to take too active a part in the business. Better to wait until they had discussed everything.

He had been to the White City that morning, and had carried back his civilian clothes to his house with a kind of amused satisfaction.

Not a bad suit, either, for what it was. True, the collar stuck out in a slight peak at the back, and the back of the jacket was inclined to 'ride up' a little. The pockets seemed too small, and the buttonholes at the cuffs were not 'practical', but he had decided to wear it for his visit to Ordingly, with some vague idea of showing how different the Emmanuel Gollantz of 1946 was from the same man in 1939. He had a mental picture of himself in those days which seemed so far away, so distant that it almost took on a sense of improbability.

He had affected stocks, had encouraged his small side-whiskers to grow and had them very neatly clipped ; he had worn wide cloaks in the evening, hats with brims which were wider than was customary. He saw himself now as an affected creature, consciously trying to 'ape' the fastidious and rather eccentric style of his grandfather. 'The world,' he thought, 'had both time and patience with such trivialities in those days. Now— after years of uniforms and uniformity—I should be ticketed as a *poseur,* and probably quite rightly so !'

The houses on either side of the road were thinning out, trees—those magnificent English trees—were becoming more frequent. The faint smell of petrol and hot tar, of humanity, the noise of moving traffic had been left behind. He saw wide stretches of open country, the sweeping green of open fields, and

24

herds of cattle grazing peacefully with grave concentration.

He turned the car into a smaller side road, where the hedges grew higher, where dog-roses and meadowsweet, with shepherd's purse and ragged robin, bloomed in tangled loveliness. Somewhere he heard the faint harsh note of the cuckoo.

He thought, fumbling in his mind for the old rhyme, ' "It's July . . ." he's changed his tune. What's the rest? "In August go he must", though it doesn't rhyme in the least!'

The lodge gate; he sounded his klaxon, and Mrs. Follie came running out, wiping her hands on her apron.

'Hello, Mrs. Follie!'

'Why, Mr. Emmanuel as sure as sure. Glad ter see you, sir, an' back in plain clothes! That's a sight fer sore eyes. Makes me feel as the war reely is over, and praise be to God for it.'

'It's been a longish time,' he admitted.

'A' endless time,' she assured him. 'My, it's brought some changes ter us all—great an' humble. Mr. Julian finished his work a week back. He's back here again—like you are, in plain clothes. Mr. Bill's back an' all, working hard in his office, so he tole me. Well, I mustn't keep you, Sir Max and 'Er Ladyship will be all excited to see you! Like the return of that Probable Son, you might say.'

He drove slowly up the long drive, where he could see the wide lawn, looking soft, green and inviting through the spaces between the big spreading branches of the tall elms. He hoped that they would have tea on the lawn—tea with ice and lemon, and later long tall glasses containing something very cold, with more lemon and more ice making a delicious clinking sound as it tinkled against the glass. Yesterday, about this time, he'd been drinking a last tepid whisky-and-soda with Bradley and Francis!

'Something vaguely degrading about whisky and tepid water,' he decided. 'Civilization, even ultra civilization, wins every time.'

He stopped the car before the wide porch with its splendid Palladio columns and wide low steps. He narrowed his eyes. Was he imagining it, or did the place look less well kept than he remembered it? Were those formal flower beds less well filled, did they glow less vividly with the brilliant colours of many flowers, were the edges of the lawn faintly ragged?

He walked up the steps and entered the cool, tiled hall. An elderly man came forward from the back of the hall. Emmanuel, his eyes still a little uncertain after the bright sunshine, frowned.

'Mr. Emmanuel, sir, this is a great joy.'

Good God, it was Hewson! But a Hewson who looked so

old, who was bent about the shoulders, whose hair was quite white.

Emmanuel said, 'That's right, Hewson—it's me. How are you?'

'Mustn't grumble, we're none of us getting any younger, sir. Her Ladyship's just going out to have tea under the big cedar. Here she is now!' He turned as Angela Gollantz came slowly down the wide, shallow stairs.

'Mr. Emmanuel, m' Lady.'

'My dearest boy!' She came down the last steps very quickly, and flung her arms round his neck. 'Emmanuel, this is exciting. To really have you home again. You've finished with the Army —yes, so has Julian. Bill's out of the Navy back working with Charles. Let me look at you. I've not seen you for nearly ten months, remember.'

She held him at arm's length, and he looked at her vivid face and took comfort to himself that she had scarcely changed. She was still charming, her hair was scarcely touched with grey, her eyes were as bright as ever. When she smiled, Emmanuel found it difficult to believe that she was any older than when he first remembered her.

With her arm through his they walked out together, and crossed the lawn to the shade of the great cedar where the shadows lay so dark as to seem solid things.

'Max is coming,' Angela said. 'Poor darling, he's not terribly well. I'm worried about Max. The days when I used to be able to whip him off to Aix are over. We tried Buxton, but—he grew so restive, and—we came back home again. Ah, here he is. Go and meet him, darling.'

A tall, spare figure, with shoulders that were bent, came towards Emmanuel. Max walked slowly, leaning on his stick. His suit appeared to have been made for a much bigger and stouter man. He was immaculate as ever, wearing clothes which were inconspicuous but admirable. His lean, clean-shaven face was thinner than Emmanuel remembered ; his hair was thin and quite white ; the eyes looked heavy and dull. When he spoke even his voice seemed to have lost its vibrance and strength.

'Nice to see you back, Emmanuel,' Max said.

'Nicer still to be back again,' Emmanuel answered.

Together they walked to where Angela sat beneath the boughs of the cedar. Emmanuel noticed that his father lowered himself carefully into his chair, then sighed heavily as if with relief that so difficult a movement should have been successfully accomplished.

He smiled at his wife, then turned to his son.

'I wanted to talk to you, it's important—or possibly I only imagine it to be important, this step which I contemplate. I am retiring from the business. I feel that I have worked sufficiently long, that I have worked hard, and that I deserve a little rest and tranquillity, such as I can still find here'—again he smiled at his wife—'thanks to your dear mother.'

Emmanuel listened. He had expected something of the kind, had tried to steel himself to show no surprise and—what he felt most keenly—apprehension. Once before Max had asked him to come into the Bond Street business, and—it hadn't worked. Max had resented Emmanuel's suggestions, and Emmanuel had chafed at the fact that the Gollantz Galleries were not what they had been. Emmanuel had returned to Milano, and since that time had taken no part in the management of the Galleries.

Now Max wished to retire. It was understandable enough ; he had grown old in the business, he was not strong, the war with its manifold anxieties had tried him heavily. In his heart Emmanuel knew that he wanted nothing so little as to take any part in the management of the Galleries. He wanted to go back to his own business in Milano, he wanted to rebuild it, to repair all the damage and make good all the losses caused by the war.

On the other hand his sense of family, his pride in the reputation which that family had gained, the probability that difficult days lay ahead, convinced him that—while he refused to abandon completely his plans for his own business—he must play what part he could in the maintenance of the Gollantz Galleries in Bond Street.

Hermann Gollantz had founded the family. Old Emmanuel Gollantz had brought his antiques to England, and had begun by showing them in an old house on Camden Hill. Max had followed, and here was the second Emmanuel waiting to continue a business which was acclaimed throughout the world as being exclusive, almost fanatically honest, and which was controlled by experts who could be neither bribed nor fooled.

He said, 'Yes, Father. I shall be interested to hear your plans.'

As his father replied, Emmanuel listened with dismay to the note of defiance which crept into Max Gollantz's voice. The words which he spoke were sufficiently just and moderate, but behind them Emmanuel heard the unspoken warning that he was not to dare to make difficulties. As Max elaborated his plans, Emmanuel's dismay grew.

'I should have liked my three sons to enter the business, but Bill unfortunately has no taste at all. He wouldn't know Chippendale from Sheraton, Dresden from Sèvres! However, he promises to be a good lawyer, and as such will be valuable to us.

'You, my eldest son, have always had excellent taste, backed by sound knowledge. You have often impressed me, you have courage and integrity. You had the privilege of being under the instruction of my father. Your own business in Milano, which I don't doubt was very profitable before the war—is probably a ruin. Have you had any news?'

'I have appointed an agent to inquire into everything. A man I can trust implicitly.'

'Not an Italian, surely?' Max's tone sharpened.

'An Italian, sir, and one of my oldest and best friends. He left England this morning. He was in the P.O.W. camp. I knew him long ago in Italy.'

Angela said, 'A prisoner! How strange for you to meet. Surely, as he was a friend of yours, that must have meant—well—complications?'

Emmanuel shook his head. 'Believe me, none at all. His behaviour was incredibly circumspect. Always.'

'And what is this ex-prisoner going to do?' Max asked, and Emmanuel heard the sudden coldness in his voice.

'Send me a full r-report immediately he has gone into things.'

'I see—then you do not contemplate an immediate return to Italy?'

'I shall have to pay a visit there, undoubtedly, but'—Emmanuel tried to make his voice sound gay—'I am virtually at your service!'

'You'll go to Bond Street? Good! I wish to relinquish all authority there. I only reserve to myself the right to approve or veto any really important purchase or sale. The sort of thing involving thousands of pounds, you understand.'

'Perfectly.'

'It may astonish you to learn that your brother, Julian, has developed a very real knowledge of antique silver, and certain forms of antique jewellery. During the war he served very admirably. He was, of course, not suitable to send overseas, or to engage in actual military operations—owing to his state of health. His career may not have been spectacular——'

Emmanuel, his pale face flushing suddenly, said sharply, 'Neither was mine!' He saw his father's eyebrows rise, his mouth tighten a little, and could have cursed himself for having spoken.

Angela leaned forward. 'Darling, your career was wonderful!'

Max held up his white, thin hand where the veins showed blue and thick. 'I was not attempting to make comparisons. I only wished to explain that during the times when Julian was unable to go down to Whitehall he studied very hard. He has a very fine grasp of his subjects, he is astute and he has undoubted taste. I propose that you shall run the Galleries between you. He'—with a slight emphasis—'is only too willing. What is your own feeling, Emmanuel?'

Emmanuel did not reply. He sat staring at the moss-covered ground, his hands hanging loosely between his knees, frowning a little. Once his mother saw him raise his head for a second, and caught a glimpse of his eyes. They were dark, puzzled and yet angry. After a long silence, he said, 'We have never managed to get on together, you r-remember?'

Max made a movement of irritation. 'Pah! If Julian is willing to forget the past, can't you be as generous as he is?'

Angela, speaking very softly, said, 'Max dear—the generosity was Emmanuel's—in the past. We can't forget that, my dear.'

'I forget nothing,' Max returned. 'I only wish Emmanuel to do his best to enter this business in the right spirit. If you begin to look for trouble, for slights, for difficulties—you will most certainly find them, pressed down and running over. If, on the other hand, you go into it determined to find the best, to offer co-operation, to be tolerant—then there is every chance of your making a great success.'

'Is Julian prepared to do all these things?' Emmanuel asked.

'He assures me that he is.'

'Then I must accept his assurance. Only, and for my own sake, I must say this—I have the greater experience, I am older than he, and I must have control. Things must be done—my way. And my way is based on experience, training and constant observation. This interest of his is a relatively new thing. Mine is of many years' standing.'

He leaned back and laid the tips of his long, fine fingers together. Angela thought how like his grandfather he was growing: there were the same small mannerisms, the same incisive manner of speaking, the same determination which was so often hidden under an air of what almost appeared to be laziness or inattention.

'I am willing to work with my brother, but I must have the last word. In such a business it is almost impossible to have dual control. Old silver'—he pursed his lips—'there is no need for me to tell you, sir, what a tr-ricky subject that is. Half the "fakers" in England work on "old silver". Antique jewellery—

29

we have never dealt in to any great extent. It is so liable to develop into a kind of "junk" stall! However, if my brother has studied these two subjects, by all means let him do what he can with them.'

'Does it strike you that you're being exceedingly patronizing?' Max asked coldly.

'I don't intend to be. I am a business man, not a sentimentalist. I love beauty in all its forms, but I want to see that it is worth something in the market. I made my very small inconvenient shop in Milano—pay. I made the Jaffe Gollantz Gallery —pay.'

'I thought that you had a soul above money!'

'Oh dear no, sir.' Emmanuel's voice was dangerously pleasant. 'I do not care a great deal for money—as money, but as the result of clever buying, correct assessment and honest selling— no one appreciates money more than I do. So with many years of experience behind me, I claim that I must have the control of the Galleries—and I think that I can promise you that you will not be disappointed. I hope that you agr-ree, sir.'

Max held out his empty cup to Angela. 'Thank you, my dear —not too strong.' Then, turning to his son, he said, his voice still cold, 'Very well, so long as it is made clear—that all limits are defined so that mistakes are not possible—I agree. How often, always supposing that there is anything left, would you have to go to Italy?'

'That's very difficult to say. It would depend upon what sales there were, what stock we still possessed—oh, on a dozen things.'

'Who would take charge at Bond Street in your absence?'

'My brother—who would naturally consult Reuben Davis on the strictly financial side, and also my own secretary.'

'Have you got a secretary?' Again Max's voice was sharp.

'I shall have—one who knows the business very well indeed. Her name is Hannah Rosenfeldt.'

'Hannah Rosenfeldt. She was my secretary, wasn't she?'

Angela interrupted, 'She's a darling! You mean the woman who has been keeping house for you while you were in the Army. Oh, Max, such a nice woman, so capable and clever. And she'll come back?'

Emmanuel smiled at her gratefully. 'I think there is no doubt of it. I shall be out all day—she told me only yesterday that with "Othello's occupation's gone" she'd like to be in harness again.'

'That's one problem at least solved,' Angela said cheerfully, then glancing towards the house, cried, 'Here's Julian!'

Emmanuel turned his eyes towards the house. Slowly descending the steps was a tall, fair-haired man, who carried a fine malacca cane with a huge ivory knob. Old Emmanuel's cane— so Max had given that to Julian! Emmanuel remembered how he, himself, had carried it when he went to bid for the famous Reynolds at Lord Howark's sale ; how Arbuthnot, Jacob Morriss with his two sons and old Lane had all gathered to see what would happen in the duel between Peters, the New York dealer, and young Emmanuel Gollantz. Bill had come, and the Claytons and—Juliet Forbes. He remembered—and checked himself, he remembered too much. Well, here was Julian, beautifully immaculate, carrying old Emmanuel's cane. The little flare of anger died, and licking his dry lips, he managed to say:

'He looks well, doesn't he?'

Angela said, 'He has been better—stronger—lately, I think.'

Julian came forward across the lawn. He had worn better than his brother and at forty-four looked considerably less than his age. He was singularly handsome, his yellow hair gleamed in the afternoon sunshine, his eyes were very bright and of a clear blue, his skin had never lost its youthful fairness. He smiled, showing beautifully even teeth.

He stooped to kiss his mother and said, 'Well, hello, Emmanuel how are you?'

Neither made any attempt to shake hands.

Julian continued, 'So you've left the Army, eh? I say, where did you get that suit!'

'At the White City, this morning. Quite good, I felt.'

'Good Lord, you didn't queue up for your demob suit, did you?'

Very equably Emmanuel said, 'Indeed I did, and some shirts, a hat and even a tie! I intend to wear them all—in time.'

'Then you've abandoned your pre-war eccentricities in dress?' The tone was light, holding a certain amusement, but to Emmanuel's sensitive ears it was mocking. Again he felt, as he had always done, that Julian had the power to make him feel rather foolish and inferior.

'Until such a time as I can afford them—yes.'

Max said, 'I have been discussing the matter of the Galleries with Emmanuel. He is quite willing to take over the management on condition that he has the chief control. How does that appeal to you, Julian?'

'I don't mind in the least.' Max shot a glance at Emmanuel, as if calling him to witness the difference in his stipulations and Julian's ready acceptance. 'After all, I'm only an apprentice, and I trust to prove an industrious one. Provided that I can make sufficient to maintain my wife and my son—thanks to your

31

generosity, Father—that's all I need. I've been working hard at old silver, Emmanuel.'

'Yes, so my father told me. Interesting subject.'

'Enthralling. I was talking to my son about it when I went down to see him. He's very taken up with the idea of going into the "shop".' He laughed, conscious that both Max and Emmanuel disliked the word applied to their dignified Galleries. 'What's your lad going to do, Emmanuel?'

'He thinks that he'd like law. I don't know, nothing is decided. Since his crash possibilities are limited, poor chap!'

Angela said, 'Lots of time and he's a clever boy, and such a nice boy. I'm devoted to him. He's going to be very good-looking.'

Julian said, 'All the Gollantz men are, darling!'

Emmanuel drove home slowly, through the sweet-scented air of the still warm evening; he wanted to think over his father's proposals. In his heart he knew that he longed for the familiar gallery in Milano, for his own comfortable apartment, for Guido's help and encouragement. On the other hand, it had been plain to him that Max was too tired to work any longer; it might be that he no longer trusted his judgment as he had done before the war. Things had changed, business was bound to be different and difficult. Even Ordingly had changed; it seemed to have become shabby, as if the people who lived there were too weary after the war to take much interest in it.

That essential feeling of unlimited prosperity which had pervaded it had gone; Angela had spoken to him of the reduced staff.

'There are no servants to get, and if there were—well, we've all got to be economical in these days.'

With everything he saw, with everything he heard, the necessity for him to return to the Gollantz Gallery became clearer. It was not what he wished; he viewed the future connection with Julian with grave apprehension, but he was determined that if it were possible he would save Ordingly for Simeon. He would make a new and great success of the business, branch out and find new methods of making money. Hannah had told him of the difficulties regarding permits for redecoration. The decorating side had fallen to nothing. Very well—there were surely other channels worth exploring.

Simeon should find a restored and prosperous business as his heritage—he should find Ordingly in perfect condition—once these things were done successfully, then Emmanuel felt that his work would be finished and he could return to that city of Milano which held so many wonderful memories for him.

He garaged his car and walked round to his house. There was no sign of depreciation here, the whole place looked bright and cared for. He smiled. The thought that he might persuade Hannah to come back into business with him made him feel happier and more confident.

CHAPTER THREE

HE had talked long into the night with Hannah Rosenfeldt, he had told her of his father's decision, and she had listened—immovable, sphinxlike and without comment, until he ended his story and said, 'Well, Hannah, what is your verdict?'

She blinked her heavy eyelids. 'Mine?' she said. 'Mine? Only this—that you have never been able to work with your brother, never have been able to make contact with him. It won't work! Go back, Emmanuel, go back to where you have worked and been happy. . . .'

He made that small movement with his hands which always reminded her of old Emmanuel; a movement which implied fatalism, acceptance and even resignation.

'Happy!' he said. 'Yes, for a year, Hannah. Then it all ended, and I went about always—looking back over my shoulder. Happy!'

Her tone was vigorous. 'Yes,' she admitted, 'but you were not actively unhappy. Perhaps melancholy would be the better word, even—retrospective. I tell you, Emmanuel, for you to work with your brother is to try to mix oil and water. You have the rigid code of morals imposed by your grandfather—Julian has no morals whatever! How can you hope to make a success of this venture? Emmanuel'—she leaned forward and laid her fat, white hand for a second on his knee—'go away as you went away before.'

He tapped the ash of his cigarette into the little jade bowl and smiled. 'Hannah, my dear friend, won't you help me? I have Simeon to think of. I want—oh, I admit it—Ordingly for him. I am to be the controlling factor. I know the business. I believe that I can make even my brother conform to my ways of doing business. But'—he paused—'I want your help. Are you willing to give it to me?'

She sighed, a great sigh which seemed to inflate her huge figure, then shrugged her shoulders.

'But of course, I cannot refuse. Indeed, it may be that my watchful eye may avert catastrophe—for a time. In addition you have always been, as you know, the light of my eyes. There is nothing that I can refuse you. It won't be easy, together we shall not be successful. This man will beat us both—and we are neither of us fools! But you ask, you wish to try to preserve Ordingly for Simeon—what can I say?

'The two people I love best in the world—no, I'm wrong—the *only* people I love in the world need my help, such as it is. One a boy—that is Simeon, the other an idealist—that is you! Yes, I shall come. Tomorrow is not possible. Simeon is coming home and I must be here to meet him. The day after, I shall be at the Gollantz Gallery at nine o'clock. I shall not go down with you, my dear. I shall go as Hannah Rosenfeldt, the private secretary of the head of the firm. There, let me give you a last drink—oh, I have always contrived to keep a little whisky in the house!'

They sat until the night was over and the dawn had begun to lighten the sky. Emmanuel—his eyes shining, his face filled with excitement—told her of his plans for the Gallery. There must be changes ; certain things were of little or no value in this post-war world, others must be found which would fit into the new scheme of things. Hannah thought that in spite of the fact that he was tired he looked younger and more hopeful. She listened, made suggestions, criticized and advised.

Emmanuel had not realized how much knowledge this elderly Jewess possessed, how keen was her brain, and how completely retentive her memory.

When at last he left her to go to bed he took her hands in his and said, 'Courage, Hannah, and faith in ourselves and we shall make something very good out of it all.'

She stared at him, her eyes heavy for want of sleep, and said, 'Ah, well, we can only try. But do not hope for too much. We shall do what we can. Good night and sleep well.'

He came down that day to find one of his old broad-brimmed hats, a clean pair of washleather gloves and an ivory-headed cane lying on the low chest in the hall. For a moment he stood staring at them—this was Hannah's way of 'dressing the part' ; she was going to make him play the rôle which had been assigned to him! He looked down at the things, his smile a little rueful. So much time had passed, so much water had flowed under the bridges since he was an antique dealer in Bond Street. Was it possible to catch at the 'skirts of time' and drag her back? Or was this the beginning of a new era? For the first time in its history one of the House of Gollantz would enter the portals of the great business wearing a 'demob' suit, but clinging to the sign manuals of the family.

Hannah herself brought in his breakfast; she set it before him and said, 'Eat and fortify yourself! The bacon is not very good, the egg is dried and the bread is horrible, but the coffee is good.'

'As your coffee always is,' he said.

He walked to Knightsbridge and took a bus to Bond Street; something made him wish to begin to school himself to a certain economy. He had—before the war began—been an exceedingly rich man, his business had prospered and he was beginning to be accepted as one of the leading authorities on antiques. Now —he had no idea what was left; there might be nothing, there might be the remains of a great business. Once Simeon came of age he would inherit the considerable fortune which had been his mother's. Emmanuel had been left complete control of her money, which he had resolutely refused to touch, and had left entirely in the hands of Charles Wilmot, his mother's cousin, and his own lawyer.

Charles had accepted the responsibility, but had asked why Emmanuel would not allow Simeon's school fees at least to be paid for out of the inheritance.

Emmanuel's lips had tightened, and his tone had been cold when he replied, 'I prefer to pay for the boy myself. I can afford it. Let him have Juliet's money when he's twenty-one.'

Charles, watching him, realized the memories which prompted the decision. Juliet Forbes, brilliant singer, beautiful woman, had been for some time before her marriage to Emmanuel the mistress of Leon Hast. Hast, who was incredibly rich, had left her everything. Emmanuel had been devoted to his wife; but he had firmly refused to touch a penny of her money, and when she died she had left him an immense fortune, partly earned by her singing, partly the legacy which Hast had bequeathed to her. He had sent for Charles Wilmot and insisted that the whole fortune should be transferred to his son, Simeon.

Charles, who was both kindly and astute, tried to argue.

'There might come a time when you needed a really large sum. If Juliet hadn't wanted you to have it at your disposal she'd not have left it to you. I drew up her will, I remember all that she said to me. You need have no——'

Emmanuel had held up his hand. Charles still remembered how it had shaken, and how white Emmanuel's face had looked. His voice was steady, but frigidly cold, when he spoke.

'I think there is no more to be said, Charles. I have made my decision.'

He got off the bus at the corner of Bond Street and walked slowly towards the Gollantz Gallery; he felt that he was absorbing the general atmosphere. The sight of damaged buildings shocked him, but Bond Street still retained much of its old character, much of its pre-war charm and distinction. He glanced with pleasure at the fine china, the good colour prints, the expensive trifles and the splendid jewels; even the ties, shirts and gloves in the outfitters' windows seemed to have their own particular and individual elegance.

The commissionaire standing at the entrance to the Gallery was new to Emmanuel; he gave the man a 'Good morning' as he entered, and then stood half uncertain in the entrance to the showrooms which had earned an international reputation.

Reuben Davis came bustling out of his office, his hands outstretched, his face wreathed in smiles.

'Emmanuel, this is pleasant. Yes, Sir Max talked it all over with me. I'm delighted! Delighted! Now, what do you want to do first? The post is in, sorted—you always used to go through the letters first—as Sir Max always does. We must find you a first-class secretary, until then I'll send in my Miss Waters.'

Emmanuel said, 'Only for today, tomorrow Hannah Rosenfeldt is coming back to us. The old team will be working together—Hannah, you and I——'

'And Julian,' Reuben said quickly.

'And Julian, of course,' Emmanuel agreed.

He let his eyes wander to the antiques displayed in the long gallery. What he saw did not please him particularly, something was lacking. The goods were set out well enough, they were well cared for but—he frowned—that additional polish, that extra gloss, that almost indefinable 'something' which marked the difference between 'well kept' and 'superbly kept' was missing.

He knew that Davis was watching him, and that he had read the expression on Emmanuel's face correctly, for he said tentatively, 'It's not easy to get staff in these days, you know.'

Warmly Emmanuel answered, 'No, no, I appreciate that. But we'll find people, good people. They must either take a pride in the place or—we'll find others. You've been overstocking a little with that brass, haven't you, Reuben?'

'Julian's very keen on brass; he's been buying a lot of it, and Sheffield and old silver. Personally, I loathe the brass, it all needs cleaning, and what's it worth!' he snapped his thick fingers contemptuously. 'Julian says that it "brightens up the place". I say that it looks—what it is—cheap!'

'Um, I'm inclined to agree with you. Makes work, and if we haven't got the people to clean it—better keep it in the showcases. Is my brother in yet?'

'Julian? Good heavens, no! It's not half past nine. He won't be here for another hour. He's got your old office. I've arranged Sir Max's for you.'

'I'll come and see to the letters if you'll send Miss Waters.' He hung up his hat in the cupboard, remembering how insistent his grandfather had always been that 'my office is not, and neffer shell be, ellowed to look like an old clothes stall!' He sat down at the big desk, which had once belonged to Benjamin Disraeli, and picked up the long slender silver paper-knife. The smooth old metal was pleasant to handle, and again Emmanuel remembered his grandfather's dislike of seeing letters ripped open and not slit neatly.

For a moment he sat, weighing the paper-knife in his sensitive fingers. How many small traditional things there were in this firm of which he was the fourth generation! Small, possibly trivial unwritten laws and observances, but all the outcome of old Emmanuel's insistence on the upholding of the dignity of the firm. Nothing slovenly was permitted, everything must be kept in the best possible way, profits were regulated according to original costs, there had never been any wish on his part to make immense profits on goods which he had bought cheaply.

'It is r-right and pr-proper that people shell pay the correct value—it is not r-right that they shell pay a sum which is greater then the value. Also,' and he would chuckle softly, 'it is a ver' bad advertisement for us.'

Only when by some astonishing stroke of luck some rare piece was bought cheaply were the profits allowed to mount. Emmanuel remembered, in his early days, he had gone down to a sale at Copsley Manor in Kent, and had returned having bought a fine set of Chippendale chairs and, in addition, a 'mixed lot'—which he described as 'a trayful of junk'.

His grandfather had chuckled and said, 'Neffer buy junk, if you please. But since you hev bought it, let me see it. I am ready to be amused.' The tray, covered with an assortment of small objects, had been placed before him, and he had examined everything, making his comments as he did so. 'Silver salts . . . Edwardian, not quite so thick as tissue paper, and far less useful. A so-called travelling inkpot. I hev met them before—they ruin everything—a gr-reat danger to linen. Ah! Now we find t'ings.' He had held up a Chelsea enamel cylinder. 'You know vot t'is is? For knitting needles. A pr-retty piece. Chairming! And—ho, ho—you are either a cleffer young man or a very lucky one—more Chelsea—a snuff-box! End spoons . . . only a mixed lot, but old silver—maybe we shell match them with some we hev! Take it avay, you have done ver' well. I am pleased.'

The bits of enamel had sold well, and Emmanuel was absolved of the sin of 'buying junk'.

He forced his mind back to his work ; he must not allow himself to sit here dreaming. The morning post lay on a silver salver, another foible of old Emmanuel's! Emmanuel began to go through them, and found one addressed to 'Miss Maureen Waters'. He laid it aside and continued his sorting ; two more were addressed to George Clough, and a small parcel bore the name of Mark Seber, with the addition 'Private and Confidential'. Emmanuel stacked them neatly, frowning as he did so. It had always been a rule that the staff were not allowed to have letters sent to them at the Gallery. Max had always refused to permit it on the ground that it wasted time, and that he would not be responsible for the letters of other people.

Emmanuel lifted the house telephone and spoke to Reuben Davis.

'Could you come and speak to me for a moment, Reuben?'

'Coming now!'

When he bustled in, Emmanuel pushed forward the pile of letters.

'I thought that my father objected to the staff having their letters sent here?'

Reuben shrugged his shoulders. 'He did, it's always been a rule. But Sir Max hasn't been here regularly for some time, and when this Seber came here, and his letters began to arrive, I spoke to Julian about it. He said that such a restriction was petty and small-minded. So—now all the staff have letters coming here.'

Emmanuel said, 'Tell me about this man Seber.'

'He's a displaced person. Julian found him. Austrian, he says ; German, I think. Specialist in old silver, brass and so forth. He found a pair of nice old gates somewhere in Sussex and a couple of good iron firebacks. That's all right, but no one is going to make much money out of that stuff. And brass—he's bought up half the candlesticks in the Home Counties. Damned stuff! Oh, we can sell it, but nine times out of ten it's not worth the trouble of keeping clean. Profits are very small. Not our style of thing at all.'

'I'll have a talk with him later. Send Miss Waters to me, will you, Reuben?'

Maureen Waters arrived with her note-book ; she was slight, with fluffy hair, bright eyes and an air of efficiency.

She snapped open her note-book and looked at Emmanuel

expectantly. He said, 'First, please, here is a letter for you, and some for other members of the staff. Will you please send a notice r-round to everyone—every member of the staff—to say that their private correspondence must not be sent here? It is against my father's r-rules, and I cannot permit it.'

He saw her face flush. 'Well, Mr. Gollantz,' she began, 'I do——'

Emmanuel smiled, 'Will you take this letter, please? There is no more to be said. "Dear Sir, I have received your letter and noted its contents . . ." '

It was nearly eleven o'clock when the door of Emmanuel's room opened and Julian walked in. He looked well, very alert and exceedingly well dressed.

'Hello, Emmanuel, I'm late this morning. Had some calls to make on my way here. I say, what's this Seber tells me about your refusing to allow the staff to have their letters sent here? I spoke to Davis about it some time ago. It's a silly kind of restriction. What earthly difference does it make to you? Seber is furious ; he's a valuable man, I don't want to offend him.'

'No necessity for you to offend him,' Emmanuel said. 'Put the blame on me. It's a rule, and a very old one, and so long as I am here it's going to be kept. Sit down, Julian, let's get down to things. The place isn't kept as it ought to be. There's far too much brass stuff. No money in it, and it takes a devil of a lot of work to keep it clean. We've overbought on it.'

'It moves, people like it.' Julian's voice was sulky.

'Possibly. But it takes too much cleaning. If it's dirty, it's an eyesore, and when it does "move", the profits are very small. We've got enough out there to last for years. I want to see the staff here in turn this afternoon. I'll go into the books with Reuben in the morning. Things have got to be both tightened up and br-rightened up. The Gallery looks'—he sought for a word —'looks dingy. We can't afford that.'

Julian flicked open the lid of the big tortoiseshell box which stood on the desk. It was empty. He shrugged his shoulders.

'Another rule,' he said, 'as we're talking about rules, has always been that this box was kept filled. Are you going to economize in that direction too?'

His brother took out his own case and handed it to him in silence. Julian took a cigarette, lit it, and blew a cloud of smoke in his brother's direction.

'You're taking a high hand already, aren't you?' he said. 'Not been here five minutes——'

Emmanuel said, 'Considerably more. I was here at nine.'

'That, I suppose, is a rebuke because I wasn't here until eleven! Look here, if we're to work together, understand that I am not going to be treated as if I were a schoolboy. I'm my own master, I run my side of the business in my own way. Mind your own business.'

'I imagined that the Gallery was my business.'

'I don't want to meddle with pictures ; that's apparently your line, as furniture is Hooper's. Leave me to manage the silver and brass, copper and so forth. We haven't sold a picture for weeks, the damned furniture hangs fire until I'm sick of the sight of the stuff. My candelabra, candlesticks, salvers and so on, go like hot cakes. Mind your own business and I'll mind mine, and don't meddle with Mark Seber. He's a valuable man, and inclined to be touchy. Is that clear?'

Had Julian been more observant, or less angry, he might have noticed that his brother's fingers closed on the silver paper-knife until the knuckles showed white. When he spoke his voice was very calm and even.

'You have only recently taken up this business. I am prepared to believe that you are br-rilliant. Max is satisfied, and he is as good a judge as one can want. I, on the other hand, have run my own business for many years. I have always believed in a policy. It appears to me that, at the present moment, a definite policy is lacking here. We have specialized in the best—pictures, furniture, silver and china. My grandfather——'

'*Our* grandfather, if you don't mind,' Julian said.

'I beg your pardon, our gr-randfather disliked what he called "oddments". Sets of dinner services, with a third missing or damaged, tea-sets in the same condition, odd spoons—unless we can match them and make up dozens, brass candlesticks of no particular value——'

Julian shouted, 'For God's sake stop talking about those damned candlesticks! I'm sick of it!'

'Those things,' Emmanuel went on quietly, 'are of no use to us. They are—fr-rankly—not good enough. Little shops in the King's Road, in Westbourne Gr-rove, or off Marylebone Road, can sell incomplete sets of china—Gollantz can't, they can't afford to. Our r-reputation is too big.'

Julian rose and stubbed out his cigarette into the big alabaster ash-tray. He stared at his brother, his face handsome and insolent.

'You've got a lot to say about your knowledge of business,' he said ; 'remember that you're thinking of the pre-war period. Things have changed. People don't spend money as they used to. However, have it your own way, but you'll find that it won't

41

work. There aren't the same profits to be made. There isn't the money—frankly, I don't think that people are such mugs as they used to be! Stick to your complete dinner services and tea-sets, undamaged Chelsea and Swansea, and Dresden figures, your fine furniture. At the end of the year I'm ready to bet that my sales will be ahead of yours! Only don't interfere with me, because if you do someone is going to get hurt—and that person will not be me. Is that clear?'

'Perfectly.'

The door closed. Emmanuel sat at the big desk, motionless, his eyes hard, his lips compressed. He had blundered, and yet he could not see how else he could have acted. It was impossible to begin this venture by allowing Julian to have everything his own way ; that could only lead to disaster. On the other hand he had always believed as old Emmanuel and Simeon Jaffe had done, that if you wished to gain a reputation you must work towards that goal unflinchingly.

Looking back on the small undistinguished shop he had once kept in Milano, Emmanuel could have shuddered at the recollection of the stock which he had been forced to rely on to sell in order to earn a living. Now he would have glanced at the contents of that shop, and with the exception of half a dozen articles, have stigmatized the rest as 'junk'.

True, even there he had begun to attain some reputation as a decorator, as a man who had ideas, and could carry them out in a manner which was completely satisfactory. He had sought diligently for the materials which he needed, and his own judgment had told him that they were good. But so far as his shop went, in those days it was undistinguished and unpretentious.

When Simeon Jaffe had taken him into partnership he had entered a new world. A world where nothing which was not beautiful, the best of its kind, complete and whenever possible unique, was admitted.

In the new Jaffe Galleries there were no pieces of mended china, no matter how skilfully the repairs might have been done. Doubtful pictures were frankly sold as 'doubtful' and they were dismissed as something which might have charm, even a certain beauty, but had no claim to be extolled or praised except in terms which held a trace of disparagement.

Jaffe and Gollantz had adopted a high standard, and had lived up to it. He had believed that he would find the same standard in Bond Street. His brief glance round the big showroom that morning had told him that he was facing a disappointment.

He frowned, drummed with his fingertips on the desk, and

42

said softly, 'The tone is wrong somehow. Reuben is as honest as the day, his taste has always been deplorable, and after all, he is here as an accountant, not as a connoisseur. My father has obviously been ill, unable to attend to business as he used to, things are slack. They've got to be tightened up.' His lips curved into a rather bitter smile. 'If I'm the man to go round with a spanner—I don't envy myself the job.'

That evening he went back to the house in Knightsbridge, feeling tired and not a little disheartened. He had made his tour of the showrooms and stockrooms, and had found little to reassure him. He had interviewed the staff individually, he had told the two young salesmen that he disliked their ties, that their knowledge of the firm's private marks was insufficient and inaccurate.

'Have the goodness,' he said to them, 'to visit Carliss and Hallett's in the Burlington Arcade—it's not damaged, luckily. Get a tie each, have it charged to me, but remember that for business I do not recommend all the colours of the r-rainbow. It distracts the client's attention from the goods which it is your work to sell. Also, oblige me by r-really setting to work to acquaint yourselves with the private marks, so that your reading of them becomes immediate and automatic. Good afternoon, gentlemen.'

He had sent for Mark Seber, and disliked him on sight. The man looked scruffy and untidy. It was not that his clothes were particularly shabby, but they were carelessly worn, dusty and the waistcoat heavily spotted with grease. Emmanuel suspected that Seber, being fair, only shaved every other day. He needed a haircut, and his nails were not beyond reproach.

Seber said, 'I am an Austrian, from Vienna.'

Emmanuel raised his eyebrows. 'Your accent is not Viennese.'

'Do you doubt my word, Mr. Gollantz?' The tone was truculent.

'Not at all. I merely commented that your accent was not that of Vienna.'

'You know that city so well?'

'Exceedingly well; my grandfather came from there. We had many relatives living there until—well, until the situation became too difficult and dangerous.'

'So! They were Jews, your relatives?'

'My family is of Jewish extraction, yes. But I did not ask you to come here to talk of my family.' He smiled. 'You are no doubt aware of the new arrangement here, and I wish to get to know all my staff.'

Seber said roughly, 'I was engaged by Mr. Julian. I thought that I was with him entirely to work.'

'Not entirely.' Emmanuel's smile was coldly pleasant. 'I should like to know exactly what work you do. If you confine yourself to the buying of old silver, that is scarcely sufficient to keep you busy. If you have other forms of business activity, I should be glad to know of them.'

'Well,' Seber shrugged his shoulders, 'I buy brass in many forms.'

'I think that the firm has now sufficient brass. Please do not buy any more for the moment. And what else?'

'I repair china—I am an expert at repairing china.'

'We don't sell repaired china, Mr. Seber, in this firm.'

'If I am ordered to make repairs, surely it is my duty those repairs to make?'

'Tomorrow I should like to see some of these repairs. Good evening, Mr. Seber, and—if you please—no more br-rass until I tell you.'

He had spoken pleasantly, he had even contrived to put a shade of cordiality into his voice, but Seber had merely bowed stiffly and gone out. Emmanuel sat still for a moment, then rose, washed his hands in the tiny room which his grandfather had installed, brushed his hat carefully, and taking up his gloves and stick followed Mark Seber.

Reuben Davis was waiting for him. His round, chubby face was grave.

He said, 'You're going, Emmanuel?'

'Yes, it's turned six o'clock. Has my brother left?'

'He didn't come back after luncheon, he rarely does.'

'Anything you wanted to talk about?'

Reuben sighed gustily. 'Many things, many, many things. It's not possible to have a real conference here, too many people listen! Can I come round and see you after dinner tonight? Before we begin this—this new régime, I must know what is in your mind.'

'At the moment, Reuben, nothing except complete weariness and a sense of frustration. Oh, that's natural, it will pass. Yes, of course, come round.' He laid his hand for an instant on Reuben's shoulder and said gently, 'Don't worry too much, my friend. I know that you're disappointed, worried, probably with every reason, but we're going to come through. I swear it! Courage, Reuben, courage!'

'Then you have noticed——'

Emmanuel interrupted him. 'I have noticed many things, and I shall begin very soon to tackle them. It's not going to be easy; very few things which are worth doing *are* easy, but we'll do it. There's an old quotation, I forget who was the author, I don't even know that I'm getting it correct—" 'Tis not in mortals to command success, but we'll do more—deserve it." There, good night—or *au revoir*. I'll expect you about nine.' He laughed. 'I can promise you Hannah's coffee and some of my grandfather's old brandy.'

He walked the length of Bond Street, feeling suddenly more content, as if the quotation which he had repeated to Reuben had been a kind of 'confession of faith'. He didn't like the atmosphere of the Gallery, he didn't care for the type of young man employed there, he disliked Mark Seber, and it was obvious that his brother was going to make every possible difficulty.

He squared his shoulders, a habit of his when he faced and realized a difficulty completely. 'All r-right,' he said very softly, as if speaking the words gave him fresh courage. 'All r-right! Before I was weak—or was I too strong? I don't know. Now, I shan't "run away". Here I am, and here I stay. *Je suit prêt!* Come the four corners—and so on.'

Forgetting his determination to practise strict economy, he hailed a passing taxi and drove home. Simeon would be there, Hannah would be waiting to give him the coffee which he loved, he could shut the claret-coloured front door, and—escape for twelve hours at least.

CHAPTER FOUR

HIS taxi had scarcely stopped when the door was flung open and Simeon rushed down the steps. His face was alight, his eyes shining, and his greeting was filled with warmth and excitement.

Simeon Gollantz was tall for his age, his colouring lighter than Emmanuel's, for his hair was a bright brown, very thick and soft, his complexion very clear, and his eyes lacking that hint of melancholy which had always lurked in those of his father and his grandfather. His voice was charming, rich and full without being noisy.

As Emmanuel took his son's hands, he thought, as he did so often, with a little stab of pain, 'How like Juliet he grows. The same voice, the same sense of radiating kindliness.'

Simeon said, 'If you'd been much longer I was going to telephone to the Gallery. Hannah's got coffee ready for you.' He laughed. 'You still stick to your continental habits.'

'I believe that my coffee-drinking is the last one. I discarded the rest when I was in the Army. Now, how are you? You're looking in such rude health that it is almost indecent.'

Arm in arm they went into the quiet little sitting-room, where Hannah brought the coffee which Emmanuel loved, served in a tiny china pot, strong and fragrant. He smiled his thanks, and sipped it with real appreciation. Simeon sat and watched him intently. He had always had a more than usual love for his father; for the first years of his life Emmanuel, Simeon Jaffe and Guido had been his world. His mother had died when he was a baby, and although Emmanuel and Guido had always conspired to make a clear and vital picture of her for the boy, there were times when her memory seemed to him to be only that—a picture. A beautiful picture of a beautiful woman, but lacking personal interest for Simeon except as a work executed with skill and loving care.

He said, 'Father, any news of Guido?'

'Indeed yes, the best. I saw him three days ago; he was

leaving for Italy, where he will act as my manager and agent in Milano. I hope to hear from him within a week or so.'

'Then he's been in England! And I didn't see him! Father, how was that?' His voice was filled with dismay.

Emmanuel spoke very gently. 'It was at Guido's own wish, Simeon. He was a prisoner of war, in the camp which I had in my charge. To him, to be a prisoner was something disgraceful, a kind of slur on his honour. He begged me not to tell you—until he was free again. Oh, you will see him, he will come here to see us, and—perhaps we shall go to see him. He has a great, very great, affection for you. He has taken back a gr-reat many photographs of you which I gave him from time to time. We've every reason to be proud of our friend Guido. He's a gr-reat character.'

'Oh, I never doubted that. Poor Guido, wearing beastly clothes, eating horrible food. Well, it's over now,' he paused—'or is it?'

Emmanuel said, 'That particular act is over. None of us knows on what—or when—the curtain will rise on the next. It's a queer time in which to live, a time of uncertainty, a time of disappointments. People say, with a kind of dogged stolidity, that we shall "come through", but how or where they very rarely explain. However, we can only hope that the sound common sense which does run through all classes will assert itself.'

'What are your political views, Father?'

Emmanuel set down his cup and smiled. 'Another continental habit I have not relinquished, the habit of calling myself a Christian Democrat, my son. Now, tell me about—what interests me most, possibly selfish—yourself. You've got plans? May I know them?'

His son flushed, frowned, and finally laughed gently. 'Oh, I've made plenty, but whether they'll be acceptable to you or not I can't tell.'

'Neither can I until you've confided them to me.'

'What about a nice long whisky-and-soda while you listen? It's not a bad idea. It will give you something to do, you can take sips in order to hide your disapproval, and it will give me confidence. Shall I get one for you?'

'Oh, excellent young man!'

As Emmanuel sipped the ice-cold drink and smoked slowly and contentedly, Simeon leaned forward, his hands clasped between his knees, his face grave and intent.

He admitted that he had 'played with the idea of lots of things'. They had ranged, as Hannah had told Emmanuel, from being an engine-driver to going to sea, from being an engineer —preferably a marine engineer—to entering the Air Force.

'Even now, although I know that it's impossible, the Air Force—flying—is what I want. Well, that's definitely—out. I was only a youngster, not a lot of experience, and now without one foot they'd not look at me, and I can't blame them, of course. You know'—his voice took on a deeper tone, he leaned forward, his hands clasped, his eyes suddenly bright as if with the recollection of days which were over—'it was a grand life. It wasn't only excitement, it most certainly wasn't the idea that you were "wiping out" cities. I don't think that ever came into it. There were "targets", and "targets" were there to be hit. They were just that—"targets". There was a tune—a march or something of the kind—called "Lords of the Air". Grandiose, I know, but you felt that. You were a "lord of the air". You were defying the rules of science as discovered by Newton, all about apples falling on the ground. It was'—he laughed—'well, it was—something.

'However, that's over, and, I began to look round for work which would mean, eventually a career. I thought of the law, with Uncle Bill and Charles Wilmot, but when I went to see them the whole thing seemed stuffy, dry, dusty. Maybe I'd got the air of the high altitudes into my lungs, I don't know.

'Then I heard that you were coming home, and grandfather told me that you and Uncle Julian were going to run the Galleries. Things seemed to crystallize. The idea fired my imagination. There they were, the Galleries which had begun on Campden Hill, when my great-grandfather came over from Vienna. He was a romantic character, wasn't he?'

Emmanuel nodded. 'I have always felt so ; that is my reason for having, more or less, tried to model myself upon him in business. Go on, Simeon.'

'It goes back further than that,' Simeon said, unable to keep the excitement out of his voice ; 'it all began in Vienna with Old Emmanuel's father, then he came to England—great-grandfather, I mean—then grandfather, and now you and Uncle Julian. I felt that it just had to go on. It all stands for something. Not just grabbing for money, but setting a standard. You see, young Max is going into the City, and from my point of view it's a good thing, because if he'd gone to the Galleries I should have been obliged to stay out. He and I don't just see eye to eye. He takes a poor view of me, and, candidly, I take exactly the same view of him. I've thought about it quite a lot, Father. I've bought some books and studied them——'

Emmanuel smiled. 'Chaffers?'

Simeon nodded. 'Yes, how did you know?'

'Because if anyone is going to study silver and the like it is the obvious book to buy. Anything else?'

Simeon flushed. 'I've been up and down the Charing Cross Road, a shop called Dobell's have been awfully decent to me, and some other people called Marks. They've found me quite a lot of books—good ones ; very useful, I imagine.'

'And all this means,' Emmanuel said, 'that you wish to come into the Gollantz Galleries?'

'That's the immediate idea, Father.'

'Hard work, my boy.'

'I don't mind that.'

'Disappointments. I remember when I thought that I knew everything and came to realize that I understood nothing. Times have changed and it would appear that we must change with them—only, Simeon,' and he leaned forward and spoke with complete sincerity, 'only never shall we change in one thing. We have a gr-reat r-reputation, a r-reputation for honesty and integr-rity. That must always r-remain.'

Simeon nodded. 'Yes, I feel that too. I don't want to shove my oar in, Father, but I've a feeling that—this is from a hymn we used to sing at school—the hosts of Midian may "prowl and prowl around".'

'Ah!' Emmanuel lifted his glass and stared at the contents, giving the glass a little twist so that the whisky-and-soda swirled in the glass. 'I'll give you another quotation—a little, shall we say, "adapted"—"and we shall shock them, nought shall make us rue, if we but to ourselves do hold but true". It's taking a certain liberty with Shakespeare, but I believe that he will forgive me.'

Simeon rose. Emmanuel's brows contracted a little as he saw the slight hesitation as Simeon settled his weight on his two feet ; then, his stance secure, he said, 'Then I can come in?'

Emmanuel found it difficult to conceal his pleasure. He had all the passion for antiques which had filled old Emmanuel ; Max had been careful, strictly honest and proud of his complete integrity, but Max had never loved old things as his father had done, or in the same degree as his eldest son.

The thought of the House of Gollantz going on gave Emmanuel a sense of keen delight. He believed in Simeon, in his sincerity ; the boy had done well at school, but he had never shown great scholastic promise. His reports had been good, his character praised, his general progress had always been satisfactory. Emmanuel looked at him keenly, noted how his eyes

49

shone, and how his lips parted a little in eagerness to hear his father's verdict.

He said, 'Naturally the thought of working with you, of teaching you what I have learnt myself, appeals to me enormously. Only, remember that we are living now in 1946, and that 1946 is not the same as even ten years ago. Money is short, and I suspect will be shorter. There are endless restrictions and limitations which will hamper us on the decorating side. My Gallery in Milano has never been run in conjunction with the Gallery in Bond Street. What remains in Milano I have not the faintest idea until I hear from Guido.

'In 1939 I was a moderately rich man ; I may be ruined for all I know. I tell you this in confidence, Simeon. The Gollantz Gallery is not what it once was. I may be able, with Hannah's help, with Reuben Davis's—and, I hope, with yours—to remake it. It's going to be very hard going. You're old enough to know that your uncle and I do not—get on. Our methods are different, our training has been different. I am not painting a very bright picture, am I?'

Simeon said sturdily, 'You've scarcely begun to paint it yet, have you? I've been to the Gallery several times, both alone and with my grandfather. It's going to look very different when you've been there a month or so.'

'You think so?' Emmanuel's tone was suddenly eager.

'I don't think, Father, I'm jolly well certain!' He grinned and looked young and excited. 'That's why I want you to let me come in. I don't like backing losers, and I'd rather back a "cert" in you.'

'There's a devil of a lot to learn. China, furniture, silver, decorating, pictures—whew! Endless! You never learn all there is to know. Hard, grinding work ; books and books to read. You'd have to go abroad to look at pictures. There are plenty to study here in London—but not enough.'

'When I was quite a small boy I remember you used to ask me things, the names of the artists who painted certain pictures, and so on. Once or twice you said that I was knowledgeable for my age. Guido always praised my knowledge, he said that it was *fantàstico*.'

He laughed, but Emmanuel detected a certain wistfulness in his voice ; he leaned forward and stretched out his hand.

'Six months' trial, without committing you to anything. Only remember you're to take advantage of the week-ends, get down to Ordingly and ride, play tennis, walk and so forth. I won't have you getting flabby and pasty-faced. Start at the bottom, no special concessions, and work your way up. I'll put everything in your way so that you can get knowledge. How's that?'

'Grand, just marvellous. When can I start?'

'As soon as I have discussed it all with your grandfather in all probability next Monday. So make the most of your holiday.'

'I shall.' He stood looking down on his father, his handsome face full of contentment. He stammered a little, as if he found it hard to speak the words which he wanted. 'I've always thought that you were the finest father a fellow could have, and I've always liked you better than anyone—as a friend, if you know what I mean. I promise that even if I don't make a startling success, I won't—won't let you down. It can't have always been very easy. I do realize that. I'll try to—to make up for a whole lot of things. Thanks a lot.'

His father rose and said gravely, 'Thank you, Simeon. So we begin with the fifth gener-ration of the House of Gollantz! I look forward to the opportunity of working with you.'

That night he sat for many hours with Reuben Davis. The little man arrived, armed with papers and books, accounts and counterfoils. His chubby face was grave, and his manner portentous

They sat at the dining-table, while Reuben talked, carefully and exactly. Slowly the position of the firm became clear to Emmanuel. Certain kinds of activity were ended, temporarily at least. It was impossible to rely any longer upon decorating and the beautiful upholstery which had been such a feature. Materials were very expensive and difficult to obtain, labour was scarce.

Emmanuel said, 'Yes, and the rest, Reuben?'

'Pictures are not in any particular demand. Here and there some very well-known painting by a famous artist arrests attention, and the dealers of repute flock to the salerooms,' but in general pictures by what Reuben called 'the lesser lights' were slow in selling. Miniatures were in a certain demand ; only a fortnight ago they had sold, and sold well, four Cosways of undoubted authenticity. 'They're small, suitable for the flats people live in in these days,' Reuben said, 'and some of them like to pretend they are pictures of their own ancestors!'

Furniture, those splendid tables, and the complete sets of chairs, six, eight, even ten, who could house them? Who could get people to polish them and keep them in good order? Little spinets, clavichords and the like, sold to be used as sideboards ; chests of drawers of the old-fashioned type sold if they were transformed into cocktail cabinets, washhand stands if they were made into dressing-tables with what Reuben designated 'frilly petticoats'—'people have a mania for something made out of something else for which it was never intended!'

Carpets were difficult, Oriental rugs sold if they were not too large, 'trivialities'—snuff-boxes, pounce-boxes, bits of ivory and the like always 'moved', but, 'you can't run a firm like ours on two Limoges figures and a couple of snuff-boxes, Emmanuel'.

'On the staff,' Reuben continued, 'two salesmen, neither of them up to much, think they're conferring a favour on us by being there—the commissionaire, three cleaners, Fred Hooper for furniture—a good man, Hooper—Seber who messes about in that back room of his tinkering with china and Heaven only knows what, and Miss Waters and now, Hannah. Ten people, not counting me, Julian and yourself—and of course, Sir Max. Then old Peters and his son Joseph, in the workshop! Those wages take some finding.'

'I take it that we're running at a loss,' Emmanuel said.

Reuben lifted his hands, and looked like the Jew he was. 'A loss!' he almost wailed; 'money going out and so little coming in! At a loss, you say!'

'What do we need? More capital?'

'To run away down the drain? No, we want reorganization, we want new ideas, we want'—with sudden viciousness—'to carry no passengers, and passengers who don't even pay their fares. That's what we want, Emmanuel.'

'And that,' very calmly, 'means, I take it, my brother Julian?'

'You've said it. Comes in at eleven, leaves for luncheon at half past twelve, comes back at three—if he comes back at all. Sits closeted with Seber for hours. Emmanuel, he is getting money from somewhere. How? Where? Who from?'

'Does he sell privately and not through the firm, do you think?'

'Maybe! How would I know? He tells me nothing!'

'He won't tell me much more,' Emmanuel said, his face grim. 'Reuben, we're up against it, but we'll pull round. We shall, you know.'

The next day Emmanuel went over to see his father. He found Max looking pale and listless, it seemed too much effort to take his son's hand in greeting. His voice was querulous when he asked how things were going in Bond Street, as if he challenged Emmanuel to dare to voice complaints.

Very patiently Emmanuel explained, and put forward his views. The great day of antique dealing had gone; for a time, at all events. The days of meetings in Max's room with Arbuthnot, old Davis and Lane, when they sat round discussing their projects and sipping fine champagne, were over.

'This is,' Emmanuel said, 'obviously the day of small things.'

Max frowned. 'I dislike those catch phrases. You'll tell me next that what we want are "small profits and quick returns"! Or you'll suggest a sale. Cut prices and the like. My dear Emmanuel, we have always run the business with dignity, and I intend that it shall continue to be run in that way—the way which is acceptable to me, to the tradition which my father laid down.'

With great patience Emmanuel smiled and assured him. 'I have no intention of relinquishing any dignity, but we must be dignified in a different way. First of all, there is the question of Simeon. He wants to learn all there is to know——'

For the first time Max's face softened. 'Ah, he wants to come into the business. That is pleasant hearing. Julian's boy is a fine lad, clever, intelligent, but he has no interest in our work. His mind turns to finance. He is going into the City when he finishes at Oxford. But Simeon—well, well. Wants to learn all there is to know, eh? I have never contrived to do that! But he's young, it may be that he will be ready to take charge when the "good days" come back—if they ever do come back.'

Slowly then Emmanuel began to outline his plans. One of the young salesmen must go, and gradually Simeon could take his place in the showroom. The place must be—he hesitated, fearing how his father might take the criticism—better kept, made more attractive.

'For the time being, at least,' he continued, 'I suggest that we introduce some new forms of merchandise. Not, most emphatically, rubbish, but things which cost less, which can be bought by people who are far from wealthy and yet like beautiful things round them. In those cupboards there are hundreds of small things, all things which would please the eye, and which have their own intrinsic value. They are,' he paused, 'stock, and they have been allowed to accumulate because the firm was occupied with other and more important matters. Now we have the opportunity to turn our attention to them and they can earn money. "Sprats often catch mackerel." ' He saw Max twist his mouth at the sound of a phrase which he had always disliked.

'Very well, for the time being—we'll bait with—sprats. Do you agree, Father?'

'I suppose there is no alternative,' Max said gloomily. 'Very well, make what alterations you wish, but—and I mean this—do consult your brother Julian. You have, I don't dispute it, greater knowledge, but he is—what's the word I want?—he's keen. Don't disregard him, I beg.'

'No, no, certainly not,' and with all the charm of which he was capable, Emmanuel began to sketch to his father his further plans and ideas.

He had spent most of the night thinking and thinking hard ; he had slowly come to see that the 'great days' were over, when 'every morning brought a noble chance, and every chance'—his mind had halted, and staring into the darkness he had added—'brought out a noble opportunity'. His mind strayed on to the words which followed, for he was a man who had read poetry widely, and in the *Morte d'Arthur* had found many phrases which delighted him. 'And I the last go forth companionless . . .' His lips had softened, his whole face looked younger. He would not 'go forth companionless'—he would have Simeon to walk with him, every step of the way.

He had outlined his plans, had spoken with complete frankness to his father, and for the first time for many years he had felt that Max trusted him, believed in him, and was glad of his presence. He had talked of Simeon and his determination that the boy should not grill in town every week-end. He heard his father's response with pleasure.

'Of course not. Plenty of room here ; make that a rule, he comes to Ordingly every Saturday. You ought to get him a horse, Emmanuel.'

Emmanuel nodded. 'Thank you, Father, that is what I hoped that you would say.'

'Plenty of room here, far too much. I don't keep horses in these days.'

'Then I may send one along, and—of course, the forage will be my business. Yes please,' as Max made a gesture of dismissal, 'I should feel happier.'

That night he went to see his Aunt Beatrice. Lady Heriot had once been Miss Beatrice Grantley, of the Gaiety chorus and she still retained the manner of speech of the Edwardian days, those days on which she looked back with regret. They had been days—and nights! Then, no man dreamed of asking you out to supper without offering you champagne. If he did you simply wrote him off your list. She had married Walter Heriot, Bart., and by him had two children : Walter and Viva. The girl had married Emmanuel Gollantz, she had divorced him—'a faked business. Emmanuel's not the kind of feller to go off for the odd week-end. I suspect that he sat up all night playing patience! However, it's none of my business. Viva was a fool to let him go!'—and married 'Toby' Tatten.

'Devoted, I b'lieve,' Lady Heriot said; 'comic-looking little bloke, not got two ideas in his head. As Marie used to sing, "A man with only one single idea"—or something to that effect. No children, Viva—well, she "rackets", always dashing about, taking up this and that and never a damned thing that's a ha'p'orth of use. Well, there it is! Poor Walter, my boy—never strong, got into the wrong set—the fast set. Died early in the war. My old man—oh, he hangs on. Heaven knows how—or why.'

She met Emmanuel with outstretched hands. 'My darling Manny!' No one else had ever used that diminutive, but then Aunt Beatrice always used them whenever possible. She called Julian 'Ju' when she spoke to him, which wasn't often. 'So you've finished with the Army? What did old Kipling call you—a "time-expired man"?'

Emmanuel said, 'Not quite applicable to me, darling.'

'Well, come and have a drink. Oh, I can still get it! What's it to be? A bottle of the "boy" to celebrate, or a B and S?'

He smiled. 'If it's possible—a W and S.'

He sat looking round the big light drawing-room, with its dozens of photographs in silver frames, its watercolours—none of them particularly good—in gilt frames; at the Aubusson carpet with its lovely bunches of flowers and foliage, and at the overstuffed, satin-covered furniture. Surely Beatrice Heriot's drawing-room was the last of its kind in London. She brought him a long glass, in which the whisky-and-soda shone yellow and the bits of ice tapped against the glass. She gave it a twist as she handed it to him.

'Two nicest sounds in the world, Manny,' she said: 'ice against glass and the crackle of a fiver. Absolute music! I'll join you.'

She fussed about, and finally came and sat down opposite to him, her knees wide apart, for her own comfort mattered far more to her than mere elegance, her whisky-and-soda—several shades darker than that which she had given Emmanuel—on the little occasional table beside her. She fired questions at him like a machine-gun.

'Gone back to the firm, eh?'

'So you heard?'

'Yes, Angela was here yesterday. She wears well. Always led a good life, never played the game!' She winked broadly. 'Oh, well, a short life and a gay one—though mine's lasted pretty well. How's the old firm going? I patronized it the other day—nothing like keeping the "spondulicks" in the family, eh? Gertie Colcroft's eldest boy is getting married. She married Colcroft when she was in the chorus at the Adelphi, now Hector's going to marry Dorette Manton's girl—she was in *Lights up in London*. History repeats itself! So do the damned politicians. I swore the other night to Walter—the old man—that I'd give a dinner for the whole Cabinet. Get all the insults off my chest at once. Morrison over the *hors-d'œuvres,* Bevan over the soup, Shinberg—beg his pardon, Shinwell—over the fish, and so on— right through the lot! Walter said, "Save your time, they've got hides like elephants! Never feel it!" So I thought better of it.

'Manny, the country's going from bad to worse. Where it's— or rather where *they* are going to land us—God knows. I say that in all respect, for I'm a religious woman! Yes, I am, Manny, don't grin like a Cheshire cat. So you're back in dear old Bond Street. Many a time I've gone there and had a glass of "bubbly" with the old man. What a lad! Always kept "a naughty little twinkle in *his* eye"—what an eye for a pretty woman! And I was an "eyeful" in those days, Manny, I give you my word.'

He said, 'I find you still a very charming "eyeful", Aunt Beatrice.'

'Well, to what do I owe the honour of this visit—I don't imagine that it's altogether for the sake of my bright eyes! Never mind, don't tell me—"you can't stop a girl from thinking", and they're pleasant thoughts.'

Emmanuel said, 'Aunt Beatrice, you're a "rattle" — an "agreeable rattle", I admit! I want to buy a horse.'

She screamed, 'A horse, Manny! Where are you going to keep it? In your office? Good God—a horse! What kind of a horse?'

'For Simeon to ride during the week-ends when he goes to Ordingly.'

'Oh, for Simeon. That's a nice lad; he'll go a long way. Comes here sometimes, makes me laugh. We'll have him hanging round stage doors before we know where we are! He'll be one of the "early birds", say what you like. Looks like his dear mother, eh?'

He caught the change of inflexion in her voice; its stridency disappeared when she mentioned Juliet. He looked at her gratefully, this was the Beatrice Heriot he loved dearly.

'Yes,' she continued, 'astonishingly like. I didn't mean that *she* was "one of the early birds". Good Lord, not likely. Lovely —gracious. They don't breed 'em like that in these days. Tarts look like society women, and society women look like tarts— most of 'em, at all events. All right, "Toby" Tatten and I will find you one. And it will be "right". You don't want some fantastic "bargain", do you?'

'I want a good horse. It may be the last decent present I shall be able to give him, and it's got to be good.'

She shot a quick glance at him. 'Not hard up, are you, Manny? I can always let you have a bit. "If you can't do a turn to a pal when he's down", y'know. Say the word!' He shook his head, smiling. 'Very well, only don't go short of anything. I mean that. Damn it, if poor Walter had been like you! Not a bad lad, y'know, but easily led. That precious brother of yours did nothing to help him. Never done anything to help anyone —except himself.

'Oh, well, don't let's spoil our cosy chat. Like to see what I bought for Hector Colcroft? Rather nice. Flatter myself I know something about old stuff, antiques. After all, I'm a bit of an antique myself!'

She rang and gave an order to the elderly butler who answered it. He returned with a pair of silver candelabra. She motioned to him to set them down on one of the numerous tables.

'Nice, eh, Manny?'

Emmanuel rose and walked over to the table. He stood looking at the pair of splendid candelabra with concentrated attention. His fingers fumbled for his eyeglass, and with studied care he put it to his eye. He said, 'Ver-ry nice, ver-ry nice indeed. A *leetle* rococo, perhaps. Lacking the simple elegance of the earlier pieces. George the Fourth, but very good. Might I ask what they cost?'

His aunt answered, 'Sixty-five "jimmies". And they're George the Third.'

Emmanuel spun round. 'The Third? No, no, my dear, impossible.'

'The Third, I tell you!' She was emphatic. 'Look at the marks.'

He gave her his old-fashioned little bow. 'Thank you—if I may.'

She watched his deft hands turn the candelabra over, saw how carefully, even lovingly, he handled them. His face was grave and intent, he bent forward to examine the marks more closely ; then carried the pieces closer to the electric light.

Beatrice Heriot thought, 'What a fool Viva was to let him go. Even if there were difficulties, they'd have blown over. Men will be men—and women should be glad of it. "Toby's" all right, but he's limited ; he doesn't come out of the same stable as this fellow. Poor Manny, he hasn't got a great deal out of life, up to date. Some scandal—I bet Julian was at the bottom of it !— then a year with Juliet Forbes, then the Army, and now setting to work to pull the business together, after Max—and circumstances—have let it go to bits. Poor Manny—the pick of the bunch!'

She said, 'Satisfied?'

He set down the piece which he had been examining and came back to his chair. He sat down and she exclaimed, 'Manny, you're not ill?'

'No, Aunt Beatrice.'

'You're looking like a peeled turnip. Have another spot?'

'Thank you. Now, who sold you that pair of candelabra, please?'

'A feller with bad teeth and hair that wanted cutting. Spoke like a foreigner. Julian told me that he was the firm's expert. Why, nothing wrong, is there? Come on, Manny—out with it, come clean!'

'I am going to ask you to allow me to r-return them to the Gallery. I shall make myself responsible for finding another pair for you, at the same pr-rice. Sixty-five pounds, I think you said? Would you do me the gr-reat favour of asking no questions. I am r-rusty, my knowledge is not quite what it was—but I am not satisfied. I shall be gr-rateful.'

'I don't understand what you're driving at——' she protested.

'Perhaps I shall be able to explain tomorrow. Until then, please tr-rust me. Aunt Beatrice, I must go. I have a gr-reat deal to do. Don't forget about the horse, will you? It's important,' he laughed ; 'everything to do with Simeon is important. My love to Uncle Walter. Good night and thank you for many things.'

Holding the candelabra with care, he walked out and found a taxi. All the way back to Knightsbridge he thought of what he believed that he had discovered, and his anger grew until it blazed. This was what Julian and his precious Seber were doing! Planning to swindle clients like Beatrice Heriot! Not that the name or status of the client mattered, but it hurt him intolerably that his aunt, who had always been so generous, who had always supported the firm of Gollantz in every possible way, should have been marked down as a victim.

There was just a chance that he might be wrong, that during the war years his knowledge had become dulled, or that after all there might be little difference between the last years of the reign of George the Third—the Regency—and the full-blooded and rather ostentatious productions of the reign of his successor in its early years.

He carried the candelabra into the house. Hannah came out to meet him.

'You're late, aren't you? Simeon's gone to bed, he was tired out. Not been buying at this time of night, surely?' with a glance at the silver.

Emmanuel set them carefully on the table; their bright sheen was reflected in its polished surface. Speaking with careful lightness he said, 'They're nice, aren't they?'

Hannah nodded. 'Quite. I'm not fond of the period. Too decorated.'

'What period?' he asked.

'George the Fourth.'

'The Third,' he insisted quietly.

She moved to examine the pieces, shrugged her shoulders and said curtly, 'The Third! Emmanuel, you're *meshuggah*!'

He shook his head. 'We shall see. Good night, Hannah.'

CHAPTER FIVE

EMMANUEL woke with a curious sense of apprehension which held, despite its unpleasantness, a feeling of excitement. He was going to pit his wits against those of other people. What the result might be he did not know, though Julian's reaction, if found to be in the wrong, was fairly predictable. Julian had always used his ill-health as a means of escape from anything which was difficult or unpleasant. Doubtless he would use it again.

For some reason Emmanuel discarded his 'demob' suit this morning and dressed with more than ordinary care. He remembered how Viva had always said that 'a really good hat gives me moral courage!' Viva—Aunt Beatrice—old Walter Heriot— all tangled up with his life, sometimes exercising a kindly influence, sometimes appearing crude and hard with the modern attitude of mind! And yet he knew of no woman who amused him as Viva did, who could look more charming, or be a more delightful hostess.

He chose his tie with care, settled his shoulders carefully into the immaculate coat which he had not worn for seven years. He slewed round before his glass and noticed the admirable fit. He felt ready to face anything!

Hannah had left the house, and Martha attended to his wants. Dear Hannah, he could picture her walking into the Galleries precisely as the clock struck nine, and staring—with a slightly offensive expression—at anyone who entered later than she did. He imagined Julian's entrance at half past ten or eleven o'clock, and could almost see Hannah's face filled with cold, but respectful, disapproval. However she might dislike Julian, she never forgot that he was a member of the family for whom she had cultivated something almost approaching adoration.

Martha said, 'I hope as everythink's all right. Miss Rosenfeldt went off early. Says she's going to walk through the Park and into Grosvenor Street and on ter Bond Street every morning. She said it 'ul get her weight down! Wonnerful energy's she's got, sir.'

This morning the commissionaire recognized him. His smile was friendly, and Emmanuel swung open the door of the Gallery ready to smile at the whole world, despite what lay before him. The place looked better kept, though it had not yet attained that pitch of perfection which was what he wanted. The two young salesmen, wearing ties of subdued and discreet elegance, wished him 'Good morning', and Hannah shot out—rather like a stout 'Jack-in-the-box', he thought, from her glass-walled office.

'Good morning, Mr. Emmanuel. The letters are all ready for you.'

'Thank you, Hannah.' She had always been called by her first name by members of the family. 'Will you come along in ten minutes?'

He entered his office, set down the candelabra which he had brought with him on a side table, and began to go through his letters. Private letters for the staff were fewer this morning, he noted with satisfaction. Only again he found a small parcel directed to Mark Seber, and marked 'Private and Confidential'.

The letters opened and read, he rang for Hannah. She came, calm, massive and efficient. Emmanuel pushed the letters—only two this morning to members of the firm—towards her, and said, 'Please send these round, and repeat my order that the firm will not accept private letters for the staff. I shall want to see Seber, please.'

He dictated carefully, and with complete attention. Anyone entering the office would have gathered than Hannah was an ordinary and elderly secretary, and that Emmanuel knew nothing of her except in business hours. No one would have imagined that these two people were bound by bonds of close friendship, trust and mutual admiration.

She gathered up the letters and rose, flinging a glance at the candelabra as she went. Emmanuel, noting the glance, laughed.

'Don't worry, Hannah. I am preparing to deal with it.'

She sniffed, 'Well, that's something, anyway.'

'On second thoughts, don't send Seber to me. I'll go to him.'

'Very well.'

He walked slowly down the showrooms; the two young salesmen displayed signs of rather unnecessary activity, for there were no clients at that early hour. He looked over the goods displayed, and called one of the young men to him.

'You're——'

'Henry Watson, sir.'

'Very good. Now, Watson, I want you to get the key of the small stockroom, the one marked, "No. 5", and tell Mr. Davis

I want you to go there and collect for me all the small—small, remember—Chelsea pieces you can find—china or enamel. Bring them out here, ready for me to look over.'

When he passed, Watson said to Clough, 'That's a pill. I don't know that I can spot Chelsea as easily as that. What is the mark?'

Clough frowned. 'Anchor in gold or red, I think. But someone else copied it later, I fancy. Whew, I don't envy you your job.'

'I don't envy myself my job, either. Suppose I'd better make a start.'

At the end of the long gallery Emmanuel found a door on which was painted the name 'Mark Seber', and beneath it the word 'Private'. Another distinct innovation, for it had been an unwritten law that no doors were to bear names, not even that of the head of the firm himself.

He knocked, his eyes hard, his lips compressed. No one bade him enter, and raising his hand he knocked again with greater insistence. Again there was no sound, but presently the door was opened about a foot and Seber looked out.

In a voice which was dangerously quiet, Emmanuel asked, 'Allow me to come in, if you please?'

Seber opened the door a little wider. 'At the moment I am very busy.'

'Then we are in the same boat, for so am I. Too busy to waste time waiting outside closed doors in my own Gallery. I wanted to have a talk with you.' Calmly Emmanuel seated himself and lit a cigarette. Seber stood, frowning and obviously annoyed at the interruption.

'First, another parcel has come for you. That practice must cease, as I told everyone yesterday. Then—and I am sor-ry to have to make so many alter-rations, your name cannot be allowed to r-remain on the door. One of the firm's rules, you understand.'

'The firm appears to hev developed a great number of new rules!'

'On the contrary, it is only that I am enforcing the old ones.' He looked towards a closed door at the other end of the small room. 'Ah, you have another room through that door? I thought that I remembered another small office. Why have you two rooms, Mr. Seber?'

'I need two for my experiments. I am too cramped as it is now.'

'Experiments! And in what do you experiment?'

62

'I perhaps should hev said—tests. Yes, that is the word—tests.'

'Of—what?' Emmanuel's voice sounded like a pistol-shot.

'Of silver, of various metals, in china—in many things. It would take too long to explain. It is a lifetime's work.' He spoke quickly and with a certain nervousness. 'I am—specialist, you know that.'

Suavely Emmanuel replied, 'I am certain of it. And also you r-repair china—acting, of course, under instructions. I should be interested to see this work. Allow me to go into the other r-room, please.'

Seber's pasty face changed to scarlet. For one brief instant his hand flew to his mouth, as if to stifle an exclamation, then, recovering himself, he said, 'It impossible is at this moment. The key is in the keeping of Mr. Julian. He is not yet arrived.'

Emmanuel smiled pleasantly. 'A pleasure deferred. Well, Mr. Seber, will you kindly come and collect your parcel, and let it be the last, if you please.'

Seber followed Emmanuel down the gallery ; young Watson was setting out a small collection of china and enamel. Emmanuel stopped for a moment and lifted two tiny figures. 'No, no, Watson. These are Limoges.' He pointed to the china mark with his long delicate finger. 'Notice the anchor . . . as in Chelsea, red, also you will find it in gold. The earliest Chelsea had of course an anchor embossed in an oval ; rather later the anchor alone, but raised. This anchor is coarser, more simple, less delicate. The texture of the china is different. Hand me that bird—yes, that one. Um—it's a nice little piece this—note the patina, the finish, and here we have the raised anchor in red. Compare the two, and relegate your Limoges to the background. I shall be back presently. Always compare the doubtful with the certain authentic, Watson.'

Clough whispered, 'Talks like a schoolteacher, doesn't he?'

Watson, to his friend's surprise, answered, 'Jolly good teacher!'

In his office Emmanuel handed Seber the small parcel. 'Let me have a receipt for it, please.'

'I didn't give a receipt for the one yesterday.'

'Believe me—an oversight. Yes, just your name—there. Ah, that reminds me, you know something of silver. I picked up these last evening. Charming, aren't they?'

Seber stood, his eyes fixed on the pair of candelabra ; he frowned, glanced swiftly at Emmanuel, and was obviously ill at ease.

'I maintain that they are George the Fourth. What exact

63

date? I have a mania for fixing the exact date whenever possible.' He pinched his lower lip in his finger and thumb. 'Say—1822, twenty-three?'

'Probably. To fix precise dates is difficult.'

'But you are an expert. There is of course the hall-mark. Shall we examine that? No, don't hurry away, this is interesting. Now, what do we find? Hello! What is this? Impossible, surely. Seber, look at the hall-mark, please. George the Third! No, no, there must be some mistake. Let me get my glass! Now we shall see more clearly. Yes, the Third! Wait—now I want your advice. In my opinion this hall-mark has been—inserted. It does not belong to this piece of silver at all. Cur-rious that you and my br-rother should have been deceived, for these candelabra were—bought here.' He sat down and laid his fingertips together ; his manner was cool and completely detached. 'Tell me, Seber, what is the histor-ry of this?'

'How should I be able to tell you? Do I buy the silver for the firm? In my opinion the hall-mark is correct, probably a piece in advance of its actual period. Possibly an experiment, who can tell?'

'That is your considered opinion?'

'Yes, why not? Better esk your brudder. He buys, I don't!'

'Thank you, you may go.'

Later, much later, Julian arrived ; he wore his hat at an angle, and was obviously pleased with life. At the sight of Emmanuel's set expression he pulled down the corners of his mouth in mock comicality and asked:

'Well, and what's wrong now! Fresh floutings of the firm's traditions?'

'I should like to see the "silver" book.'

He saw Julian's eyes flicker for a second. 'Why? That's my business.'

'I want to know where a certain piece was bought, what was paid for it, and if it carried a guarantee. Those candelabra there. Any information?'

Julian recovered himself, he looked at the silver, snapped his fingers, and said, 'I can tell you all that. A fellow who was leaving for Canada. Hard up. I don't believe that I even knew his name. Told me they'd been in the family since the reign of George the Third. I bought them as a private speculation. Thought that Amanda might like them. She didn't care for them. Very choosy, y'know, my wife! I paid—now what did I pay? Fifty, I think—yes, I'm certain it was fifty. Now are you satisfied?'

'When was this?'

'Good Heavens, man! Don't be such a bore! About a week ago.'

'And you sold them to Aunt Beatrice for sixty-five. She has had them several days. That Seber of yours is a quick worker!'

'What the devil do you mean?'

'I'm not quite certain, but I'm going to make certain—certain beyond all doubt. That's all, Julian.'

He sat there, his chin resting on his hands long after the door had closed behind Julian. He was as certain as he was capable of being certain of anything that the hall-mark on the silver which Lady Heriot had bought was superimposed. It had originally belonged to some other piece, and some clever craftsman had transferred it. Emmanuel, using the strongest magnifying glass in his collection, which he kept in the drawer of his desk in its neat leather case, could see certain irregularities near the edge of the mark. It had not been 'stamped on'; rather it had been 'stamped in'.

For all he knew this kind of work might be what constituted Seber's 'experiments'—he had slipped badly in using that word, and then changing it to 'tests'. In Heaven's name, what tests did Seber have to apply?

Emmanuel sighed. He had been back at the Gallery for less than a week, and already Julian was loathing his presence; he was suspecting Julian, and the tense atmosphere was growing with every hour. He knew how useless it would be for him to go to his brother and try to 'make friends', to talk plainly about the danger of such tricks played on the public, and the disgust which old Emmanuel would have felt. He knew that such arguments would lead nowhere. Julian would only suspect him of being afraid to carry on his investigations, he would have stigmatized his ideals and longing to maintain the high standard of the firm as 'sentimental and weak', he would laugh at scruples, and finally dare Emmanuel to go to Max and tell him all that he suspected.

If he went to Max, he could imagine his father's tired face and the voice from which all strength and colour seemed to be fading. He could picture Max's quiet but unmistakable exasperation, his feeling that until the arrival of Emmanuel 'things had run smoothly', and that only with his advent had the domestic difficulties in the firm begun.

Bill would grumble and growl that he'd better give Julian the thrashing which he deserved, better pay him off and get him out of the place for good and all; Angela listening, her heart heavy because she knew that such reports would worry Max and tax his small remaining amount of strength, would say, 'Darling, can't you and Julian try a little harder to pull together? Try, Emmanuel. Things are so difficult, and I am so desperately worried about my beloved Max.'

No, there was no help to be found there. Even if Angela spoke to Julian it would have no effect. Julian would contrive somehow to throw the blame on other shoulders—his brother's for preference.

Who else remained? It was not in Emmanuel Gollantz's character to contemplate washing his dirty linen in public, and for this reason he found it impossible to visit any of the dealers which his father had always liked and in whom he had believed.

Old Jacob Lane was an invalid, scarcely alive, people said ; his secretary, who was his heir, for the old man had never married, was a thin, dark-eyed reticent fellow, who might be brilliantly clever, but who Emmanuel had never really liked. There were the two Morris brothers, sons of old Augustus—Joseph and Samson. Good fellows, both, and men who knew their business. He might go to them.

There was only left the very old Marcus Arbuthnot, who still wore his fantastic high collars and talked rather as Lady Heriot did, using the pronunciation and jargon of a past age. Arbuthnot—born Abrahams—had not always been too scrupulous, but he belonged to the former generation, the generation of old Emmanuel. He might understand, at all events. Emmanuel felt that he might get sound advice from him without actually incriminating anyone.

He telephoned to the workshops, and told Peters to bring round a small case, giving him the rough measurements. 'Got anything about that size, Peters?'

'It 'ul be round almost before you've 'ung up that telephone, sir.'

'Bring some tissue for packing as well.'

While Peters packed the candelabra, Emmanuel telephoned to the Arbuthnot Rooms ; years ago they were called 'salons', he remembered. The secretary said that Sir Marcus would see him—Emmanuel had forgotten that he'd been knighted—and that the visit would give him great pleasure.

Emmanuel drove round to King Street, and at the sight of Arbuthnot's rooms felt a little pang of jealousy. This was how he wanted his own place to look. There was too much Empire and rococo furniture, but Arbuthnot had always specialized in that. He liked the ornate furniture, disliked the severe English style, and boasted that he wouldn't give Chippendale or Shera-ton house room. But everything was kept in perfect condition and set out in the most admirable manner; the delicate gilt and rosewood gleamed and shone, the brocades looked fresh and bright, the fine carpets might have been laid only that morning.

Arbuthnot's secretary met Emmanuel; he had known her for years and had always liked and admired her. She was no longer a young woman, her hair was heavily streaked with grey, but she had an air of confidence and efficiency which pleased him.

'Nice to know you're back, Mr. Gollantz,' she said. 'Sir Marcus is quite excited at your visit. What's in the case? Have you found us a bargain?'

Marcus Arbuthnot half rose from his elaborate gilt armchair and held out a hand which was white and thin, which, when Emmanuel took it, felt brittle. His hair was white and very sparse, his head seemed to be supported by the tremendously high collar which he wore, from which it emerged—the neck looking like that of some old bird.

'Hello, hello, my dear fellah,' he almost whistled, so thin and high had his voice become, 'nice to see yer. Bai Jove it is! How's yer father? Didn't look so good when I saw him last. Tired, but damn it, we're all tired. How'd you get on in this disgusting war—eh? Nasty tedious business, and look at us now? By gad, Salisbury, Chamberlain, dear old Bonar Law, would have had something to say. We ought to have stuck to Winnie Churchill.

'Howevah, let's hear your news. Miss Carnforth, d'you know, I don't believe that "another little drink would do us any harm". Ha, ha, dear old George Robey, still as good as evah, they tell me. Give it a name, Emmanuel, my deah fellah. No need to ask mine, same tipple—brandy. Nothing like it for making old blood run quicker, at least nothing except the sight of a really pretty lady! Now, my boy!'

Emmanuel said, 'First, I've come as a customer. I want a pair of George the Third or Regency candelabra. They've got to be absolutely—right. Got such a thing, Sir Marcus?'

'Got everything—except money! Miss Carnforth, send for Briggs, if you please. He'll fix you! He's got a nose for silver! By the way, I heah that yer brother's dabbling in it. What the deuce does he know about it? How the dickens can he hope to get away with it—against a fellah like Briggs, been in the business for nearly forty years? Ah, Briggs,' and he told the small, stout man with the rather shiny blue serge suit what Emmanual wanted.

Briggs scratched his chin with a stubby forefinger, drew a deep breath, and said, 'We—have—the very—thing!' He spoke with long pauses as if each word were a matter for deep consideration. 'Yes, the very thing. Might I use the telephone, Sir Marcus?'

'Of course, my deah Briggs, of course. Give him a "snifter", Miss Carnforth. That's a new one, Emmanuel, eh? "Snifter". I like to keep up with the times.'

Briggs, who had been speaking rapidly and decisively, using, Emmanuel noticed, numbers with fluent exactitude, hung up the receiver and, reverting to his old manner of speech, said, 'They'll be over—in a minute. Yes—a minute. Thank you—Sir Marcus. Mr. Gollantz—your very—good health.'

'And yours,' Emmanuel said. 'Now, I want you to look over these pieces I've brought with me, as a favour to me. I found them. I should value your opinion very highly.'

Strange how, at the sight of the silver, both men seemed to Emmanuel to take on a new personality. Arbuthnot sat bolt upright in his chair, his long thin neck thrust forward, his eyebrows drawn low over his eyes. Briggs seemed to sniff the air like a dog picking up a scent; his nostrils twitched a little, once he ran the tip of his tongue over his lips. Emmanuel set the candelabra on the desk and stood back watching the two men. He saw Arbuthnot's figure lose its rigidity; he leaned back again in his chair, his eyes watching Briggs.

He said, 'Want to sell 'em, my deah fellah?'

Emmanuel shrugged his shoulders, 'I've not decided—yet.'

Briggs lifted one of the pieces, found the mark, stared, then frowned. His fingers went to his waistcoat pocket, the old movement which Emmanuel knew so well. Out came the little glass which these experts always carried. He carried the silver to the electric light, switched it on, and continued to stare at what he found.

'This—piece—was in your—stock, Mr. Gollantz?' he asked, without raising his eyes.

'No,' Emmanuel said, 'I found it.'

'Um—um. Got the history?'

'No—I'm afraid not.'

Arbuthnot said, 'Nevah, evah, buy silver without a history. The country without a history—may be happy, we are assurahed that it is so; silvah is anothah mattah, remembah.'

Briggs, returning to his brisk manner said, 'Might I trouble you to cast your eye over this? Thank you.' With his short thick finger he pointed out certain things to his master, who merely nodded, his lips pursed. Briggs kept muttering, 'There, see?' and 'Look at that, eh?' Presently he set the candelabra down and stuck his hands in his pockets.

'You've been sold a pup, Mr. Gollantz. That is—the thing's all right for what—it is. You understand me—for what—it—is. A piece of George the Fourth, I imagine about 1822 or even a little later. Now, the hall-mark is definitely—George the Third. No mistaking that. What's the verdict? In looking at the hall-mark, you might have observed that I pointed out several marks to Sir Marcus. What was I pointing out? Small scratches, minute places where—frankly—the hall-mark—didn't fit. In other words—fakers have been at work. Am I right, Sir Marcus, or am I right?'

Arbuthnot nodded. 'Undoubtedly and indubitably—right. It's a serious thing, Emmanuel. If you can trace the fellah who did it—well, you can make trouble for him—if he's in the trade—and he must be—you can make bad trouble. Ah, here are your pieces, Briggs.'

A young man carrying a piece of green baize came forward, spread it on a side table, and set up a pair of silver candelabra of great and real beauty. Emmanuel could scarcely suppress an exclamation of pleasure at the beautiful lines, the dignity and the grace of the things. Both Briggs and Arbuthnot watched him closely.

The latter thought, 'I've seen his grandfather look like that a hundred times! It's an expression you only see on the faces of men who know the best when they see it. This "yen" about finding those fakes, all stuff and nonsense! Emmanuel's much too wily a bird to be caught like that. Something behind it all. He's in partnership with his brother, his brother's posing as an authority on silver! Pah! the damned fool. He'll land himself in Queer Street, I shouldn't wonder!'

Aloud he said, 'How d'you like them, eh?'

Calmly Emmanuel said, 'Very fine, I imagine. And the price?'

'I nevah know—Briggs, what are we wanting for them?'

'Sixty-five, Sir Marcus. And they're worth more. That's the sober truth, Mr. Gollantz. I'm not talking dealer's "hot air". To the trade——' He glanced at Arbuthnot, questioningly.

'Going to sell again, Emmanuel?'

'No, sir, I want them for a present.'

'Right, usual discount to Mr. Gollantz, Briggs.'

Briggs answered smartly, 'Forty-three-six-eight, sir.'

'Could you send them round to the Gallery, addressed to me?' Emmanuel asked, as he wrote out his cheque in his usual neat and very characteristic writing. 'Thank you, Mr. Briggs, and thank you, sir. I'm grateful.'

'And—the—others, Mr. Gollantz?'

'Send them at the same time, if you please.'

69

When he had gone, Arbuthnot motioned to Alice Carnforth to give him another brandy-and-soda. He leaned back in his chair and sighed.

'Funny business, eh?' he asked.

'Unlike that firm to deal in—doubtful stuff,' she admitted.

'Um—that fellah who's just left us nevah would. He's got to fight othah influences. If he's not very clever, he'll lose—lose badly. I once, and I don't mind admitting it to you, though I'd not do so to anyone else, tried to get him to dabble in something which was not—well, not quite the thing! He was only a youngstah, but he made me feel small, confoundedly small. But—and heah is a point—I nevah felt active resentment, nevah! If at any time we can give him a helping hand, safeguard his interests, I shall be glad if you will let me know. You might convey that to Briggs, will you? Yes, a nice fellah, honest cove—too damned honest for this wicked world and this equally wicked business. Now—the lettahs . . .'

Later in the day Julian entered his brother's office ; the first things which caught his eye were the candelabra which he had seen before, and standing near them a pair which—even to his inexperienced eye—were obviously excellent.

He said, 'Hello! You been buying silver? I thought that was my province. What's the game?'

Emmanuel answered very calmly, almost as if the whole matter had ceased to interest him, 'I have taken a fancy to the —Georgian pair. The others I have bought as a present. They're pleasant pieces, I think. Georgian too, I fancy, although the hall-mark is Henry the Seventh.'

'What are you talking about!'

'Candelabra, their hall-marks and dates,' Emmanuel said coolly.

'What do you mean about a hall-mark of Henry the Seventh? I've never seen such a thing—except possibly in a museum.'

'Oh, that remark! That was just a piece of additional information ; you're not likely to find such a thing. I'm no expert, Julian, but I advise you to be ver-ry careful in buying silver. Always be certain to get the histor-ry of every piece. It's a wise policy.'

Julian, his pale face suddenly scarlet, returned, 'Oh, damn you and your lectures. I know all I need to know. Look after your business and I'll look after mine.'

'Unfortunately—the greater includes the less.'

That evening he telephoned to Lady Heriot. He heard the butler's voice saying, 'I will tell her ladyship,' then someone called, 'Hello! Emmanuel! This is grand. It's Viva speaking. Can you come round? Why not? ... Yes, of course. You'll dine here ... Oh, do. ... Only Mummy and—possibly my father and me. Toby's away, buying a horse somewhere. ... You will! Eight—as they say on invitations—eight for eight-thirty. S'long.'

He told Hannah that he would be dining out ; she nodded like some Eastern god. 'Yes, it's good for you to go out. Get the taste of that Gallery out of your mouth. Pah!'

'That taste is going to be altered very soon, Hannah. What's Simeon doing? I don't want the lad to feel that we're neglecting him.'

'He's dining with Colonel and Signora Mancini at the Savoy. They wanted you, but Simeon said that he couldn't promise for you. Will you telephone? You might go on after your dinner, eh?'

He hesitated. He wanted to see Simeon at the Savoy, he could picture him dancing with Iva Mancini—Iva Alfano, as the operatic world knew her. He wanted to correct that mental picture which he had made. Simeon in his severe evening clothes —Emmanuel remembered with a kind of start that he didn't even know if the boy wore tails or only a dinner jacket!— moving easily over the floor with Iva in his arms. Iva still lovely, even though she had allowed herself to grow a little heavy.

Paul—his old friend, who had done so well in the war, whose father had been an Italian ice-cream merchant! Paul, more British than men who had no foreign blood in their veins, who had promised to be one of the best tenors of his generation, and had known what it was to see his hopes dashed to pieces, because of some small and apparently unimportant growth on his vocal cords. He'd taken it very well ; he had listened to advice and finally had married Iva and managed her affairs with skill and great ability. Then—the war. He had enlisted in the British Army, and here he was—Colonel Mancini, O.B.E., and half a dozen other decorations as well. Nice to see Paul and Iva again.

And Viva—the woman who had once been his wife, how well he remembered their house, with its careful and lovely furnishing. What a vivid person she was! Not restful, assuredly, but vital and amusing and completely charming. She had married 'Toby' Tatten, the man who looked like a good-tempered edition of Adolf Hitler, with his funny scrubby moustache ; only 'Toby' had the kindest heart in the world. A passing likeness—nothing deeper. Emmanuel remembered how when they had met, in the early days of the war, Tatten had said:

'I say—I hope that it's not embarrassing for you to meet me.'

Emmanuel, looking down from his considerable height, had smiled and said, 'Not at all—if you mean about Viva and me—believe me, there is no one I like better than—your wife, Captain Tatten. My sincere congratulations ; you're a lucky man.'

Tatten, who looked like a jockey, had grinned engagingly and said:

'Then that's O.K. by everyone, for Viva's got a great admiration for you. She's always comparing me to you—to my grave disadvantage.'

Emmanuel's eyes had twinkled ; he had leaned slightly forward and spoken very softly, 'My advice is—don't permit that kind of thing. As a matter of fact, Viva knew very little about me, but she has a wonderful imagination. The thing which is out of reach will, to Viva, always assume the qualities of perfection. Within reach, nothing could please her less.'

Tatten had continued to grin. 'Sounds pretty good, but upon closer examination—not so hot. You see, I'm "within reach". I shall always be, so far as Viva's concerned.'

'There are exceptions to every rule,' Emmanuel had said gravely.

Now he dressed with extreme care, for he was always something of what his grandfather would have called a 'dandy', and took out his clothes with a certain satisfaction. He was the least conceited of men, but he had never seen why he should not wear clothes which pleased him, and in which he felt well-dressed. These fine silk socks, the exquisitely tucked shirts of the softest linen—he had always detested piqué—the collar with its slightly old-fashioned shape, and his suit of the smoothest material ministered to his personal comfort.

The sensation of wearing good clothes was, he told himself, good for his morale. Those years spent in the Army had taught him to wear rough clothes, harsh shirts and underclothes, but though they had shown him that such things could be worn, they had never, he felt, raised his spiritual attitude towards life.

He wanted very little. His tastes were simple, he could work for long hours and be content with a sandwich and a cup of coffee to last him through the day ; but—and he smiled when he reflected what an important part that small word played—but the sandwich must be thin and well cut, the coffee 'black as night and strong as love'.

Possibly he was a sybarite, but he was one whose gratification cost comparatively little. He took a distinct pride in his clothes, his ties and his beautiful old jewellery, but everything he had lasted him for years, and was always beautifully kept.

On this evening the thought of meeting his friends again blotted out the disgust which he had felt during the day. How he had hated it all! He had realized that Marcus Arbuthnot had known that there was 'more than met the eye' in his story. He had caught the quick exchange of glances between Sir Marcus and Briggs, he had sat in his office later smarting under the knowledge that they thought—and probably with good reason —that the House of Gollantz was embarking on some dubious transactions.

Emmanuel felt that something was going on which was detrimental to the business. He almost felt that he could put his finger on the cause of the trouble, could almost give his reasons and prove his theories. He longed to demand that Julian came out into the open, but his wiser self warned him to wait.

'Collect your evidence,' it whispered, 'tabulate your evidence, have all your facts ready, and then—and only then—speak!'

'Even then,' he thought as he tied his cravat, for he clung to them even though they were out of date, and people preferred bow ties to the long strips of incredibly fine linen which he wound so carefully and meticulously round his collar, to end with a bow tied with mathematical exactitude, 'even then, who knows if I dare use what I knew! My father with his intense dread of scandal, and my mother with her love for Julian which nothing will ever change. I've hidden things before—I may have to hide them again.

'Only one thing'—he stared at his reflection in the mirror; 'Juliet's son shall never be sacrificed to Julian—never. He shall have everything that I always wanted, and God help the man who tries to spoil his life!'

He sprayed his hair with the least possible amount of Cuir de Russie, his sensitive nostrils quivering a little as the scent reached him. He sniffed with appreciation and his thoughts flew to Paris. Paris, Chanel, the lovely shops, the restaurants where, as his grandfather had said, 'one does not merely eat—one dines'.

With those thoughts came the remembrance of Louis Lara and his lovely wife, Olympia. Where were they? He must begin to make enquiries. Dear Louis, who was not content to be slightly eccentric in his dress, but who, like Guido, must always go to extremes. Olympia—overblown, but like a wonderful rose may be overblown, losing nothing, but rather gain-ing in beauty. Emmanuel sighed—the world was full of fine people, and he was fortunate to know so many of them. Life might be so pleasant without—his mind halted, but he knew that the thought which he had expelled from his mind had been —'without Julian'.

CHAPTER SIX

VIVA TATTEN sprawled on the large, stiffly upholstered sofa in her mother's drawing-room, a cocktail glass in one hand, a cigarette in an immensely long holder in the other. She was talking with her usual animation to Bill Gollantz, the youngest of Angela's sons.

Bill had recently come out of the Navy, where his career had been useful and generally unspectacular. He was a heavily-built, broad-shouldered man in the late thirties. His face possessed none of the good looks of either Emmanuel or Julian; there was something essentially ordinary about Bill—his features, his clothes, his completely sane and well-balanced outlook. He was in partnership with his mother's cousin, Charles Wilmot, and was already making a success as a solicitor. Charles, who was no longer young, liked to take life at a more leisurely pace than he had done before the war, and he found Bill Gollantz quite ready, and certainly able, to carry much of the weight of the business.

At the moment he was listening to Viva with grave attention. He thought that he had never seen any woman who could 'sprawl' so gracefully; that was typical of her, she never looked clumsy, her movements were always endowed with that peculiar charm which was one of her greatest characteristics. Bill reflected that while he might not approve—wholeheartedly—of Viva's manner of speech, of the rather 'rackety' life which she and 'Toby' Tatten lived, there was no woman who amused and interested him more.

She was saying, '. . . is Emmanuel's trouble. He will cling to his old romantic ideas, he will allow himself to remain sensitive, and he expects everyone to live up to those ideals to which he—poor old-fashioned creature—has always adhered. The result is that he is—bound to be hurt! Oh yes, Bill, whatever happens Emmanuel is always going to get the kicks; that's because he will "stick his neck out". He asks for it!

'He falls in love, and imagines that he's discovered the philosopher's stone and that everything will automatically be turned into gold. Not, believe me, that he sets such a devil of a lot of store by gold—he's the least mercenary person I know. I doubt if he's ever been really happy except for that year when he was married to Juliet. He certainly wasn't happy with me——'

Bill said, 'Were you happy with him, Viva?'

She considered for a moment, sipped her cocktail reflectively, and answered, 'Fairly, yes. I liked him so much, you see. I always shall. Oh, admittedly it was rather like living with Sir Lancelot and Sir Galahad, with a dash of King Arthur thrown in as make-weight, but it was'—she sighed—'it was very pleasant. There was some dignity about him—I've never had a scrap of dignity, neither has "Toby". I think sometimes that if Emmanuel had taken me by the shoulders now and again, shaken me until my teeth rattled and said, "Behave yourself, you unutterable bitch!" things might have lasted.'

Bill laughed. 'Can you imagine Emmanuel doing such a thing? I doubt if he's ever used the word "bitch" in his life!'

'That's what I say!' Viva retorted. 'That's why it all—didn't work. I know that he couldn't do it—now "Toby" could, can, has done, and in all probability will again! But then such words come as trippingly to "Toby's" lips as they do to mine! "Toby" talks like a stableman ; I talk like a coster's moll. Now, Emmanuel has gone into the firm—with Julian! My God, you'd think that he might have learnt sense! Oh, your mother and father know all about that damned Julian, believe me. One night at Ordingly I lost my temper and spilt the beans.' She laughed, as if the memory gave her satisfaction.

'I'd been waiting to do it for years and years. I began— Julian stood there with a face like chalk. He tried to make a bolt, but "Toby" stood in front of the door and looked like a terrier baiting a bull!'

Again she chuckled at the memory. 'Can you imagine it, Bill? That room at Ordingly, so packed full of dignity and tradition, decency and reticence, Max listening with a face like stone, Angela wondering who she hated more—Julian for having done these things, or me for referring to them!'

'And the upshot of it all?' Bill asked.

'The upshot? Need you ask. I think that it made a difference to Angela. I believe for the first time in her life she realized what a jewel of a fellow Emmanuel was. Max'—she shrugged her shoulders—'I don't know. Julian of course fell back to his last line of defence, his "ill health". Then Max begins to do a spot of analysis, and to discover that even if Julian is what in his heart he hopes him to be, there is not some good and sufficient reason for it all! I like your father. I respect him—that's a damnable thing to say, really, of anyone—but he's like the bloke in Julius Caesar, he thinks too much, and he doesn't always think quite straight. He imagines that he is a great observer. He may be as regards old masters and old furniture, but when he thinks that he sees "right into the hearts of men", then he's backing a loser every time.

'So, Emmanuel having done his job in the war, with no great flourish of trumpets, although he went to that ghastly P.O.W. camp as a second "loot" and came away in command of it, and got the D.C.M. in Africa, he's to go into the business and put it to rights, with the weight of Julian to pull along—doing his best to put it all wrong! Emmanuel ought to have had more sense than to go into the blasted business! He ought to have gone to Milan to see what was left, and stayed there. Pooh! Give me another cocktail, Bill—talking makes me thirsty.'

'And you talk such a lot too,' Bill said, grinning. 'Never mind, Viva, your humble servant likes to listen to you. You know that young Simeon's going to join Emmanuel?'

'Umpa! I heard so. That's a nice lad, Bill. Never grouses about losing his foot ; told me the other day that the boot on the artificial foot always fits better than the other. But it was another smack in the face for Emmanuel to know that his son was maimed. Simeon said to me the other day too, "My father feels far more badly about the loss of this foot than I do. I forget all about it, except at night when I take my boots off!" I say, where is everyone, Bill?'

'I dunno, we must have been frightfully early. Who is coming?'

She ticked off the names on her fingers. Bill thought that he had never seen such a brilliant red on any woman's nails. He said, 'I say, your nails, Viva! Knowing that Emmanuel's coming, you might have toned them down a bit. He hates it!'

She glanced at them, then said, 'My beloved child, can't you get it into your thick head that I'm not married to Emmanuel any longer? I'm Mrs. "Toby" Tatten, and my husband adores my nails like this! Well, Emmanuel's coming, and you and me—then there's a woman called Wilmot, used to be rather sweet on Emmanuel, I fancy, married to a bloke at the F.O. called Gregory Wilmot. I find them a couple of drears, but she plays the piano, and my mother thought Emmanuel might like it. So we shall have a session of Bach and Company inflicted on us, and we have to behave nicely and pretend that we like it!

'Then Bill Masters is coming. I say, Bill, does it ever strike you that before the war we were the young generation, and they were just "young elderly" people? Now, we are the "young elderlies" and they're a couple of generations behind. Queer to think that neither of us will see thirty-five again! Angela is coming if Max is well enough. That's the lot. Just like my mother, bless her, to collect a nice ungainly party, not big enough to be fun, and not small enough to be intimate. Hello, Mother dear, we were just talking about you! Are we frightfully early, or is everyone else damned late?'

Lady Heriot, wearing a considerable amount of excellent jewellery and a dress which was—in her daughter's opinion—cut far too low and was far too elaborately made, sat down rather more heavily than one would have expected.

'Probably a bit of both,' she said. 'Billee, darling, give me something to drink. These stays of mine are agony! I swear that I can hear them creak when I move. I'm half inclined to chuck up the sponge and just let my figure go to hell.'

Bill, handing her a cocktail, said, 'Oh no, Aunt Beatrice, I couldn't bear that! Surely the wholehearted admiration of your favourite nephew is worth a little discomfort!'

'Get along with you,' she retorted. 'A little discomfort! I wish you had my stays on! Where's Manny? He's my favourite really, y'know. Poor boy. Well, well—oh, Simeon's coming in.'

Viva made a gesture of despair. 'Not another person for dinner! My dear, how your wretched servants keep track of your guests I don't know. It will throw your table all wrong, you know.'

Her mother smiled placidly. 'Oh, to hell with the table! Yes, give me another quick, Billee, before people come!'

Emmanuel arrived, entering the room as he always contrived to do, without noise, but bringing with him an indefinable air of dignity. Lady Heriot shouted, 'Hello, Manny—how are you, my angel! How's the shop? What have you got there? A present for me?'

Emmanuel stooped and kissed her, went over to Viva and taking her hand raised it to his lips. She flushed, and as he raised his head, their eyes met and he smiled at her.

She said, 'Bill warned me that you'd hate my nails!'

His smile widened a little. Viva felt that it had actually reached his eyes.

'Naturally I was looking at you, and didn't see them. Bill should know me better. Now I have seen them,' he held her hand palm downwards on his own, and gave a small shudder, 'Bill was right. Now I have seen them—what's the phrase?—

"raw in tooth and claw". Frankly, so revolting that they are fascinating.'

Tilting her chin, she replied, ' "Toby" adores them like this.'

'Then, of course, subjugating your own feeling, sublimating your own taste—which, forgive me, was never really good—you sacrifice yourself to him. In this present Year of Grace such thought is very highly to be commended.'

His aunt flung back her elaborately dressed head and screamed, 'That's the stuff, Manny! You ought to write another verse and a couple of choruses to that one! Now, what's in this parcel?'

He carried the parcel to a side table, talking as he did so.

'You remember showing me the wedding present which you had bought the other day?'

'Hector Colcroft—yes. Nice things too, Manny.'

'But, if you also remember, we had a slight argument about them. I came to the conclusion that they were not quite good enough. I took the very great liberty of finding others. There you are!' He stood back, and made a movement of his fine hand with its long sensitive fingers indicating the candelabra.

Lady Heriot said, 'By Jove, Manny, they're beauties, Eh, Viva?'

'Emmanuel's taste—unlike mine—is always impeccable,' her daughter returned.

Emmanuel took a slip of paper from his pocket and handed it to his aunt with his little ceremonial bow. 'And costing less than your original wedding present, Aunt Beatrice. My cheque for the difference.'

She unfolded the cheque. 'Good Lord! Twenty-one pounds thirteen and fourpence! Manny, you're a wizard! I shall always get you to buy for me in future.' She slipped the cheque into the enormous embroidered bag which she carried. 'That, me old cockalorum, goes on a gee-gee to-morrow. Thanks a lot, Manny.'

With a sudden gravity, he said, 'I wish that you would give me a promise that if you should buy anything of this kind'—with a gesture towards the candelabra—'and come to Gollantz for it, you will allow me to—guide your choice.'

'Oh, I'll promise you that. They're heavenly. Again, thanks a lot.'

Viva, watching Emmanuel's grave face, found herself thinking, 'So there's something on foot already, is there? Mother's been sold a pup, and Emmanuel's spotted it. I wonder—whose "pup" it was, and why it didn't come up to Emmanuel's standards? Trust him to find trouble; he simply can't miss it.'

Other people began to arrive—the Wilmots, he thin and desiccated, she charming, Emmanuel thought, as ever. He remembered how for a time he had wondered if Vivian Mallet—as she had been then—was not the solution to his intense loneliness. They had so much in common ; he found her voice restful, her ideas good, and had found, too, a certain quiet pleasure in her companionship. Something had held him back from asking her to marry him, some sudden realization that he could never offer her anything but 'second best' and that she was too nice a person to be given what at most could only be a kind of substitute for the love which a woman had the right to expect.

Bill Masters, limping badly, inclined to be irritable, never ceasing to grumble at the misdeeds of the Government and the present plight of England ; Angela Gollantz entering and, Emmanuel felt, bringing a sense of warmth and sunshine with her. And following her, his son. He noted with relief that the boy could scarcely be said to limp at all. There might be a faint stiffness, a kind of brief hesitation, but to the average observer it would not be noticeable.

Angela smiled at everyone, and, with her hand on Simeon's arm, said, 'This nice child brought me from Ordingly. Wasn't it sweet of him?'

Bill Masters growled. 'Sweet? In Heaven's name, why sweet? All your life people have been ready to take you anywhere at any time, and you know it, Angela.'

She replied, 'Oh, Bill, dear, not many—you and Simeon!'

Emmanuel, standing near her, asked in a low voice how Max was. Some of the brightness seemed to fade from her vivid face—a face which time had not been able to rob of its charm and vivacity.

'Not very well. It's this continual sense of being tired. So unlike my darling Max. Oh, Emmanuel, how I wish that we could put the clock back! Those were such lovely days, things were—were fun. There isn't much fun in these days. I'm sure that the Government is doing its best——'

Emmanuel laughed softly. 'Darling, what a terrible thing to say of anyone—any government!'

'No, seriously, I am sure that they are, but it's such an uncomfortable best. I don't believe that the normal human being is capable, at the moment, of getting up in the morning and going to bed again at night without having broken the law in some way or other. There are so many restrictions, and our memories have grown too short, and we're too old and tired

80

to remember them at all. I never thought to regard myself as a consistent law-breaker, Emmanuel.'

Bill Masters, who had limped over to them, pulled down the corners of his mouth. 'Don't let it worry you, m'dear. Evolution has been flung overboard, everything is rushed, badly digested, and—what's the result? I could tell you, but politeness and decency forbids. Ah, there's dinner! Far too late! To-day it's cocktails *ad lib.*, and what they're made of Heaven alone knows —and dinner far too late everywhere.'

Angela slid her arm through his. 'Bill, you mustn't get disgruntled. One day things will be—I don't say "as they once were", but either we shall have grown used to everything, or——'

He said sharply, 'Or we shall be dead. Sorry m'dear, I'll behave nicely during dinner.'

Emmanuel found himself sitting with Viva on one side and Mrs. Wilmot on the other. He felt a sudden spasm of amusement at the general *décor* of his aunt's dining-room. He supposed that Sir Walter was dining in his room ; at this hour of the night he was rarely fit for company.

He thought what a plucky woman Beatrice had been, for life couldn't have been easy for her. Her only son, Walter— dead some years ago—had consistently lived a life which was no particular credit to anyone ; her husband—and he remembered what a firm affection his grandfather had had for Walter Heriot—had steadily deteriorated, mentally and physically. There were periodic disappearances into what were euphemistically known as 'nursing homes', but which could have been given a more specific title. At long intervals he appeared at his wife's dinner-parties, looking like a mechanical figure, speaking with a certain difficulty, and invariably excusing himself immediately dinner was over on the grounds that he had letters to write. The excuse deceived no one, and he tottered out, his legs stiff and not very certain, and did not appear again.

The room was what constituted Beatrice Heriot's idea of the ideal dining-room. True, in the old days her husband had relied upon the taste and judgment of old Emmanuel. There were the chairs which he had chosen, the dining-table was really admirable—Emmanuel's fingers delicately felt the patina of the lovely old wood which lay beneath the elaborate lace cloth— but the rest! A nightmare. A heavy red flock wallpaper, the equally heavy Turkey carpet—red and blue—the heavy furniture ; in the fireplace brightly polished brass, and far too much of it. The suffocating dark red velvet curtains, with their pelmets and swinging tassels, the pictures in their wide gilt frames, the two enormous Rockingham vases which flanked the immense black marble clock, all made up a setting which, to him, was completely hideous.

Viva's crisp voice at his elbow said, 'I couldn't agree more.'

He turned. 'I'm sorry ; I wasn't attending. How did you know?'

'My dear, I watched your face. You show too much in your expression, Emmanuel. It is a hideous room—so hideous that it almost becomes a "period piece", eh?'

He replied gravely, 'A period which I, for one, would be glad to forget.'

'Yes, but it's such a help to young theatrical designers. They scrape acquaintance with my mother, come here and make notes—and incidentally eat remarkably good luncheons or dinners! "Toby" will be sorry to have missed you, he's riding somewhere in the country. He sent me a telegram this morning, hoping that Simeon liked the horse.'

'I have barely set eyes on Simeon since he went to Ordingly this morning to inspect the animal. Judging from his expressions he seems satisfied enough. A great thing that, even with his disability, he can ride.'

Her voice sharpened a little as she answered, 'Listen, Emmanuel, don't go on harping on this—disability. It's not amusing, we know that, but how many of us are going about actually—intact? Tonsils, appendix, lots of other things missing, and no-one is regarded as a pitiful object. Well, to lose a foot is only to go one step further forward. I mean in these days it's not noticeable. There's no great discomfort ; it doesn't hamper a man's career. Look at—what's-his-name—the film star ; he lost his leg in the last war. He's not allowed it to interfere with his career. Treat this as something—quite ordinary. Much better for Simeon, believe me.'

He nodded. 'Yes, you're right. Only—perhaps as his father— it does matter to me a great deal.'

'What ought to matter most to you is that he's here, fit and well, and not a handful of ashes under a burnt-out airplane.'

'Again—you're right.'

'I am—invariably,' she said, and turned to the man on her right. Emmanuel twisted in his chair so that he could see Vivian Wilmot. She was talking in that full, deep voice, which he remembered, to the man on her other side. He waited and presently she turned and smiled.

'How nice to meet you again,' she said.

Emmanuel said, 'You spoke too quickly. I intended to say that!'

'And that's your son—over there?'

'That's Simeon. I remember how kind you used to be to him when he first came to England.'

'I imagine that quite a number of women will be ready to be kind to him. How good-looking he is!'

'I think so, but then I am biassed. He's like his mother—too much so sometimes. He was in the Air Force—perhaps you have heard?'

'Yes, Lady Heriot told me. Too bad, but,' she smiled, 'how much worse it might have been! And you?'

Briefly he told her of his work and his plans, and as he spoke thought how probable it was that his brother might overturn all his hopes and schemes for the business. She was interested, she made intelligent comments and replies, but Emmanuel found himself wondering how he could ever have imagined that this woman could have been his wife and achieved happiness for either of them.

She was what he would have described as a 'trained hostess'; again and again, though her replies were immediate and to the point, he caught her eyes wandering to where her husband sat, talking gravely and with a kind of cold concentration to Angela. He could imagine their small, carefully planned dinner-parties, where everyone was chosen as if they were part of a jigsaw puzzle and would 'fit' into the general scheme. Those dinner-parties where, if certain subjects arose, they were immediately frozen to death without argument, without discussion. He could imagine how the conversation was skilfully steered into safe channels, and how, when the guests had left, Wilmot would suggest that 'So-and-so' was not asked to dine again.

'Bad *gaffe*, that! I dislike that kind of thing, Vivian'; and how she would reply warmly, without heat, 'And so do I, Gregory.'

He hazarded, 'Your husband looks well. I remember that he was the first person to tell me that Italy was entering the war against us. Poor Iva Alfano was there—how upset she was!'

Vivian answered calmly, 'I'm afraid that Greg was a little precipitate on that particular evening. Most unlike him, he is so careful. Yes, I think that he is well. Of course, in his position at the F.O. life is pretty wearing. He is one of the permanent officials, you know.'

'Ah, responsibilities are heavy.' He was talking like a parrot.

'Very, oh very. I don't want to boast, but I have heard—not

from my husband, of course—that he is marked down for promotion. Very considerable promotion.'

'Splendid! I am sure that your help will be invaluable.'

Her smile was charming, he thought, but mechanical. So many people had said that kind of thing, so many more would say it in the future.

'I sincerely hope so.'

She turned away to speak to the man on her other side, and Emmanuel saw that Viva, too, was in the midst of an animated conversation. He let his eyes wander round the table. There was his aunt, wearing, as Bill would have said, 'everything but the kitchen fender', laughing at every remark which was made to her, making the speaker feel that he was one of the world's great wits. His brother Bill, already growing a little heavy and beginning to develop a slight 'jowl', his eyes dancing and his mouth always ready to smile. His mother—Emmanuel had never lost the affection which amounted to adoration which he felt for her—looking beautiful.

And yet Angela Gollantz had never been a strictly lovely woman: her features were irregular, her nose was a little too short, her chin a fraction too long. She had charm, and what was more—her eldest son smiled at the thought—she knew how to use it. Bill Masters, grey as a badger, his face wrinkled and sagging, his hair rapidly thinning. He'd been Angela's faithful adorer for years and had never attempted to conceal the fact. Poor Bill, he had been so good to Juliet, and she had understood him so perfectly. For that, and that alone, he commanded Emmanuel's respect and a certain affection.

Then there was his son—how handsome the boy was, what charming manners, and possessing the ability to make everyone who spoke to him feel that he gave them his full and undivided attention. How like Juliet—Emmanuel knew that his thoughts shied as a spirited mare might shy at a piece of fluttering paper on the high road. He must prevent his thoughts always wandering back to Juliet; he must not allow himself to use her standards as the criterion for everything and everybody; he must not continually make comparisons between Juliet and every other woman with whom he came in contact.

'And yet,' he thought, 'how can I prevent myself from doing so? How can I attempt to shut her out in any way—however small—from my life as it is now? The habit has become too strong—or I am too weak to deny myself the vicarious pleasure that it gives me.'

His eyes turned again to Viva. She had ended her conversation and her gaze met his; she smiled and he noticed how her eyes crinkled at the corners. Viva wasn't quite young any longer—how old was she? Nearly forty, and still retaining her zest for life—or what to her passed for 'life'—for enjoyment and amusement. How often had she said to him, 'I can bear anything, my dear, but boredom. That I will never tolerate, never! It's lingering and painful death!'

She said, 'You were loking very serious. Not that it is anything new—you're a serious person, eh?'

'It may be that I find life a serious business,' he said.

'Who said that life was a slightly exaggerated form of comedy?'

'I've no idea,' Emmanuel assured her. 'It would not surprise me to know that you invented the phrase yourself.'

'Oh no, that's not my style at all, and you ought to know it.'

'During the last few years I have had no opportunity to study your particular style.' He laughed. 'The war robbed us of so many opportunities.'

'Anyway, you never took advantage of those opportunities when you had them!'

He leaned forward and met her eyes squarely, conscious that he was enjoying himself, that she was amusing him.

'Viva, my dear,' he said softly, 'don't be provocative!'

She whispered, 'Go and talk to Vivian Wilmot, then. Didn't you find her—provocative at one time, Emmanuel?'

'There again, time has impaired my memory. Frankly, I don't believe that she's the same woman I used to know.'

Viva wrinkled her short, well-shaped nose. 'Of course she is, exactly the same. She put on an act for your benefit—Bach and Beethoven! Oh, women who play the piano are terribly dangerous to susceptible men.'

He laughed. 'I am—susceptible?'

'Terribly—almost pathetically. Unless I play a perpetual guardian angel I can see you leading some dreary woman to the altar for no reason except that she is fond of Simeon, or plays classical music or enjoys reading Charles Morgan! There —my mother is growing restive! Come along. Thank Heaven we've abandoned the awful segregation of the sexes after dinner. Do you remember those hours and hours, when women talked scandal in the drawing-room, and men talked more concentrated scandal mixed with improper stories in the diningroom? I believe that we're growing more civilized.'

He answered, 'I find that difficult to believe in the light of present events.'

As they walked across the hall the butler came forward.

'A telephone call for you, ma'am. I've put it through to the morning-room.'

Viva turned to Emmanuel, 'That's "Toby", he always telephones about this time—he's marvellous in remembering where to find me, like a bloodhound. I shan't be a second. Our conversations are highly affectionate, but invariably brief. Any message?'

'Thank him for the trouble he took about the horse for Simeon. I am writing to him to-morrow.'

He watched her disappear into the morning-room, heard the door shut, and turning, followed the other guests. Coffee was handed round ; his aunt screamed, 'You'll find my coffee better than most of the muck they give you in town, Manny ! Where's Viv? Oh, "Toby", eh? Devoted feller, never forgets to 'phone her. Simeon, come and tell me about this horse he found for you. If it's not all right, we'll send it back damn' quick. I shall have to come down and run an eye—probably both eyes—over him ! Walter—my husband—always says there isn't a woman in England with a better eye for a bit of blood! And after all the interest I've lavished on the brutes they consistently let me down ! By Jove, I've only to put a quid on any horse you like to choose and either the price shortens to nothing or the damned thing breaks its neck ! The bookies ought to pay me to back the favourites.'

Simeon, standing near his father, turned and smiled at him.

He said softly, 'She always makes me laugh ! I adore her, don't you?'

Emmanuel answered, 'I have done ever since I can remember. More, I've a tremendous respect for her. Under that rather "out-moded" manner she's kind and loyal and very shrewd. Do you like the horse?'

The young man's eyes shone with pleasure. 'Like ! That's much too moderate. He's a smashing fellow. Bay with dark points. Lovely wide-open intelligent eyes, and a mouth as soft as velvet. I hadn't time to give him much of a trial, but it's like sitting in an easy chair, but all the time you realize he's got no end of reserve power. I can't thank you enough, Father. He's magnificent.'

'Splendid ! Tatten's a good judge of horseflesh. Now go and tell Aunt Beatrice about him.'

The door opened and Viva entered. She came to where Emmanuel stood sipping his coffee, and said, 'Put the cup down. Come out into the hall. I want to speak to you,' then turned and walked out.

He set down his cup and followed her. She was leaning

86

against the back of a tall oak settle, and as he came nearer he saw her jerk her shoulders back and stand upright, very stiff and straight.

He said, 'Yes, Viva——'

She blinked her eyes rapidly, as if to clear her sight, then said in her usual tone, 'Emmanuel, I don't want a fuss made. Make my excuses to my mother later, when people have gone. That,' jerking her head in the direction of the morning-room door, 'wasn't "Toby". It was a pal of his, Major Carteret. "Toby's" at his house near Esher. He's had an accident. His horse fell. I'm going to him now. No!' as Emmanuel began to speak, 'I don't want anyone with me. *Please.*' She held out her hand and Emmanuel took it in both his own. Her voice shook suddenly. 'I'm rather frightened. Carteret said, "He's rather badly hurt— the doctors are with him now." I believe he's lying.'

Emmanuel said urgently, 'Let me come with you, Viva. I won't talk. You ought not to drive there alone.'

'What I ought to do and what I'm going to do are two different things,' she said. 'No, stay where you are. I'll telephone later. There, I'm going. Car there? Then give me my coat.' To the butler, 'I shan't be very long. Good night, Emmanuel.'

He stood watching her walk down the long paved hall, saw the door swing open and close behind her. Then he turned and walked back to the drawing-room.

CHAPTER SEVEN

EMMANUEL walked back into the room; he heard the babble of voices which seemed to rush towards him and envelop him. The noise, he felt, was too much for his nerves; he longed to cry suddenly and imperiously, 'Be quiet all of you!' He stood for a second watching them all, feeling detached and as if he were a stranger who had come there through a mistake. Then, recovering himself, he went over to where his aunt sat talking to Angela.

His face felt stiff as he forced himself to smile. They both glanced up and Lady Heriot said, 'Hello, Manny dear, where's Viva?'

He stooped down to speak to her, keeping his voice very low.

'She's gone off to collect "Toby",' he said. 'He's over at Colonel Carteret's at Esher. He's broken a collarbone or something of the kind, and she's driven over and is taking him back to the flat. You know that "flivver" of Viva's, most uncomfortable for a chap with a broken bone. I had a smashed collarbone, do you remember, Angela, when I was about twelve? I thought that I'd follow her in my bus. You know what Viva is! She dashed off and wouldn't wait. What's Carteret's address, Aunt Beatrice?'

She said, 'Poor old "Toby". I've always said that his seat isn't half as good as he likes to believe. Hands all right—seat . . .' She pursed her lips. 'However, a collarbone's nothing much. Probably stop him 'chasing this season, though.'

Gently Emmanuel said, 'And this man's address—Carteret?'

'That's "Buster" Carteret, used to be in the Guards. Good feller, bit of a thruster, but always well up! Never seen "Buster" look for a gap or a gate. Breeds cockers, or is it bull-terriers? I forget——'

'And where does he breed them?' Emmanuel said.

'Carteret—breed 'em? Got kennels at his own house. Plenty of ground. It's first turn when you come to the green, house with big yellow gates. What the devil's its name? Forget my own name next! I've got it—Forley Lodge. That's it.'

'I'll find it. Angela dear, I meant to take you home; forgive me, won't you? Oh, Max is sending the car! That's all right then. Aunt Beatrice, thanks for a marvellous dinner ; all Black Market, of course.'

'Every scrap and crumb! Good night, Manny.'

Angela followed him out and laid her hand on his arm. He turned and smiled down at her.

'Is it only a—collarbone?' she whispered.

'I don't know—yes, I do know that it's not a collarbone. It's something more serious. That's why I'm going. There, good night, darling. My dutiful love to Max. Good night.'

That was an old expression of theirs, to send their 'dutiful love' to their father. They—Bill and Emmanuel—had decided years ago that 'love' sounded sentimental, and they had decided that 'dutiful love' expressed both affection and filial respect.

'Good night, my very dear. I hope—well, you know what I hope.'

He ran down the wide steps and found his car, sandwiched in between a very sober-looking Humber which he felt certain belonged to the Wilmots, and Bill's rakish but shabby Alvis. He swung out of the wide stretch of Portland Square and turned the car towards Esher. He drove fast, but with care. Conscious of his own powers as a driver he never overestimated either his own skill or his car's speed. He had a trick of steadily eating up the miles without any appearance of over-driving. His hands were sensitive, and he always felt completely at one with his car.

Now, under the light of the street lamps, his face looked white and intense, his whole figure rigid with concentrated determination. In his heart he felt as Viva had done, that 'Toby' Tatten was dying ; why he felt this he could have given no clear reason. From the moment she had begun to speak to him of the accident Emmanuel had been conscious of a chill, a sense of apprehension, and an inability to offer protestations which carried any conviction.

Poor Viva—she and her queer little husband were devoted to each other. They were tolerant, they made no great demands on one another's time ; each went their own way, but the bond between them existed nevertheless. Emmanuel had never seen either of them in the least demonstrative, he had never heard Viva eulogize her husband ; the most she had ever said of him and in his praise was that he was 'one of the most decent blokes I've ever known—ever hope to know'. Tatten, in a wild burst of confidence, had once admitted to Emmanuel that 'Viva's a great girl, straight as a bit of string—and I don't need to tell you that, do I?' Then, realizing that he had made a *gaffe*, he had grown scarlet about his somewhat protruding ears and stammered, 'I say—I didn't mean that—but well, you know what I did mean. Damn it, have another drink!'

The houses were beginning to thin out, there was less traffic; again Emmanuel squared his shoulders. He was getting very near to Esher, and—what was he going to find there? He feared and dreaded the unhappiness of the people he either loved or liked. Years ago he had loved Viva Heriot, now he liked her more than he liked most women; he knew that he hated the thought that she might be suffering.

He reached Esher, and leaning from his car scanned the names of the houses intently. There were the yellow gates, wide open, and he turned in and saw several cars standing on the wide gravel sweep before the house. He glanced up at the house as he walked towards the front door.

'The blinds are down!' He felt a sense of dismay, then reminded himself, 'You fool, it's nearly eleven. Of course they're down!'

An elderly maid opened the door to him and said, 'Excuse me, sir, are you Sir Hearvey Franks?'

'My name is Gollantz. I've called to drive Mrs. Tatten back to town—if she's going. How is Mr. Tatten?'

She answered him in a hushed voice, as if already she were speaking in a house which death had visited.

'Unconscious, sir. We're expecting Sir Hearvey Franks at any moment. Excuse me—this will be him, sir.' They turned to watch a very large, heavy car swing into the drive; it drew up noiselessly and carefully. The uniformed chauffeur jumped down and opened the door. A tall, thin man got out who seemed to peer nervously at the light which flowed out through the open door. He moved tentatively, frowning and uncertain.

The maid said, 'Would you be Sir Hearvey Franks, sir?'

'Yes .. yes.' Nodding towards Emmanuel, he asked, 'Are you Major Carteret? Carteret—that's the name, isn't it?'

Emmanuel explained, the doctor nodded—quick, nervous little movements. A huge man with thick reddish hair came down the stair. Emmanuel said, 'This, I think, is Major Carteret, sir.'

Again that queer shuffling forward, again the quick hurried questions. Carteret's voice sounded like the baying of a mastiff by comparison.

'Hello, Gollantz, isn't it? I'll come down in a minute. Go in there; help yourself, will you?'

'How is Tatten?'

Carteret answered, looking over his shoulder, one foot on the stairs. 'Bad, poor chap—very bad. Now, Sir Hearvey—please.'

In the stiff comfortable dining-room Emmanuel waited. He heard doors open and close, someone ran down stairs very quickly—then there was complete silence again. Once someone opened the door of the room where he sat, said, 'Oh, I beg your pardon,' and disappeared again, shutting the door quietly.

A large black marble clock ticked loudly, the sound seemed to grow and swell until it filled the room. The table was still laid in readiness for a meal which had not been eaten ; mechanically Emmanuel fingered one of the forks, twisting it in his fingers, soothed by the smooth feeling of the silver.

He held the fork so that the light shone on its markings, his lips moved soundlessly. 'The Castle—thistle instead of the old Deacon's mark—maker's initials. Date about 1780. Very nice— very nice.' As he laid down the silver he frowned. The memory of his brother's activities came back to disturb him—Julian and Mark Seber. The future wasn't going to be easy!

He moved restlessly, mentally rebuking himself for being so engrossed in his own worries that he had—for the moment— forgotten the reason of his visit. What was happening? Where was Viva, with her husband or waiting for the verdict? Emmanuel could almost visualize 'Toby', lying immobile, his little dark moustache looking black against the whiteness of his face.

The door opened once more, and the huge bulk of Carteret entered. He pulled out a chair from the table and sat down heavily, puffing out his lips, saying, 'Give me a drink—will you? Whisky—not too much soda—thanks. And you—good! Puff! This is a bad business, eh? Known Tatten since we were kids— prep. school. Decent bloke, good type.' He drank deeply and set down his glass. 'Puff! That's better. Gut-twisting job, watching your pals snuff out.'

Emmanuel said, 'He's not dead!'

'He will be very soon. Broken his neck. I knew a chap in the Brigade who broke his neck—or his backbone—forget which. They patched it up for him. Apparently they can't patch up— whatever poor old "Toby's" broken. I dunno—don't understand their jargon. It's a bad business. He was riding this youngster— promising youngster too. "Carillion" . . . and—I'll tell you. "Toby's" always had good hands, lovely hands, but his seat was never what it might have been. Anyway, this wasn't his fault. Horse stumbled, threw him, and then came down on top of him. By the time we got to him, got the horse up, the damage was done. He's not made a sound since, not a sound.' He drank again. 'Lot of bother to find his wife. No-one in her flat, servants out, I suppose. Finally tried your father's place; they told us she might be dining with her mother. At last we got her. Nice woman, eh? Give me another drink, old man, will you? Thanks. Have another yourself, do! Yes, nice woman, plucky woman. Taking it on the chin. Poor old "Toby", worshipped that woman—positively worshipped her. He's her second husband, she divorced the first one.' He set down his glass suddenly and stared at Emmanuel, 'Damn it, I beg your pardon. I'd forgotten. I say, I'm sorry.'

Emmanuel said, 'Don't distress yourself. I don't mind.'

'And you're still good pals?'

'The best of friends, I assure you. I was dining at her mother's, who is a kind of aunt by marriage through some cousins of my own mother's. All very complicated and not nearly so close as it sounds. Viva told me of your telephone message. She refused to let me come with her, and so,' he shrugged his shoulders, 'I followed in my car.'

'Very sporting effort!' His large rather protruding eyes were suddenly suffused; then, cocking his head like one of the gun-dogs which he bred, he listened intently, 'They're coming! My God! This is going to be terrible.'

Sir Hearvey Franks entered, and with him a smaller, stouter man. The great doctor advanced with his strange mincing gait, the other man followed respectfully in his rear. Carteret, his hands pressing on the arms of his chair, half rose; Emmanuel stood still and composed before the fireplace.

Sir Hearvey said, 'Very sad—I say, very sad.'

Carteret gulped noisily. 'It's—over, eh?'

'Yes, oh, yes. Poor fellow. No hope from the first.'

Irritably Emmanuel thought, 'The first! The first of—what? This man only got here half an hour ago!' He said, 'And Mrs. Tatten?"

The smaller and stouter of the doctors said, 'Wonderful. Great strength of will, composure.'

Carteret asked, 'Sir Hearvey, have a drink, will you? You too, Caddingly?'

Dr. Caddingly replied with an implied rebuke, 'Sir Hearvey—Carteret. Will you take something to drink, Sir Hearvey?'

The tall, thin man lowered himself into a chair. 'I shall be glad to, glad to. In the course of my long—and extensive career, I have never—never been able to accustom myself to death. It has always . . . always . . . held a certain shock for me. The whole scene has never lost its——'

Emmanuel said, 'Whisky-and-soda?'

'I prefer brandy, thank you.'

He turned to Carteret. 'Got brandy here, Carteret?' The other man nodded, and pointed to the bottles.

He was obviously deeply moved. Emmanuel saw that there were tears on his light, thick lashes, his whole face looked distorted in his effort not to break down. He said, thickly, 'Give me another, Gollantz. Whisky—that's it. Thanks. Shot to bits! Oh God, she's coming!'

The door swung open and Viva entered the room. She stood for a moment in the doorway. Carteret half rose, muttered something which was almost inaudible. She laid the tips of her fingers on his broad shoulder and said, 'Thanks, "Buster". Thanks for—everything.' Then turning, her eyes met those of Emmanuel, standing there, his face very grave and almost colourless. He smiled, a smile which held complete kindness, understanding and sympathy.

Viva said, 'I knew that you'd come—Emmanuel.'

He replied, 'But, my dear, naturally. Sit down, let me give you something to drink. Yes, I insist.'

'You know——'

He inclined his head. 'I know, my dear. I'm terribly grieved for you.'

'And for him!' She flung the words out like a challenge. 'And for him. He did enjoy being alive so much.'

Carteret said, 'Y'know, I always believed he'd win the National one day. His hands were so darned good, only his seat——'

Viva stared at him, then her lips curled into a smile. 'I know, "Buster", his seat wasn't awfully good. As well for it to happen here as at Becher's.' She sipped her drink, then, turning to Emmanuel, snapped her fingers. 'Give me a cigarette, please.'

He handed her his case, lit her cigarette and said, 'Then let me take you home, please, Viva. Where will you go, to Aunt Beatrice or to Park Lane?'

He watched her sagging in her chair, picked up the glass which held her drink. and whispered urgently, 'Drink this— yes—now. That's better—again. Now, lean back.'

The drink seemed to restore her; she turned to the stout little doctor; her voice was very clear and crisp.

'Is there anything you need me to do, papers to sign? No?' as he shook his head. 'Then I shall make all arrangements from town. You don't mind "Toby" staying here until to-morrow, "Buster" dear, do you?'

'Me mind?' he barked. 'It's an honour! By God, I tell you, I'm proud to have him here!'

'Darling "Buster". Good night, Dr. Caddingly, and thank

you. Good night, Sir——' she hesitated. Caddingly prompted her.

'Sir Hearvey——'

'Good night, Sir Hearvey.'

'Can I drive you home, I say, can I drive you home? My car is here.'

'Many thanks. Mr. Gollantz is waiting for me. I'll just go and say good night to "Toby", Emmanuel, then we'll go.'

The door closed behind her ; there was silence in the room, only broken by the ticking of the ugly marble clock. Emmanuel saw Caddingly tiptoe over to Carteret, lean over his shoulder and whisper. Carteret blinked, as if he pulled himself back from a great distance, and said, 'Wha'? Didn't catch wha' you said.'

Emmanuel said, 'Dr. Caddingly, if Major Carteret allows it, will you come with me for a moment. Got another room down here, Carteret? May we use it?'

Carteret nodded. 'Yes—why not?'

Emmanuel thought. 'Poor chap, he's rather tight. He's been fond of "Toby"—nice fellow this man.'

Carteret continued, 'Breakfas' room. First onner right.'

The stout little doctor followed him ; they found a small room, which Emmanuel decided must be cheerful and sunny on pleasant mornings. He sat down and pulled out his cheque book. 'Now, Sir Hearvey's fee!'

As they stepped out into the cool night air Emmanuel glanced at Viva's white calm face. He saw her look upwards to where the stars hung, spattered across the sky. The whole atmosphere was peaceful, the night was very still, and the great arc of the sky seemed limitless and completely removed from the events of ordinary human lives. Life, death, birth—these things left the stars untouched and unmoved ; what did they know of wars, and crises, what would they care if they did know?

Viva, apparently sensing his thoughts, laid the tips of her fingers on his arm. 'They make you feel dreadfully unimportant,' she said.

'Possibly that's what we actually are,' he answered.

'Probably, but we're not unimportant to—ourselves, just the same.'

She said, 'Good night, "Buster", you've been so good. I'll send for my bus in the morning. Don't worry, everything will be arranged.' Then to Emmanuel's surprise she leaned forward and kissed him on his large round cheek. Emmanuel heard his gasp of surprise, and heard his hoarse voice mutter, 'Bless you, Viva, it's been a bad knock.'

As he drove back to London she lay back with her eyes closed. He made no effort to speak to her, and only when they reached Brompton Road did she sit upright and begin to talk to him. Her voice was as crisp as ever, but he noticed a brittle quality in it, and decided she ought to have something to make her sleep. She was too tightly strung, too near to breaking point.

She talked rapidly about 'Toby' Tatten, quoted things which he had said, things which he had done, places they had visited together. Nothing which held any particular interest, only rather disjointed statements and comments. Through all she said, which amounted to very little more than mere babble, Emmanuel caught the real and deep sense of affection which she had felt for the dead man. Not that she ever grew sentimental, her remarks were almost painfully commonplace, but the very fact that she had remembered so much, so many trivial things, and could recount them now, showed him how she had identified herself with Tatten's interests and amusements.

As he drew up before the great block of flats where she lived she seemed to relax, her voice had lost its tautness, and she said with a sigh, "Oh, it's a bad show. I do resent it so much, not only for myself, but for him. It's so damned unfair! No-one ever wanted less to die than "Toby". Coming in, Emmanuel?'

'Will your servants be up still—it's turned twelve?'

'Louise will be, she always waits for me. Yes, come up for a minute. I'd like you to.'

They entered the hall, with its vulgar decorations of coloured glass and gilt mouldings, its plants in gilded stands, its over-thick, over-heavy carpet, and its profusion of electric lights in chandeliers of grotesquely twisted and distorted brass.

She said, 'Hideous, isn't it?'

'Dreadful.'

'But the central heating is good, and the lift works.'

He smiled. 'Then everything else is forgiven and forgotten.'

The lift carried them silently upwards. Viva opened the door of her flat and her maid hurried forward. He saw a stout Frenchwoman, with dead-black hair and a sallow skin, but her dark eyes were bright and intelligent.

Viva let her coat slip from her shoulders to the floor, put her hands on the woman's shoulders, and said in a curiously level voice, 'Listen, Louise, you've got to help me. Mr. Tatten is dead—no, don't scream! If you do I shall do all the screaming for both of us. He was riding and had an accident. To-night I must sleep ; it will'—she turned to Emmanuel—'take the edge off things. Get me some hot milk and a couple of luminols.'

'Oui, madame.'

The woman picked up the coat. Viva walked into the big sitting-room. She said, 'This must set your teeth on edge!'

He said gravely, 'It does—rather.'

'We like it.'

'Then nothing could be more satisfact-orry.'

'A last drink?'

'If you are having one—thank you.'

She sipped her drink, her eyes staring vacantly. Emmanuel sat and watched her intently. He longed to say things which might comfort her, and then asked himself how he dared to imagine that any words of his could mitigate her grief. He felt instinctively that Viva would resent the commonplace sympathetic utterances; she would be, he thought, inclined to sneer, to mentally shrug her shoulders on hearing them. Better and wiser to continue in the key which she had chosen, to voice commonplaces, to behave as if poor Tatten were not lying at Esher with a broken neck.

She broke the silence by saying abruptly, 'We've been frightfully happy, "Toby" and I Somehow we just—fitted in. We neither of us made great demands on each other, and yet—if the opportunity had happened—there wasn't anything he wouldn't have done for me, or that I wouldn't have done for him. He wasn't clever, but then neither am I. I'm intelligent, so was "Toby" in some ways—horses and land, cars and cattle. God! It's going to be damned lonely, Emmanuel.' She shivered. 'How I am going to hate it all. Loneliness—it's a grim thing being lonely.'

'It is,' he said. 'I know, my dear.'

She nodded, her eyes still staring blankly. 'Yes, you've been through it, haven't you? I suppose, compared with you, I've had better luck. I had a good many years with "Toby"—you only had——'

'A year,' he said, 'that was all.'

'Nearly twenty years ago,' Viva said musingly. 'Does it ever really—heal, Emmanuel?'

He shook his head. 'Not really. Oh, the wounds don't go on bleeding, but they ache and burn and throb at the slightest provocation. It's rather like a person with a broken limb; you spend your time trying to avoid jarring it, giving it reason to—remind you of its existence.'

'I understand.' She turned to glance at the elaborate electric clock. 'My dear, it's so late. You must go and I must get some rest. I've a great deal to see to in the morning.'

'Can I help you? Can I do the——' he hesitated, 'the tiresome details? I could attend to them, perhaps.' He added gently,

'It would give me a certain vicarious pleasure—to do anything that I could to help, Viva. I'll drive down to Esher early in the morning and see Carteret. Hannah can see to the announcements in the papers——'

'Would you? You mean that? Emmanuel, what a nice chap you are! You don't know what it would mean—or how damned grateful I should be.'

'Then—that is settled. Good night, and try to get some sleep. I'll send Hannah round in the morning about ten to see you. You can trust Hannah to do everything, and do everything well. God bless you.'

'Thank you. I could wish that He'd turn His attention to showering a few blessings on you, my dear! You get precious few.'

'Pr-robably as many as I deserve. Good night, Viva.'

He sat in his own room, his long legs outstretched, his hands hanging limply at his sides, his eyes closed. He was terribly tired. The last few days had been filled with appointments, interviews, in giving facts to journalists, then rushing back to Park Lane to tell Viva all that he had accomplished.

Carteret, poor fellow, hadn't been a great help. He was anxious to do everything possible which might add to the honour of his dead friend, but so many of his proposals were fantastic and impractical, and when Emmanuel had to shake his head and murmur, 'A fine idea, but I don't think we'd better do that,' he saw the other man's face fall like that of a disappointed child. Carteret had wanted a regimental band, a troop of soldiers in uniform, tenants brought down by special train from 'Toby's' place in Westmorland; Irish pipers imported from the estate in Limerick; whenever Emmanuel saw him he was ready to begin, 'I've been thinking, Gollantz, it might be a good idea to have . . .' and then he would recount his latest plan for making 'Toby' Tatten's funeral 'something just a little out of the ordinary'.

When he told Viva of these brilliant ideas she said irritably, 'Oh, for Heaven's sake, no! It's a funeral, not a garden party! Carteret's a fool!'

'Possibly,' Emmanuel agreed, 'but it's his idea of doing honour to "Toby"; it's his glor-ry he wants, not anything for himself. He's rather a fine fellow. I like him ver-ry much indeed.'

'Oh, you always make excuses for everyone, you always did, you always will. It's become a habit with you.'

For three days Emmanuel had devoted himself to 'Toby' Tatten. His intense love of detail had made him plan everything with the greatest and most meticulous care. He had been thankful for Hannah's help, and that astonishing Jewess had amazed him by her knowledge of the routine of Christian funerals.

He had spent very little time at the Gallery; in fact he knew that he had avoided going there as much as possible, because he was vaguely afraid of what comments Julian might make. His brother had walked in the morning after Tatten's death and entered his office.

He said, 'Hello! My mother told me this morning that Tatten's dead. Accident, eh? Were you there?'

Coldly Emmanuel said, 'At the time of the accident? No.'

'I mean when he died. I heard that you went over with Viva.'

'I was in the house when he died. I followed Viva and brought her home. Is there anything else you wish to know?'

Julian grinned suddenly. Emmanuel felt his hands clench instinctively.

'Quite a lot,' Julian said, 'but I doubt if you'd tell me.'

Very gently Emmanuel said, 'Be careful.'

Still smiling, his brother asked, 'Careful—of what?'

'I dislike impertinence. Also your amusement str-rikes me as being in particularly bad taste.'

'Good Lord, you get more pompous every day!'

He had gone out without troubling to close the door. Hannah rose and shut it gently. Emmanuel—white-faced—said, 'Hannah, one day I shall kill my br-rother!'

She shrugged her massive shoulders. 'Ach! Leave his death to someone else. Now—this announcement for *The Times*. . . .'

Now the funeral was over, and he lay back remembering his grandfather's funeral leaving from Ordingly, with the whole of the Gollantz foreign contingent following the Head of the House. They had come from Holland, Vienna, Paris and Budapest—Bruchs, Hirschs, Jaffes, and de Laras; with them were the Davises, the Lanes, Harrises and Harts. Angela's family—Drews, Wilmots, Heriots, William Masters, and his own Juliet, little Gilbert and dozens more. He remembered his father's drawn, white face, heard little Bernstein's whispered assurances that he would not leave Angela's side until Max returned. Recalled his father's hoarse reply, 'Don't let her die, Meyer, don't let her die!'

She hadn't died, though her life had been hanging by a thread for days. Meyer had pulled her through; Meyer and the devotion of her husband.

That other funeral in Milan, when it seemed to him that the

stream of people would never end—musicians, composers, great conductors, singers, representatives of musical societies, others from the many charitable institutions who had benefited by Juliet's generosity. Guido and Louis Lara weeping without restraint, little Gilbert white-faced and tight-lipped, Charles Wilmot who had been Juliet's solicitor, old Simeon Jaffe, immense, unwieldy, puffing and panting whenever he moved. The vast cemetery, with its huge monuments and elaborate memorials, the long trail of dark-clad people passing along the road which led to the chapel. The rain falling, softly and persistently, the even, slightly over-cultured voice of the English chaplain sounding strange in his ears, the sight of the coffin being lowered and his own instinctive movement forward. The touch of his brother Bill's hand on his arm, his voice saying 'Steady, Emmanuel, steady.'

He shivered at the recollection of his return to the flat. The silence, the loneliness, and then little Simeon's wailing had reached him. He had not moved, at that moment Simeon meant nothing to him, his own sense of loss was too great.

Guido, his face still puffed and swollen with crying, had said, 'Poor leetle baby! I bet he's lonely. *Poverino!*'

Emmanuel had not moved or spoken, and Guido had listened intently to the sound of the baby crying.

'Eet is not kind to let a leetle baby cry,' he said reflectively. 'Eef no ozzer chaps have hearts—Guido has! Watcha me, eef you pleaze!'

He had gone and reappeared with the child in his arms. The crying had ceased, and he offered him to Emmanuel, saying, 'Efter all, t'ain't the fault of poor leetle baby—this tragedy. Cannot hand him the blame!'

Emmanuel remembered how he had taken the child and stared at him. Then a great wave of emotion shook him, and holding the child close he felt the tears run down his cheeks, and the sobs shake him.

And now, today, he had followed what was left of 'Toby' Tatten, he had watched the crowd of well-dressed people—his mother and father, Lady Heriot, and with her old Walter looking shaky and tottering a little, his own son, Simeon—tall and erect, his young face grave and intent ; more Drews, Heriots and Wilmots, Masters limping badly, 'Toby's' trainer, several jockeys with wizened faces and quick nervous movements. 'Buster' Carteret, and with him a small crowd of men of his type—tall, well fed, bulky and apparently uncomfortable in their dark, well-cut clothes. Men from Ireland, men from the North, representatives of coal mines, agents, stewards and the rest. Viva entering the church alone, looking straight before her to where the coffin lay covered with a pall and banked with wreaths.

The little knot of clergy, headed by some clergyman who looked not unlike the jockeys, and who 'Buster' Carteret had told Emmanuel, '. . . ought to be there. Great pal of "Toby's", only parson he ever liked. Great sportsman—"Chalky" White. Knew each other overseas.' Two other clergymen who Hannah had told him were 'the local products—Vicar and his head curate,' and lastly the Bishop, who was some distant relation of the Wilmots, tall, dignified and immaculate in lawn sleeves. Emmanuel stood at the back of the church, watching and listening.

The thin, sweet voices of the choirboys reached him, the deep richness of the men's voices, the soft tones of the organ ; the beautifully spoken phrases of the Liturgy, and the smooth ease of the movements made by the clergy as each one took the part of the service allotted to him.

He thought how soothing it all was, as if the church laid kindly fingers on hearts and minds which were disturbed and full of pain. With something like regret he wished that he had retained a definite faith. School had meant what appeared to be endless chapels, and at Ordingly neither Max nor Angela professed much interest in the church. Both of them gave liberally. Angela went to church on the great festivals, and the Vicar came to dine at regular intervals ; the children—once they had left school—were neither encouraged to attend the services, nor were they in the least discouraged. Emmanuel felt that if any of them had felt an urge to go to church twice every Sunday, the last thing that either Max or Angela would have tolerated would have been that anyone should sneer at their inclinations or the form which their religious ideas took. Angela because she was essentially kind-hearted and sympathetic, Max because he regarded any form of intolerance as unwarrantable and impertinent.

He thought that in all probability his religious beliefs had never been very strong, and that they had wilted and died through lack of attention and exercise.

The organ had begun to play—what was it? A 'dead march', but one which was only vaguely familiar to him. Men were beginning to move the flowers, presently they would carry 'Toby' out to make the last stage of his journey. Emmanuel stood stiffly erect as the coffin was carried past him, then followed to fulfil the last of his self-imposed duties.

'Buster' Carteret stood near him on the pathway of the

100

church. He whispered, 'Jimmy Holdforth said just now what a pity we didn't arrange for the "Last Post". Too late now, but it's a pity, great pity. Can't be helped, I suppose.'

Later he had sat in Viva's flat, while Charles Wilmot, with Bill Gollantz seated near him, had outlined 'Toby's' will. Emmanuel had scarcely listened. He heard Sir Walter grunt in approbation from time to time, heard his aunt sigh, rather than actually say, 'Poor fellow . . . poor fellow,' and saw Viva—white-faced but calm—listening with a kind of contemptuous attention, as if she lacked interest in 'Toby's' instructions as to the disposal of his money.

Walter Heriot said to him when they were leaving, 'Well—one thing—the poor fellah's left Viva a hell of a lot of money. Pooh! a hell of a lot! She must be a damned wealthy woman! Damned wealthy!'

Viva herself gave Emmanuel her hand, saying, 'I shall never be able to thank you sufficiently. And that kind woman, Hannah. What a tower of strength she's been—in fact'—with the ghost of a smile—'you've been twin towers! I'm going away as soon as possible. I hate this place—without "Toby". It's all so pointless—this, everything. I'll get away as quickly as possible. For long? I hope so. I'll see you before I sail. Oh, didn't I tell you? America—plenty of space there. Good-bye, and again thank you, Emmanuel dear.'

He opened his eyes and sighed. To get away, to leave London, the Gallery, behind, to forget that his brother Julian existed—he couldn't ; he must stay and stick to his work. If only Guido would write!

CHAPTER EIGHT

At his desk Emmanuel turned over the letters, and suddenly gave a suppressed cry of excitement. There, with its row of unfamiliar postage stamps, with the label stating that it was *espresso,* and also *raccomandato,* was the long envelope bearing the name of the Jaffe-Gollantz Galleries on the flap.

He knew that his fingers trembled a little as he picked up the fine paper-knife and slit open the envelope. He drew out the sheets, sheets of closely typed statements ; then reluctantly laid them down again and turned to the other letters. Guido's report must wait.

Offers to sell—everything imaginable—tables, chairs, chests, books—not much sale for those at the moment, particularly if they held any real value—china, glass—anything and everything. Some of it no doubt good, much of it the worthless gleanings of old attics, and the result of the present ingrained conviction that 'anything will sell'. He leaned forward and rang his bell ; a second later Hannah entered, and smiled her usual, 'Good morning.'

He said, 'This and this—yes, and this too—are of no interest to us. Just Victorian and Edwardian junk ! Here is a lady— and obviously a lady—who has a Pembroke table. I don't like them much, but they are useful and the wood is often good. She lives at'—he read the address—'Maidstone. She also has a tea service which she believes to be Crown Derby. Let Simeon go down and see them. There may be something else. He's quite capable of acting on his own.'

Hannah nodded her massive head. 'So ! this boy has a flair. One day, with experience and some encouragement, he will fill a great place.'

He nodded, and turned to another letter. 'Someone here with what he calls "a fine set of Bartolozzi prints". I know what they're like, framed and all the borders cut to fit the frames ! He's also got three sporting prints—he writes, "rather spotted but no doubt they could be cleaned". I know that type too. "Foxed" all over ! No, not for us. Six Chippendale chairs—two

102

with arms. And a table. Get Hooper to go down, they're at Maidenhead. Some lace—this is at Kingston—we don't want lace. And several fans.'

Hannah watched his face lose its keenness. He repeated, 'Several fans.' Then said, 'Ask this lady to bring them here, we'll pay the expenses of the journey if we don't buy them.' He added reflectively, 'I have a weakness for old fans. There is something ver-ry charming about them, they belong to another time, a time when people moved with dignity. Yes, I should ver-ry much like to see them. Here—this I find amusing, because I am not certain that the law—as it exists today—allows me to buy, but I am pr-repared to r-risk it. A case of Normandin Cognac, the date 1875. Make the usual enquiries as to how it has been kept, and so forth.

'Now, enquiries. Have we a dinner service, Coleport? Must be perfect, for twenty-four people. I suppose,' with a hint of regret, 'that must go to my brother. And this—Sheffield Plate entrée dishes, with the mark of Thomas Law.' He repeated, 'Law—that's about 1755 to 1760, isn't it? Pass them on, please, Hannah. There, that's the lot for this morning.'

She shuffled the letters together, and stood hesitant for a moment. Emmanuel, his fingers longing to pick up Guido's letter, said, 'Yes, what is it?'

'I suppose you couldn't deal with the china and the Sheffield?'

He shook his head, 'I don't think that it is wise. Better leave it.'

'I suppose so. Very well.'

The door closed behind her, and Emmanuel, conscious that his heart was beating furiously, opened Guido's letter. There were several sheets of typewriting, several lists which he laid aside. He turned to the letter itself.

Master, Friend, Instructor, I have good news. On my sad return to find Milano if not in actual ruins at least having suffered a real bashing. Nevertheless the vermins, our enemies, were not so full of brains as to put anything over this Guido. I bet now they are mad as hell. Good job, first rate. I laugh when I think—and I think often. The monumental wall in the cellars had such an air of oldness that nothing was suspected. I had laid outside of it with loving care a great deal of junk. Speculative Reubens, possibility Carlo Dolce, maybe perhaps be but not guaranteed Titian. Beautiful set of fine china from Japan! Of an ugliness not to be believed if you recall. Several nice pieces of old plate and jewellery from Birmingham—tasty and horrible. All were gone. Maybe we hope lost on the Brennero! Also many Hun thieves.

Down comes the ancient looking wall. I laughed like a great collection of drains. Pictures—a small Boucher, a very smallest Mantagna, two Caroto—but of great beauty. One Englishman painting, name of the gent, Reynolds. A 'credited' and I believe with reason, Giorgione. Many packing-cases of china, the glass of Venice, of Waterford, of Bristol. China of Derby, Worcester, Dresden, Meisen and more than I have time to shake sticks at! Furniture—old painted of Florence, French of the Empire and also of Ré Louis. This very good-looking. Brocades, embroidery of Churches and priests, velvets from Genova, and so on. Silver of much kinds. In short it was like to enter the cave of this chap Aladdin who had that goodish lamp!

Have no fear, soon I shall have you here, and together we shall make the Galleries like Paradise. You are rich bloke, dear Emmanuel. Now you must get a crack on, and hurry here. I shall tell you stories which will make your hair very curly! I believe when you see what we have—lists included on other sheets of paper—your eyes will leap from your head with joy and smiling-ness. As I did, crying loudly, 'Not bloody possible truly!' But really completely bloody possible thanks to Guido and his cleverness and the kind aid of Almighty God. Come soon, I am well, people say, 'Handsome Guido, bettern ever,' but I am sad at heart whiles you shall be to share out our joy.

Emmanuel laid down the letter and wiped his forehead. Then there had been things saved, and if all Guido wrote were true, a very great deal that was of immense value, and which would be sufficient to set the Galleries going again. He turned to the lists, and as he studied them his satisfaction grew. These things were not merely good, many of them were unique.

This dressing-table by Gillow, with its long slender legs, its concave front and beautiful little ivory handles; that set of Hepplewhite—how well he remembered their dignified simplicity. Here was the carved chest, perfect Gothic, which he had bought scarcely believing that it could be genuine, so perfect was it, and of such superb beauty. The enamel of Limoges, he could recall its rich colouring still, that wonderful blue, which looked like velvet; the shimmer of the old glass of Murano, some of it with threads of gold imprisoned in the glass. That touchingly simple Chardin, which he had found dirty and neglected and had carried home in triumph, swearing that he would never sell it to anyone who did not love it as he did. The cases of ivories of the 16th century, the little bronze virgin of

1359, standing on her beautiful casket, looking shy and rather timid. He would see them, handle them again. Tanagra figures, Greek vases, even those fragments of antique beauty which he had never cared for very much, because he disliked loveliness which had been damaged and disfigured—but they were waiting for him!

For a few moments Emmanuel appeared to have shed years, he looked younger and very alert, his eyes shone, and his lips lost the somewhat harsh line which they had assumed during the past few weeks. He wasn't sitting in the Gollantz Gallery, he was back in Milano, going through cases and crates, unwrapping bales of material, holding little ivory figures tenderly in his hands, while Guido kept uttering little cries of delighted surprise as each new treasure came to light. He was among his own things, he was sorting out his own collection, the things which he had found and housed with care.

Years ago old Simeon Jaffe had said to him, 'Emmanuel, alvays veel you be no dealer in antiques but alvays a collector. R-really, you don' like much to sell, you vould r-rather keep zese t'ings in your Gellery for the pleasure vot dey giff to you. Tell me, am I r-right?'

The old man had been right, he felt an actual love for his things, he had sufficient practicality to know that they must be sold because to sell was his work and the way in which he made his living, but he did not enjoy selling as Guido, for example, did.

Then as Emmanuel finished reading the long list, the smile faded and his eyes lost their bright intensity. He wasn't in Milano, he was here in Bond Street, and the problems which Guido's letter had caused him to forget all came rushing back to him.

He locked the letter and the lists away in his desk, and set out on his daily tour of inspection. Young Watson, who had conceived a complete and violent admiration for Emmanuel, came forward, blushing and stammering.

'Mr. Julian has been round, sir, about the Coleport dinner service. He said it was exactly what he wanted for an order.'

Emmanuel nodded. 'I remember, twenty-four persons; must be perfect.' He added, 'In these days it's a fairly tall order. Works out at over a hundred pieces, eh?'

Watson, with an air of subdued pride at the exactness of his knowledge, yet unwilling to throw the slightest doubt on the infallible knowledge of his master, said, 'I think, sir, rather more. I made it a hundred and ten.'

'Quite likely. My intimate knowledge of Coleport is rusty. Is it perfect, Watson?'

'Practically——'

Emmanuel's voice sharpened suddenly. 'What do you mean by "practically"? It's either perfect or imperfect.'

'Mr. Julian is examining it, sir.'

Emmanuel walked swiftly to the office where he knew that he would find his brother. Julian was lounging in a chair, smoking and reading a letter; whatever were its contents they were causing him considerable amusement. Emmanuel thought, 'It's from some woman, I know that expression on Julian's face!' then blamed himself for being petty-minded and captious. Julian glanced up, put the letter in his pocket, and said, 'Hello— want anything?'

'That Coleport . . .' Queer how he always felt at a disadvantage when faced with his brother's easy nonchalance. 'Is it perfect—that's the stipulation, you know.'

'I've not had time to look it over,' Julian said; 'it's there, waiting until I've a minute to spare.'

'Can't Seber look it over?' Emmanuel asked. 'I should like a reply to go to them today, and one piece.'

'Seber isn't working here any longer. He didn't like the— atmosphere. He's an independent fellow, a craftsman, and —well, he decided to work elsewhere. Which means—if you want a plain answer, that he disliked your interference, Emmanuel. As for the china, all right—you can leave it to me, I'm perfectly capable of managing my own part of the business. Like Seber I'm growing a little tired of this being called to book about every single thing! Frankly, you're intolerable!'

'Where is Seber working? Is he still working for the firm?' Emmanuel refused to be drawn into argument, he determined to cling to the business in hand. 'If not——'

Julian interrupted him. 'Seber is working for me. He isn't working for the firm, as you call it. He's valuable and I find him useful. I'm paying his wages. Again mind your own business.'

The whole atmosphere was growing tense; Emmanuel felt that only by an almost superhuman effort could he control his temper. He stood there watching his brother light a cigarette with elaborate care, and wondered how long he would be able to tolerate the present position.

'But surely,' he said calmly, 'this is part of my business. I am only concerned with the fact that this man, who you assured me was an asset to us, has left us suddenly. Did he leave without notice? Was he paid in lieu of notice? In what way is he useful to you, where is he working? Why did he not give notice in the usual way?'

Julian stubbed out his cigarette with a movement which was vicious in its intensity; he stared at his brother, his face overcast and furious.

'He didn't give notice; he merely took himself off, because his dislike of your interference was growing every day. He did not wait to be given notice, which he felt was only a question of time, as you took so little trouble to hide your general disapproval of him. Where he is working is my business, what he is actually doing is my business also. You've got Davis and young Watson under your thumb; you've got your own precious son dragged into the business, and that fat old Jewess eats out of your hand! Surely that's enough for you, unless you contemplate making conquests of the charwomen! You'll have a report on the china by four this afternoon, a piece will be posted in time for the afternoon post. . . .'

Emmanuel said, 'Providing, of course, that the set is perfect.'

'Oh, don't quibble! I implied that. There are a pair of Sheffield dishes, but the mark isn't what these people want. Law, wasn't it? These are three scrolls—knots—I don't know what the devil they are.'

'Unidentified,' Emmanuel said, 'about the same date . . . possibly a year or two later.'

'Trust you to know, eh? I know where I can put my hand on a pair with this Law mark. Since you know so much, how does it go exactly?'

Emmanuel drew a sheet of paper towards him and taking his slim gold pencil from his pocket made a drawing; his hand moved smoothly, there was no hesitation; he handed it to his brother.

'Small "T.L." in italics, larger stamp with L.A.W. in block letters, followed by another smaller stamp like the first, again with "T.L." in italics. The maker's name has always been one of the——'

Julian interrupted him. 'All right, all right. I didn't ask for a lecture on Sheffield Plate! I believe that you actually take an interest in all this stuff! Good Lord, we're only shopkeepers after all; drapers don't sentimentalize over a length of silk, or bootmakers grow lyrical over a pair of shooting boots. It's all this damned assumption that we're better, more exclusive, than other—tradesmen. Very well, I can show you the dishes, probably the day after tomorrow. I know a man who has quite a few. Now, if you've finished your lectures and homilies—will you remember that I have work to get done?'

It was a relief to get back to his own office, to send for young Simeon and tell him of the good news from Guido. Emmanuel watched the young man intently as he read the letter, a smile touching his lips from time to time when Guido's somewhat unconventional phrasing amused him.

He handed back the letter, saying, 'That's quite marvellous. Will you go over?'

'As soon as possible. I don't know what conditions for export are. I imagine that as I exported quite a considerable amount before the war I shall be permitted a certain percentage of that amount. Then there is America ; I used to send a great deal over there. I shall have to get on to the Board of Trade. I'll let you know. Oh, Simeon, for the time being—for the time being, don't mention this to anyone.'

'No, of course.' Then his eyes shining again, he began to talk of his journey into the country. 'I'm rather excited about this job, my first. I've looked up Pembroke Tables and Crown Derby. If they're all right, am I to buy them? How much can I give for the china? And if there should be anything else, can I buy that if it seems all right?'

His father smiled, the boy's excitement reminded him of the days when his grandfather used to send him on similar journeys. He said, 'Nothing must *seem* all right, you've got to be able to give chapter and verse why it *is* all right. Let me show you . . .' Again he took out his pencil, again he drew the various monograms of the great china, giving dates and writing particulars regarding colour. 'There, take that with you, study it as you go down. As a matter of fact, although it's a later date, I have a great liking for the Bloor. Charming! Only remember Limoges copied the cornflower, and in all probability Bloor copied it from a piece of Angoulême.'

It did Emmanuel good to watch his son's face, so eager and intent on concentrating on the matter in hand. He seized the paper, folded it and put it into his inside pocket, saying, 'That shall be my reading for the train.' He laughed. 'Save me buying a thriller from the bookstall, eh?'

Emmanuel said, 'We must begin to make a collection of books for you ; unfortunately they're difficult to get, but I have some of your grandfather's which might interest you. They have his own pencil notes in them.'

'Really! How marvellous. I have a few, you know. I've got Chaffers ; he's monumental, isn't he?—and two by E. A. Jones

108

on silver, and one, I forget the name, on English furniture. Of course, I need a great many more.'

'Learn to trust your eyes, and your fingertips,' his father advised. 'There, off you go on your treasure hunt! Come and show me the spoils in the morning. Oh, and Simeon—if this lady is old, and—well, looks as if she needed the money, be gentle with her. Try, unless her price is prohibitive, to give her what she asks.'

The boy nodded, and went out smiling. As he passed Hannah's small office he opened the door and looked in. She turned, her eyes shining with pleasure at the sight of him.

'Well,' she asked, 'what is it now, please?'

'I'm going off to buy some things! My first job!'

'*Mazaltov!* Your father's sending you, no?'

'Yes, he's been giving me tips about Crown Derby. I say, Hannah, what a grand bloke he is! He's got everything at his fingertips.'

She nodded. 'Old Emmanuel was a great man, your grandfather is also great—in a different way—but I am not sure that Emmanuel the Second is not the greatest of them all. I, Hannah Rosenfeldt, know what I talk about!'

He found Julian's report waiting for him the following morning, neatly written in the careful, rather studied hand which he affected.

'One hundred and nine pieces. One small plate missing. Perfect except for one superficial crack in a large plate. Mark—scroll with letters C.S.N. Panels of flowers on crimson ground, gilt edges. Price £356. One small plate sent as sample. Insured and registered.'

And lower on the sheet: 'Two Sheffield plate covered entrée dishes. Perfect. Mark of Law, date 1758. In process of cleaning. Communicating with client today ; sending photograph and measurements.' The sheet was signed 'J. E. Gollantz.'

Emmanuel was conscious of a sense of satisfaction. Julian was doing his best, and that best was very good. His reports were concise, and he had been admirably prompt in procuring photographs. Possibly this was one of the ways in which he used Seber. Perhaps the fellow acted as a 'scout' and brought word of pieces in unlikely places to Julian. He telephoned to Julian's office, and rather to his surprise his brother's voice answered. Again Emmanuel felt that thrill of satisfaction. It was barely half past nine ; early for Julian to be in.

'Julian? Many thanks for the reports. Pity the one plate is missing, hope it won't put them off. I should very much appreciate a glimpse of one of the pieces. I forget if I've ever seen that particular set.'

Julian's voice sounded cordial as he replied, 'Only too pleased. I'll send one along with young Watson. Lovely thing, never seen a better.'

'And perfect?'

'Barring one plate and this superficial crack. I'll send that one along. The Sheffield plate dishes are pretty nice too. The mark is exactly as you said. What kind of a price should I ask?'

'Let me have a look at the photograph, Julian. It's a good period.'

'Very well. They'll be along in a minute.'

'Thanks, and congratulations.'

A moment later Watson entered carrying the dinner-plate. Emmanuel took it, and held it almost reverently in his hands. What a lovely thing it was with its deep, rich crimson ground, and the exquisite panels of flowers and foliage. The gilt edges so bright and of such a clear gold. He ran his fingertips over the surface, noting the smoothness, and realizing the hardness of the glaze.

He said to Watson, 'What a lovely thing. Since 1790 this particular ware has never deteriorated. There is something of perfection in Coleport. It's worth studying. Yes—very fine. Now the photograph. Small beer compared with the china, of course.' He examined the photograph with care. 'Very pleasant, but Sheffield is Sheffield and not silver, after all. I suggest—let me see . . . Thirty pounds as it's an early mark. We might take twenty-five. Thank you, Watson.'

He returned to his letters, still filled with a sense of satisfaction, perhaps things had taken a turn for the better, perhaps Julian sensed his determination not to be drawn into a quarrel, perhaps from now on they might find it possible to work in some kind of harmony.

He sat for a moment allowing himself to dream of the chances of the Gollantz Gallery working in close conjunction with the Galleries of the same firm in Milano, pictured them building up a great and flourishing export trade, buying from all parts of the world, still retaining their right to be regarded as international dealers and experts.

Simeon's entrance disturbed his dreams; the boy came in smiling, obviously longing to tell his father of his experiences during the previous day.

Emmanuel said, 'Well—let's hear all about it.'

'She was a very nice old lady,' Simeon told him, 'living in a small, but not uncomfortably small, house; everything very

110

neat and beautifully polished. She showed me the table—I think that it's a good one, nice wood, mahogany, well kept. It belonged to an aunt who left it to this old lady. She showed me the china—said that it was made the year of the Battle of Waterloo.'

'The year that Robert Bloor took over the factory from Dewsbury.'

'It's a beautiful set—twelve cups and saucers, sugar basin, slop bowl and cream jug. The teapot has the smallest little chip out of the spout——'

Emmanuel said, 'They so often have. That is the tragedy of teapots.'

'It's scarlet, blue and gold, it feels like silk when you touch it. It really is'—he checked his enthusiasm as if he feared that he were saying too much in praise of his purchases, and added a little lamely—'it really is very pleasant.'

'Then suppose that you bring this marvel for me to see,' his father said, 'and then we must send for your uncle. It's really his province, you know. By the way, what did you pay for them?'

'The table, what she asked, which was eight pounds. The china—I rather took a chance on that, Father. She said that she didn't know, that she realized that the teapot had this chip, and asked if I thought that twenty guineas was too much. I thought for a long time, and honestly she did look so—well—anxiously at me, that I said I thought that you would wish me to pay a little more, and I gave her thirty-two pounds. There was a tea service sold in 1908 for that price, and surely values have risen.

'Perfectly r-right, you were looking at me as anxiously as your old lady must have looked at you! Now—let me see the china.'

Simeon was right, the set was beautiful, the patina exquisite, the colours rich and clear. Emmanuel examined it carefully, then said:

'You've made a very good beginning. Hannah will tell you that "a good beginning makes a good ending"—so your career ought to be successful. Let's telephone to Julian.'

It was evident when Julian entered the office that he was in one of his best moods. He came in smiling, nodded with easy affection to Simeon, and said—with considerable eagerness, 'Now, let's see what kind of spurs our young knight has won in his first encounter!'

He examined the china, nodding and continuing to smile.

'Ah, the usual tragedy of the teapot spout!' he exclaimed.

Simeon said, 'That's exactly what my father said!'

111

Julian glanced at him, his expression comical, 'That is what every dealer has been saying down the ages, my boy. Awful thought, some heavy-handed maid, washing up this beautiful stuff, bangs the spout against the tap and—knocks off not only a piece of china, but a considerable amount of money! However—I can sell it. You've done well, my boy.'

Emmanuel, watching them, thought how capable Julian was of making people like him—when he cared to exercise his personal charm. Young Simeon at the moment was listening to him with an air of being completely absorbed and interested.

He said, 'I got a table, too, Uncle Julian.'

'That's not my province, Simeon. I never wander from my own ground. As a matter of fact,' he lowered his voice, but the sound of the laughter came filtering through, 'I am not sufficiently certain of my step, if I do. Your father is the clever fellow with the immense all-round knowledge; I'm just trying to understand a difficult subject at a time when my brain is beginning to grow a little rusty. By the way, I bought a pair of candlesticks, Emmanuel. I'm damned if I could find the mark, and yet I knew instinctively that they were "right". I found it eventually hidden among the decoration. That's unusual, isn't it?'

Emmanuel considered, then said, 'It depends how cleverly it is hidden. There were certain makers who considered—with some justice—that the marks were unsightly on a highly decorated piece. They went to the greatest pains to conceal them among decorations, leaves and general embellishments. No, when it's well done—it's not very unusual. Badly done—you don't often find it.'

Somehow Julian's quick turn to Simeon, and his smile as he said, 'I told you, he knows everything!' gave Emmanuel a sense that his brother was putting him in a disadvantageous light. Simeon appeared not to notice it, but Emmanuel felt that some of the content which he had felt had dissolved, leaving behind it a deposit of faint bitterness.

He said, 'Have the china entered, Simeon, please, and supply your uncle with all particulars. Note if all the pieces are really perfect, and how many are marked. I must get on with some work.'

Julian slipped his arm through his nephew's. 'We're turned out!' he said. 'I have always called your father "The Industrious Apprentice" and he never disappoints me. I'll send someone for the china. Come, Simeon—"life is real, and life is earnest".'

The door closed behind them; again Emmanuel experienced that queer sense of having been 'put in his place'—and that place

112

a very dull, rather uninteresting one! Then he returned to his desk, telling himself that he was hypersensitive, it might be even a little jealousy of Julian's ability to attract Simeon, to make him smile. How foolish; as if it mattered! Simeon was excited; he wanted to talk about his first small success. Emmanuel turned again to Guido's letter, and later telephoned for Hannah.

'Get me an appointment with Mr. Bird, at the Board of Trade, will you? The sooner the better, but I won't be fobbed off with some understrapper who will waste my time as well as his own. If Bird can't see me—I'll wait until he can.'

Hannah said, 'You've had news? Good news?'

He nodded, 'Better than I dared to hope for, Hannah. Only for the moment I don't want it talked about. Simeon knows, and you and I.'

Hannah grunted, 'That's enough! It concerns no one else.'

'My own feeling exactly. Now, get me that appointment, please.'

Later she returned to say that Mrs. Tatten was on the telephone and that his appointment with Bird was fixed for four that afternoon.

Viva's voice, clear and faintly hard, reached him. 'That you, Emmanuel? Can you possibly lunch with me? No, here at the flat. I'd be glad. I'm leaving almost immediately—yes, America. Can you make it one o'clock? Good! Come right up in the lift. I shall come back from America calling it the elevator! Good-bye.'

So Viva was going away. He felt vaguely disappointed. He would have liked to know that she was in England, have enjoyed talking to her of his excitement over the Milan Galleries; she had always given him advice which was sound and unbiassed. There was something about her which had the effect of a tonic, slightly astringent, leaving a pleasant, clean taste! True there were times when he deplored her taste, or lack of it, when he wondered how she could tolerate the things which she gathered round her. Comfort at the expense of elegance. He had said so often when she had shown him some new purchase, 'But in five years' time—what will it be worth? Possibly three pounds!'

She had replied, 'Exactly, but by that time it will be worth even less to me. I shall be sick of it, and glad to see the last of it.' Or, in her more impatient moments, 'Oh, I know, I know— what Old Emmanuel used to call "The best Tottenham Court Road period"! All right—I like it, I wanted it, I've got it!'

He had never found the friends which she and Tatten

gathered round them in the least attractive—the men who looked like country squires or alternatively like jockeys; the women who all pitched their voices too high, who were addicted to a great deal of make-up, and who rarely appeared to be without a glass of something or other in their hands. Not that they weren't pleasant and kind. 'Toby' had always been amazingly nice to him, and again and again he had found it difficult to refuse the many invitations which both 'Toby' and his wife had showered upon him. The fact that Viva had been his wife did not appear to worry either her or 'Toby'; he had, very tentatively, mentioned this fact to her when they were alone. Her blank stare showed him that the idea had never occurred to her.

'Good God!' she had exclaimed. 'What a funny mind you've got. Always pulling things up to see how they're growing. What on earth does that matter? We like you—both of us. "Toby" knows you sufficiently well to realize that you'd probably be the safest man in the world to leave me alone with. He knows, too, that he's the only man who matters to me. That marriage of ours is all over and done with—we all know it. You're not contemplating making a sudden pass at me, are you?'

'My dear Viva!'

'That shook you, didn't it? I've certainly no idea of seducing you, and "Toby" isn't setting the stage for you to make a "come back". Oh, Emmanuel, dear, don't be so silly.'

He walked to Park Lane, and he had scarcely reached the door of Viva's flat when it was opened to him by her maid.

She beamed at him, 'I 'eard zee leeft, saire. My 'earing is ver-qvick. Madame is waiting for you.'

Viva came to greet him, and he admitted that her black clothes were effective against the white carpets and upholstery which she declared to be the only scheme for this particular room. He disliked it as a scheme, only the two pictures pleased him; they were of the modern type, but not so excessively modern as to be, to the average observer, completely without meaning.

She said, 'Nice of you to come. I'm going the day after tomorrow. Bill and Charles somehow managed to get everything through for me. I'm damned lucky the way the Gollantz family always turn up to do any hard work for me.'

'The Gollantz family are very honoured to be of help to you.'

Her smile deepened, 'Running true to form, as always, Emmanuel! No one else uses those easy running phrases. I shall stay away as long as I'm finding America amusing, and shall leave the instant it begins to bore me. No, probably about six or seven months will see me back again. Not here—I'm getting rid of this—except the pictures.'

He said, 'Running tr-rue to form, I was about to make you an offer for them.'

'Sorry, I want them. "Toby" liked them. And that, too.' She pointed to a design in dark wood, with strings stretching tightly from side to side.

Emmanuel frowned. 'What is it, and why did he like it? It doesn't look like "Toby" somehow.'

'What a relief to find that about some things you're an ignoramus, my dear. It's—modern form. By this new man. Hengist Matchlet. Some misguided person persuaded "Toby" to go to his exhibition—it was somewhere in Bond Street. "Toby" came home with this, and declared that this Matchlet was a humorist. I looked at this piece of rubbish—he'd paid fifteen guineas for it!—and asked why? He said,' she chuckled at the recollection, and her face looked suddenly younger and less strained, ' "In the catalogue it was called 'The Truth'. Can't you see—this thing's a *lyre*! I don't say that the chap's made it awfully well, but that's what it's meant to be. It's a joke!" He bought another later, of two round bits of wood stuck one on top of the other, and a tiny one tacked on somewhere or other. It was called "The Lovers", but I found that he grew so ribald about it, and his remarks were so unspeakabl᷍ ᷍hat I made him give it to "Buster" Carteret. It's probably bri᷍ntening his young life at the expense of his morals at the moment.'

Emmanuel held the twisted wood and string object in his hands and stared at it closely ; then, setting it down, he said, 'The man who made that is either sincere—but no artist, or he is an artist—and completely insincere. In either case, the thing is a cr-rime.'

'Can sincerity be a crime?' Viva asked.

'When it is as offensive as these preposterous pr-roductions, I think so.'

When lunch was over they sat and talked over their coffee. In spite of the decorations of the room, Emmanuel felt soothed and comforted. They had discussed many things with frankness and complete honesty. Once or twice, he knew that Viva had lifted the veil which hid her deeper feelings, and allowed him to see something of her mind.

'I want to get away, really to run away from everything that reminds me—of things I want to forget. I don't want to forget "Toby" ; one day I shall be able to remember him and smile, and not feel as if someone is twisting a knife in my guts. But I don't want to remember two doctors—one tall and thin, the other short and stout ; starched nurses, the smell of disinfectants, the tinkle of steel instruments on a tray, and "Toby" looking like a yellowing wax effigy of himself. Not even a very well-made effigy. I want to run away from that.'

As he was glancing at his watch she said, 'I wanted to give you something of his—it was difficult, because you'd never wear tiepins with horseshoes or foxes or racehorses, would you? You don't wear watch-chains, do you? Will you have these links? I had them made for him. Yes, they are rather nice. Please wear them. I'd like you to. And one thing more, Emmanuel—I've known you for a long time ; I've always liked you, very, very much ; I've admired your integrity and dignity. I've—more than once—tried to advise you.'

'My dear, you've always been wonderful to me!'

She shrugged her shoulders. 'Well—more or less. However, do be wise. Don't allow anyone to pull wool over your eyes. Don't let sudden bursts of energy deceive you, or a few pleasant words cheat you into hoping that the leopard has succeeded in changing his spots. These things—don't happen!'

He said, 'I am afr-raid that you mean my brother Julian.'

'Of course I mean Julian! The man's a skunk and a blackguard. Well, let him be . . . but be sufficiently clever to see that he doesn't pull you down with him. There! In other words—have a little common sense! Yes, I know that you must go. Good-bye, my dear, and thank you for everything.'

BOOK TWO

CHAPTER ONE

ANGELA said, 'You'll have coffee, Max?'

Her husband stared at her for a second as if he had not heard exactly what she said, then recovering himself he replied, 'Yes, yes—I'd like to. In the drawing-room?'

She nodded, thinking how strange it was that he should question that. For years they had taken coffee in that wide, spacious room which Max had always loved. Tonight he had eaten very little, but had kept losing interest in what was on his plate, and allowed his eyes to wander, half vacantly, about the dining-room.

She had said nothing, but she realized that this was a definite step in his illness. They had kept it at bay for months ; he had been patient and uncomplaining, always to her the same Max she had known and loved for so long. She had admired his alert brain, his ability to come to decisions, his quick and exact fashion of arriving at just conclusions ; now to watch him losing his grip, to be fully conscious that his clear brain was growing clouded, was intolerably painful to her.

He stood up now, raising himself stiffly by pressing his hands on the arms of his chair, and—with what Angela felt to be an effort—smiled at her across the dining-table. He stood upright, a tall, spare man, with broad shoulders, and it seemed to her that in some strange way he had shrunken. It was as if his skin were too large for him, like a garment which has stretched, or the wearer of which has grown much thinner.

They had been married for something approaching fifty years, and their love for one another had grown, Angela felt, with every year they had spent together. She had always boasted that the Gollantz men were the nicest in the world, and that Max was the nicest of them all. She had loved and admired old Emmanuel, his somewhat spectacular personality, his wisdom and his essential kindliness had appealed to her. Max had never been in the least spectacular, he would have been horrified had anyone suggested that he possessed that quality ; he had never

117

been as good-looking as either of his elder sons—Emmanuel and Julian.

There had been a pleasant quality about him, a sense of essential honesty which made people believe in him and trust him. He had never created a stir when he entered the great sale rooms, he had never held all eyes when he began to bid for some treasure; his method had been quiet and convincing. If Max Gollantz bid £40,000, men knew that his bank would honour a cheque for that amount without question. His name in the antique business, his reputation as a connoisseur and his character as a man had all been unquestioned. The best, and only the best, was good enough for Max Gollantz and the business which he had inherited from his father.

Now he was failing, and Angela went round to where he stood and slipped her arm through his; not only in order to give him unobtrusive help, but because she suddenly longed to be close to him, to realize that he was really and actually still with her.

They walked together into the drawing-room, the room which Max had always liked, and on which they had both lavished such care and attention. He sat down a little heavily, as if there was not very much strength in his body, and glanced around him.

'It's a nice room,' he said, 'don't alter it, darling.'

'No—no, of course I shan't. It's the nicest room in Ordingly.' She carried his coffee to him, and set the cup on the small table beside his chair.

'It is going to be difficult about Ordingly,' Max said. 'It will go to Emmanuel, and that means that Julian, Amanda and Max will have to find other quarters. Emmanuel and Julian will never be able to live together. A pity—a great pity. But'— quickly—'believe me, I do understand the impossibility.'

'Max, Max, dear,' Angela said urgently, 'don't talk in that way. For years you and I are going to live here. Don't speak as if—we were coming to the end of things.'

He raised his head and met her eyes squarely. 'Darling, I am coming to the—end of things. We haven't ever found it possible to lie to each other, surely we're not going to begin now? Oh, it won't come today, or tomorrow, it may not come for weeks, but it *is* coming. I've always wanted to "set my house in order", I've always disliked things left with a lot of loose ends.' He smiled. 'I've got a mania for order and tidiness, you know. So help me to get everything decently in order. You will'—with suppressed eagerness—'you will, won't you?'

She came over and kissed him. She was too wise a woman

118

to protest, to bring forward arguments which she knew to be specious. Max was just 'running down', the machinery was slowly losing speed and precision; one day—it would stop, and that would be the end of her years of happiness.

'I've always tried to do everything that you asked me,' she said.

'I've never failed to take advantage of that fact,' he said, still smiling. 'Angela, I'm not good at saying charming things. I've never been able to turn delightful phrases—oh, all quite sincere!—as my father and Emmanuel could and can. I've always been a "plain, blunt man"; but it's been a wonderful life—yes, even taking into consideration the bad patches, when you have always shown so much more sense than I have. We'll not spoil it now! You're wonderful, I adore you as I always did, and I am going to rely on your help as I have always done. That is something of a threat, my dear.'

'I'm not afraid. Yes, we'll make it a good time, Max dear.'

Carefully and without ostentation, Angela Gollantz set to work to alter the central point of Ordingly. Where the drawing-room, the big dignified dining-room, and Max's library had been the focal points of the house, now his bedroom, their joint sitting-room, her own room and her small drawing-room became the 'heart' of the place.

Max, she knew, had given his ultimatum. He had talked with Meyer Bernstein, and he knew that his life was slowly coming to an end. He faced it in the calm, dignified and rather matter-of-fact way that he had faced most difficult things in his life. She felt that he had made a definite appeal to her to co-operate with him, to prevent any waste of strength or energy which might be left to him. He never came downstairs again. Slowly she reorganized the whole life of Ordingly, and it became recognized—without any definite statement having been made —that Max and she had virtually retired to the suite of rooms where the windows looked out on the great beeches and elms which Max had always loved and in which he had taken such pride.

Slowly she eliminated such pieces of furniture as she judged useless or unsuitable; slowly and almost imperceptibly adapting the rooms to Max's taste and to suit his requirements. She knew that he watched her, that he appreciated what she did, and his smiles when she declared, 'That desk from your own study is far better here than stuck away in a corner downstairs,' repaid her. She realized that he was not in the least deceived, that he understood her anxiety to make his chosen quarters exactly to his taste.

Julian was the first person to speak to her openly about her changed method of life. He met her on the wide, low-treaded stairs one morning and said almost irritably, 'Hello, darling. Don't you come down to dinner in these days? Pretty gloomy with Amanda away for me to dine there in that vast room alone.'

'Why not have your dinner served in your own dining-room?'

He grinned suddenly, 'Several reasons. I hate dining alone, and if I dine downstairs with you and my father it saves my household bills. That's quite frank!'

Angela nodded. 'Charmingly so. No, I don't think—unless there is some special reason, that Max and I shall dine downstairs—not yet, at all events. We enjoy quiet meals, in a quiet room. He likes the view from the windows.'

Julian said sharply, 'He isn't ill, is he?' and she remembered his hatred of illness, his strange, almost morbid, fear of death.

'He's been ill for a long time, Julian. He feels that he wants to conserve his energy——'

'Is he going to die?' His fingers closed tightly on the broad banister rail. 'He's not going to die, is he?'

She shrugged her shoulders and said lightly, 'We're all "going to die"—sooner or later. Neither your father nor I are very young, you know.'

Julian scowled, 'Ought I to pay a visit every morning?'

She answered with an edge to her voice which he had never heard before when she spoke to him. 'You *ought* to wish to do so. If you don't—I, at least, prefer that you keep away.'

Meyer Bernstein came, and when Angela told him that she and Max had moved to the first floor he nodded. 'A good move, yes? I t'ink that the air is clearer, fresher. Yes, I approve very wholeheartedly.'

By no sign did he show that he considered his patient to be worse, in itself something which convinced Angela that he and Max had discussed the whole matter before her husband had spoken to her. They were strange people, these Jews. After nearly fifty years she could not understand them and their motives completely. Either they endowed their wives with almost superhuman understanding and adaptability, or they calmly disregarded them, believing that they were obedient and tractable and that they had learnt to refrain from asking questions.

She could not think that Max held the latter view; she knew him very well. There were only rare occasions when she remembered that he had Jewish blood in his veins. He had always trusted her, and she felt now that the great faith which he had always had in her sanity and commonsense had crystallized, and become completely clarified. After all the years which they had spent together, he knew that he could rely upon her understanding, and particularly on her innate knowledge of him.

During the later years of their marriage Angela had experienced several shocks at the attitude which Max had adopted regarding various matters. He had been intolerant concerning Emmanuel, too ready to condemn without having facts at his fingertips. There, she admitted, she had not been altogether free from blame. There had been, too, the business of poor Juliet Forbes—the divorced wife of Vernon Seyre, and the mistress of Leon Hast. Angela frowned at the thoughts which came rushing into her mind. She had never cared for 'whitewashing' people ; they made mistakes, went against the laws of society—and they paid ! She had always set her face against making excuses for people because she liked them fundamentally—but Juliet . . .

In some strange way Juliet had been the exception. Old Emmanuel had loved her in that strange way he had of falling in love with women from a purely mental standpoint. How often had she listened to him—even when he was growing very old—talking to Juliet, bringing into his voice the tones of a lover ! Max had never possessed his father's imagination, and his attitude towards Juliet had been rigid and conventional. He had admitted her artistry, the beauty of her voice, her charm, but he had felt that for his son to marry her was little short of a disaster.

Now, when he sat quietly in his room which opened out of his bedroom, at his desk writing, holding long discussions with Charles Wilmot, his broker or his bank manager, or more often only staring out over the park at the great swaying trees, he seemed to have changed. When Angela entered, he turned smiling at her.

'I've done a good morning's work. Emmanuel is coming to see me this afternoon. He tells me that Simeon is showing great promise.' Then with a change of tone, 'This is a very pleasant room, Angela.'

'Yes, I've always liked it.'

'I'm very pleased with Emmanuel.' There was a long pause. 'I wish that he'd had more happiness in his life. Partially my fault, I'm afraid. I was—stiffnecked over that business. Juliet was a fine woman. My attitude'—again he paused—'my attitude was narrow and provincial. How foolish we are to make mistakes and not try to put them right before it is too late to do so. I would give a good deal to be able to welcome Juliet to Ordingly.'

Angela came nearer and laid her hand lightly on his shoulder. How distinctly she could feel the bones beneath the cloth of his jacket!

She said, 'May I repeat that to Emmanuel, please, Max?'

'My dear, I hoped that you would say that! If I were sufficiently courageous or sufficiently near to Emmanuel I would say it to him. There is a broad bridge to be built before he and I can be really near to each other. It may not be finished— that bridge—but I've made a start! Yes, tell him what I said, I shall be grateful to you.'

Emmanuel listened to what his mother told him; listened gravely and intently. When she ended her story of what Max had said, he spoke:

'And he wished you to tell me this, Angela?'

'Specifically.'

'I am very much pleased. Additionally pleased—because Juliet will be glad, too. Perhaps you will thank him from me.'

'Sit down,' Angela said. 'I know that it's all been very difficult. Max is a splendid person, but Max is, always has been, always will be, conventional. He *fears,* yes, definitely fears any deviation from the normal social code. Have you ever wondered why? His mother—that entrancing Juliana Lara—well, there was a time when her behaviour made Max doubt if Algernon, his brother, was more than his half-brother. It's an old story. I don't propose to tell it to you now.

'Then—I have mentioned this to you once before—then I, when I was very young and incredibly silly, fell in love with Max's brother, Algernon. I didn't know that he was Max's brother, he'd changed his name. Again that sense of instability rising from something which was—unconventional—touched Max. The whole wretched story—and fundamentally it was innocent enough—made a terrible impression upon him. He died—Algernon—as I think I told you once—he was drowned trying to get away from the Secret Police in Switzerland. Max tried to save him and failed. Again that fear of scandal! Old Emmanuel saying, as he always did about anything of which he disapproved, "This offends me!"

'That has been Max's attitude. "It offends me!" Darling, I have always adored the Gollantz men, but really their attitude towards certain things is almost preposterous. They have such standards. Oh, I approve of them wholeheartedly, but they're a little difficult for everyone to live up to. They're not censorious—oh, dear me, no! They simply dismiss people, actions, furniture, pictures—everything which swims into their orbit—as "unworthy", if these things don't happen to conform to their criterions.

'Now, my dearest, Max is "sitting and thinking", he's not only setting his financial affairs in order, he's setting his own "house in order". He's looking back, admitting that this judgment was harsh, that some other verdict was too rigid. He can't be enjoying it, poor darling, but he's doing it, and he's happier for doing it. Do you understand, Emmanuel?'

He answered gravely, 'I think that I do. Respectability has meant security. He knew that that was threatened by—whatever action my grandmother Juliana took. That might have meant the wreck of his home. His brother's behaviour might have meant the collapse of his hopes for a life with you. So respectability, correct social behaviour, have come to be more important to him than—motives. Isn't it the Jew asserting himself? That intense longing for security after generations during which everything was insecure? I've watched it evinced in the longing to gather great possessions, wealth, power, but it all means the same thing . . . "In a changing world, I at least will be safe and secure." Yes, darling, I do understand. I'll go and talk to him.'

He entered the cool, quiet room. Max was at his desk, the pen had fallen from his hand, and he was staring out over the parklands of Ordingly. As Emmanuel came in he turned, and his son was shocked at the change in his appearance. His face was colourless, his eyes were sunken in his head, the bony structure of the face and head showed clearly under skin which seemed to have grown very thin, and to be stretched too tightly. The sunken eyes brightened as Emmanuel came towards him.

'Ah, Emmanuel, thanks for coming to see me. I know that you're busy. The returns show me that. You're doing remarkably well.'

Emmanuel stooped and kissed his father's forehead. 'It is always pleasant to be pr-raised. Yes, we're doing quite well. Nothing, as yet, spectacular, but—quite satisfactory.'

He went on to tell his father about the news from Milano, adding that for the moment he was not making it public. He said that he hoped to get away within the next ten days.

Emmanuel saw the eyes narrow, the mouth tighten at the corners.

'How long will you be away?' The voice was suddenly sharp.

His son thought, 'He knows that he is going to die. He

doesn't want me to be away when it happens! Poor Max—he's worried about it all.'

Very calmly Emmanuel answered, 'Not more than a week— ten days from Victoria to Victoria. It will only be a sort of spying out the land. Giving instructions, coming back with lists, having more interviews with the Board of Trade and so forth.' As he spoke he saw the strained expression leave his father's face, and thought again, 'Meyer Bernstein has given him a limit. I shall be back. He's relieved.'

Max said, 'Splendid. I am delighted. And there seems plenty of your old stuff left, eh?'

'Thanks to Guido Moroni.'

'And if everything turns out as well—as we hope and trust it may, you'll have a sufficiency—financially?'

'Rather more than an actual sufficiency, I imagine.'

'And Simeon? Forgive me if I seem intrusive, Emmanuel.'

'Not at all, sir. Simeon will have whatever I can leave him. In addition he will have his mother's money—which is considerable. There is also the money which old Simeon Jaffe left to him. Simeon will be—unless the world turns upside down—a very wealthy young man.'

'It seems remarkably likely that the world may turn upside down, judging by the trend of present events. However, for the sake of our own argument, we will disregard that possibility. You like this place—Ordingly?'

Emmanuel's smile came very readily. 'I love it; it has always meant a great deal to me. Always.'

'In the event of my death, could you keep it up? I should of course leave you—what I could. I must provide for Julian, although he appears to be doing quite well in the Gallery, eh?'

Some of the colour had vanished from Emmanuel's voice. 'He seems to be working very hard, sir.'

'I have not yet fully acquainted myself with the figures. The Gallery, even with things as they are at the moment, is worth a great deal. A great deal,' Max continued reflectively, 'because it carries with it a kind of "hall-mark" of straight dealing and rigid integrity. Ever since my father opened his place on Camden Hill our name has stood for something on which men could rely. I can safely promise to leave you and Julian something fairly substantial. Your dear mother is, of course, amply provided for. Then . . .'—again a long pause—'you would keep on Ordingly?'

'As long as changing conditions make it humanly possible, yes.'

'You give me your word?'

'I do indeed. And Simeon will feel exactly as I do.'

Max leaned back in his chair ; some of the strain had left his face ; he looked, Emmanuel thought, better and relaxed.

Max said, 'I know that it is early—what is it?—nearly five. I rarely drink during the daytime. I am going to now. Ring the bell, if you please, and pass me the cigarettes.' As the door opened, he said, 'Oh, Hewson, whisky-and-soda—for two. Now I am going to be quite frank. My fault is that I have not been sufficiently so in the past. Or have I been too frank, stupidly, possibly brutally so? It's difficult to say. As my eldest son, you have a right to know the position. Ah, thank you, Hewson. Not too much soda! No, leave it here' ; he smiled at the elderly butler. 'I'm having a holiday. Celebrating with Mr. Emmanuel.'

Hewson said, 'And very glad I am to see it, Sir Max. All work and no play—well, we all know the rest. Thank you, sir.'

As the door closed Max turned again to Emmanuel.

'I'm rather ill. Not so much actually ill as that the machinery is worn out and they don't know of any way to get—spare parts. The heart wants new valves—it can't have them, the liver is doing something rather tiresome which cannot be corrected, the blood is not circulating with the right amount of pressure, and so on. Very annoying, and also completely tedious. Oh, don't look so grave. I'm not going to die tonight or tomorrow. In fact, I shall be here waiting anxiously for your return from Milan.

'This place comes to you. Julian has never liked it, he only lives here because it suits him to do so. I cannot see you both living under one roof—I regret it, but I understand it. I should suggest that you let him have your house in Heber Square. That is merely a suggestion. Young Max will go a long way ; he's got ability and he's—yes, he's hard. His grandfather in America, old Van der Hoyt, has made—they say—millions out of the war. He likes young Max. Keep Julian with you in the firm while you can—I repeat, *while you can*. Charles approves of the terms of my will, and I have always relied on Charles. I think that is all. Have another drink, Emmanuel?'

'Thank you, sir—and you?'

Max laughed. 'I ought not to—but I shall! Hope that my news hasn't worried you——'

'Believe that it has gr-reatly disturbed and upset me, sir. I knew that you were not in your former health, but I had no clear idea how bad things were. I am deeply distressed.'

Max watched his son's good-looking sensitive face ; noticed the expression which was tender without being sentimental ; heard the very gentle tones of Emmanuel's voice and thought,

'He means it. He really regrets that I'm going. God, I wish that I'd had more tolerance!'

'No use being distressed,' Max said, with an attempt at brightness which was not completely assumed. He had become used to the idea of death, and except that he hated the thought of leaving his wife, he could almost have welcomed it. He had worked very hard, and it seemed for very long. He had faced loss, disappointment, and he had seen what he had hoped might be a devoted family disintegrate and split into factions. He had always disliked divorce, yet he had seen Viva Tatten divorce his eldest son.

He continued, 'I'm not young any longer. In fact I'm older than my age warrants. I've had the inestimable privilege of spending nearly fifty years of my life with the most charming and delightful woman in the world . . . well, "I am ready to depart"! I should like to feel that now and again you'd give me your help and advice should I need it, Emmanuel.'

'Both—if they are of any r-real value are always at your disposal. I feel honoured that you should even say such a thing. I shall tr-ry to leave for Italy immediately. I will wr-rite to you from there. Good-bye, and,' he hesitated, 'God bless you.'

Max sipped his whisky. 'I'll be waiting when you come back, only don't be too long.'

'Not a moment longer than is necessary, r-rely on me.'

Meditatively his father said, 'You know, I believe that I do—more than you know. Good luck, Emmanuel.'

Emmanuel leaned from the window of his carriage on the Orient Express and watched the long train wind into Milan station. He glanced up at the roof, where the glass was still missing; the whole station which he remembered as a source of pride to the Fascist Government looked shabby and slightly dilapidated. He called a porter, and the man came running readily enough. Emmanuel slung his two bags through the open window to the waiting man, then walked along the corridor and descended to the platform. He had not notified Guido of the exact time of his arrival, merely of the date on which he hoped to reach Milan. He followed the man down the long platform, glancing to right and left, listening to the chatter of Italian which was going on around him. Passing through the barrier, a man touched his arm.

'You veesh changa money—ver' goot, yes?'

Emmanuel shook his head, 'No, thanks.'

'Veesh goot 'otel, nice price?'

'No, thanks.'

'Veesh Eengleesh cigarette—American cigarette, yes?'

Emmanuel stopped and replied in Italian, 'I wish nothing but for you to go away immediately. You give me a headache!'

Driving through the busy streets, he passed the petrol pumps where the mob had hung the bodies of Mussolini and his companions after their death. The names still showed clearly. Emmanuel shivered. What a finish to a career which had opened so magnificently, if only from the standpoint of achievement, and which had ended so ingloriously, so wretchedly. His mind went back to what he remembered of the rise and ultimate fall of the Fascist Régime, the growing power of greedy Ministers, headed by an even more greedy Leader, who abandoned himself to a life which was—in the main—repugnant to the people whose 'Duce' he claimed to be. The Axis—the jokes concerning 'The Leader of Our Leader', 'His Master's Voice' and the like. Those men who had strutted and swaggered, who had bawled and bellowed, who had 'monarchized and killed with looks'— and now, what traces of them were left except a poverty-stricken nation, ruined cities, a depleted exchequer, and widespread misery?

He watched the ruined buildings as the taxi sped towards the centre of the town; he recalled that he had dined in this house, had designed the decorations for another, to the owner of a third he had sold a set of Sèvres china.

The taxi stopped at the entrance to the Jaffe-Gollantz Galleries. Emmanuel paid the man, and taking his bags walked up the wide steps and so came again to the place which held so many memories for him.

A young man, carefully if shabbily dressed, came forward. Emmanuel frowned. His hair was too long and he needed a shave.

He said, 'Is Signor Moroni here, please?'

The young man glanced at the bags. 'You wish to sell something?'

'I wish to see Signor Moroni. My name is Gollantz.'

'Gollantz!'

'The partner of Signor Moroni. Allow me to tell you that your hair is too long, you have not been shaved this morning, and your manner is not good. Now—be quick, if you please.'

The young man sped away along the Gallery. Emmanuel stared round him. The place was shabby, but perfectly clean. There appeared to have been little or no damage to the building. The antiques were set out well; they were obviously well kept and scrupulously polished. Here and there he noticed pictures which seemed vaguely familiar. He smiled; things were better than he had dared to hope.

Down the long gallery came a small figure, running and waving its hands in greeting. A small, grey-haired man, with large and limpid brown eyes, who cried, 'Master! Master! Emmanuel has returned!' then flung himself upon Emmanuel, laughing and crying at the same time.

'This is a miracle!' he cried. 'You have come home again. Now please come into your own room. The first thing which was put in readiness was your office.' He flung open the door. 'Look! As you left it. Here are the pens which you used, here the inkpots filled in readiness. Your chair, everything—now we shall get busy pushing back the old clock!'

Emmanuel looked round the room, everything had been arranged as he had left it, even to the little silver ashtray which years ago Simeon had bought for him. He had an ingrained dislike for ashtrays made of anything except glass or porcelain, but Simeon had decided that silver was more elegant, and there on his desk it had remained, although he never by any chance used it.

He said, 'Guido, we can't put clocks back. You should know that it is very bad for the works. But what we can do is to re-wind the clocks and allow them to go forward, recording good hours, eh?'

'Indeed. You have not looked at the Gallery. Poof! All Milano marvels at its beautifulness. However—sufficient. You will care for the old whisky soda, no? That too I saved! Yes, I can offer, and good mark. Your favourite—Red Hackle. How well I remember the kind English mi-lord who used to send, "One case Red Hackle. Kindly acknowledge." One moment I shall recall his honoured name! Hip—Hipburn.'

'Hepburn,' Emmanuel corrected; 'and in these days he cannot send out cases of whisky. Times have changed——'

Guido held up an exquisitely manicured hand. 'One moment, please. I remember, "Tim-es change, end we change with zem, boot not in wayzz of friendliness." Ah, how I recall many t'ings.'

'Now, while you get ready the whiskies-and-sodas, with ice, my dear Guido, I shall have a walk through the Gallery. You understand, quietly and alone. Then I shall return.'

'It is understandable, my dear.'

At the door, Emmanuel halted. 'That assistant of yours. His hair is too long, his nails are dirty, and he has not been shaved this morning.'

'Ah, Alfredo Bassano. On him I am working in the manner of your admirable self, as you worked with me. I shall attend to it. Come soon, the whisky will be ready. Oh, what happiness is mine!'

Guido walked to the desk and pressed the electric bell. The young man who had spoken to Emmanuel in the Gallery entered. Guido eyed him sternly.

'Now, let us get down to little brass nails. I prefer to use English idiom. How often have I told you about hair, beard and nails? Not once but ten millions of times. Now—a disaster! Arrives the great Gollantz. He comes filled with happiness to find his Gallery in good shape. One fly in 'is face cream! The unspeakable dirt of Bassano! Now, with a quickness which is incredible, you will run to the nearby barber. Why did I engage you, tell me? Because you are able to speak ver' bad English and write nice handwriting. What is good handwriting with nails which offend my noble patron? What is bad English when the beard makes the speech inaudible to hear? Go! Return when you are shorn of too much hair, when your nails are like driven snow on the Dolomites and when your face is of a smoothness which will make the bottomside of a baby seem like the hair of a mule.'

The unfortunate Bassano bowed his head, and murmured that this was Wednesday and that he never shaved—or was shaved—on Wednesdays. As for his nails, he had been working in the store.

Guido snorted in his indignation. 'Wednesday! In the week there are seven days. On each well breeded men are shaved! Nails! *Dio mio,* do you try to tell me that my storeroom is dirty? There is not sufficient dirt there to fill your nails, even though they are too long, like the nails of "Turandot". Return when you are in a state of hygiene, and do not offend the eyes of my patron! *Via—subito!*'

When Emmanuel returned there stood on his desk a beautiful salver with a gadroon edge, two splendid beakers of Waterford glass, and whisky in a magnificent step-cut decanter of old English glass. The syphon, standing in an old silver coaster with a beautiful pierced gallery, was placed beside them.

He touched them gently, 'Guido, everything is beautiful. How shall I ever be able to thank you?'

Guido beamed at him. 'For me all replies are *facile*. It is simple. Remain here, work with me, or, better, permit that I work with you. I shall clean up Bassano, in fact even now he is being—how did we say?—deloused.'

'Deloused!' Emmanuel exclaimed, 'Guido, you don't mean it!'

With a certain easy and yet respectful patronage Guido replied, 'Not in the most strictest sense, but if dirt remains too long, louses come round. When you see him tomorrow, he will shine like a sixpence in——'

Emmanuel said quickly, 'My dear fellow, where did you pick up some of these expressions? I shall have to "edit" your English. Now'—he poured out two whiskies and added the soda, pushed one glass towards Guido, and, lifting his glass, said, 'Guido—to our partnerhip . . . Jaffe, Gollantz and Moroni of Milano, London, New York, Vienna and Paris!'

CHAPTER TWO

EMMANUEL flung himself into one of the huge arm-chairs which stood on either side of the big fireplace in his Milan flat. The room was quiet and cool, there was nothing there which he did not remember with affection. Guido had succeeded there as he had done in the Gallery ; in some way, best known to himself, he had enlisted the services of kindly and faithful people who had helped him to safeguard Emmanuel's treasures. True, during the occupation the Germans had been installed in the apartment, but they had found it bare of everything except mere necessities.

Now, because of the housing shortage in Milano, owing to the destruction of so many homes, it was needful to fill every room in the flat. Guido lived there, and also Casimiro Boccolini, once 'podesta' of Milano. Here, too, lived many people who came and went in transit—Louis Lara and his wife, Paul Mancini and Iva Alfano, little Gilbert whenever it happened that he came to accompany some singer on an international tour. Now, Emmanuel Gollantz had come back, and Guido beamed at the whole world, unable to hide his content and complete satisfaction.

The various hidden treasures had been recovered by Guido, and were once again installed in their accustomed places. Emmanuel lay back, tired to death, aching in every limb, but with his mind at peace. Not for years had he experienced such content. All day he had been in the Gallery with Guido at his elbow.

What a strange fellow he was, this Guido Moroni. That morning he had arrived in the big dining-room at the flat, having cast off his sober clothes of dark grey, and had shown himself again like a small bird of Paradise.

Even the old swagger had returned as he entered and saluted Emmanuel.

'Ah, the first day of the new era!' he declared, then turned to the grave Casimiro Boccolini and gave him one of those dazzling smiles which were at once so childlike and yet held so

131

much wisdom. 'Conte, am I not right? The darkness is past, and we now come rushing out like transcontinental trains searing—no, one moment!—haring out of tunnels! Today the life of the Gallery begins anew. For this reason, notice the change in Guido. For months I have worn only sad, miserable clothes like gents wear at funerals. Now I wear the clothes of bridegrooms on their *luma di miele*—only better!'

He executed a brief *pas de quatre* to exhibit his change of costume. True the clothes were not of the latest fashion, it was obvious that they had been laid away, and on being brought out had been carefully pressed, but they were of an elegant cut and made of light materials. They grey coat and trousers had a sheen which was almost silver, the pale heliotrope shirt matched the fine silk socks, the tie was, in itself, an achievement, and the handkerchief which was so carefully folded in the breast pocket was mathematically correct in its shape and angles.

He beamed at Emmanuel, 'Only one matter preoccupies me,' he said ; 'for the sake of business—will it be better if my hair—changes its colour? Will people argue in this manner: "Ah, Guido! Once his hair was admired for its darkness, now the lack of business in the Gallery has changed it to—silver"? Is this what they will say?' Again he smiled at both men impartially.

'No,' Emmanuel said, 'leave it as it is. It gives you an added dignity, my friend.'

Boccolini added, 'People will be all the more inclined to trust your judgment, I feel.'

Guido sighed. 'Then it must be much, much more grey. Now it is of the unadmired colour of mices—no mouses. I wish it as snow on the mountain tops. Now I shall leave you. I await you, Master, in the Gallery.'

Later, after a long talk with Boccolini, during which they had discussed the future of Italy, the prospects of the recovery of trade, the necessity for a strong government, and the need for a sense of personal responsibility in the heart of every Italian, Emmanuel walked down to the Gallery.

How good it was to find Tommaso waiting with his hat and gloves. The same kind Tommaso, making enquiries for Simeon, and wiping his eyes with the back of his hand at the thought that 'the bambino' was now a grown man ; the news that Simeon had lost a foot reduced him to tears. Tears, Emmanuel felt, which were not merely the outpourings of easy sentimentality, but the proof of real affection for the little boy Tommaso had once known.

He walked down the quiet dignified street, and then into

132

the wide thoroughfare, where the trams were clanging past, where cars rushed by, and over all hung the strange, indescribable smell which is inseparable from Italian towns. Just as London has its own particular smell, as the scent of Paris cannot be mistaken for that of any other city, so the great Italian towns held their own perfume. A mixture, Emmanuel thought, and not unpleasant! Dust, petrol, a harsher smell which was undoubtedly the result of using petroleum in motor vehicles, somewhere a hint of fruit rapidly growing overripe in the sun ; here and there at the street corners a whiff of flowers, a suggestion of expensive scent as some well-dressed woman passed. Added to these a perfume which was undoubtedly hair-oil or brilliantine ; a trace of chemical used to keep away moths told of a suit recently retrieved from its wardrobe because the day was sunny and warm ; oil—Emmanuel sniffed—yes, decidedly oil, and a suggestion of garlic. The whole going to make up the unmistakable scent of Milano.

He turned from the busy street into what seemed like a dignified backwater, and there were his Galleries, with their great dark marble pillars, and the wide stone steps which led to the splendid doors which old Simeon Jaffe had brought from Vienna and in which he had taken so much pride.

How well Emmanuel remembered his first visit there ; years ago, when he had possessed only one suit, and that one terribly shabby ; how his boots had holes in them through which the water seeped steadily, and how old Simeon Jaffe had ordered him to drink brandy, hot water and lemon to keep away the cold which he predicated was inevitable.

How the old man with his arrogance had offended him! How he had disliked his obvious opulence, his certainty and his various demands, and how good the old man had been to him, how kindly and understanding he had proved himself to be ; how completely generous in every possible way. But for old Simeon Jaffe, Emmanuel reflected, he might well be still struggling in a small and undistinguished antique shop in a small insignificant side street in the city of Milan.

He walked into the Gallery, feeling a thrill of pleasure at the thick carpet beneath his feet ; true it might have lost some of its original beauty of colour, the design might be worn in places, but it retained a dignity and sense of luxury which was unmistakable.

The young man he had spoken to the day before came forward. Emmanuel's dark eyes twinkled as he looked at him. The overlong hair was cut, the youthful face had been shaved until it glistened, and when he waved his hand indicating the

133

way to Emmanuel's office—a gesture which might be elegant, but which was completely unnecessary—Emmanuel noticed that the nails had ben manicured and cut in a most drastic manner.

He smiled at the young man, wishing him good morning, and the lad replied, 'Ent to you, all-so, good morr-neeng, Meester Gollantz.'

A moment later Guido rushed in, bearing ledgers, notebooks and lists.

'Here we are once more!' he cried; 'this is what English comics say! Now to begin. . . .'

Emmanuel said, 'Have you forgotten? Oh, Guido! Always first my coffee!'

'*Dio mio!* Forgotten, never! Here comes the lady! Look, the same, our invalueless Signora Incisa!'

The elderly woman who had worked for them for so long entered bearing a familiar porcelain tray, on which stood a tiny coffee-pot of French china, a cup and saucer of fine make, and the wonderful aroma of hot coffee freshly made reached Emmanuel. She looked older; he remembered her dead-black hair, always drawn so smoothly towards the nape of her neck. It was heavily streaked with grey. Round her eyes were hundreds of fine lines, traced there he thought by peering into the darkness fearful of what she might find hidden there. Her lips, too, had lost their fullness, even her smile came slowly as if to smile were still something new and strange.

He rose and held out his hand. 'Signora Incisa, this is a great joy.'

The smile became a little easier. 'Signor, I am happy.'

'As I am,' he replied. 'And I shall be even happier when I taste your superb coffee again.' He sniffed with appreciation. 'A—ah!'

As he sipped his coffee Guido fidgeted nervously, longing to begin their tour of inspection. Emmanuel said, 'Man, you've waited for years, give me time to drink my coffee!'

Then at last the tour began. Through the long Gallery, Guido calling out the number and value of everything they passed—china, porcelain figures, bronzes, pictures and enamels; there were long halts before glass-covered cases which held what Guido called '*Magazzino di giocatoli*', or the toyshop, cases which held bits of beautiful old silver, pieces of jewellery set with strange unfamiliar stones; there above them hung the splendid chandeliers of Murano, some glistening clear and white, others composed of tinted glass representing fruit and flowers in their natural colours.

On the walls hung carpets—Aubusson, Spanish, and from

the East ; velvets from Genova and the great French factories ; tapestries, some from France, others from the Low Countries, a few of Italian origin. There were delicate chairs from France and England, heavy carved chairs from Spain and Italy, leather-seated furniture from Africa and Russia, cabinets inlaid with ivory or precious woods—it seemed as if the whole world had been scoured to find goods for the Galleries.

Emmanuel checked, examined, noted and listened. He went with Guido into the inner rooms, where they kept the most precious of their goods, things which were only offered to special clients and connoisseurs. Here Guido told him of a young Englishman who had come with his wife and had bought a picture—'one which he liked although I assured him it was not a Solario, and we never pretensioned that it was such'. 'A nice young man,' Guido said, 'with a difficult name. Fly-it Maisteira.'

Emmanuel said, 'Flight Masters, the chap who had the gallery in Bond Street. I wonder where he is now. The gallery was bombed ; someone told me that he'd been killed at Dunkirk, poor fellow. Let's hope that it isn't true. He had a nice taste in pictures.'

He looked at the pictures slowly and carefully, as if they did his eyes good. There were not very many, for Guido kept reminding him that 'only the really pearls are left, the Huns took all the—Oriental pearls!'

Back at his desk, having only eaten sandwiches for luncheon, Emmanuel, his face propped on his hands and elbows on the desk top, talked to Guido.

His voice came even and quiet, it seemed to the listening Italian to be the finest music in the world. More than once Guido wiped his eyes with the back of a hand which—despite the care which was lavished on the Gallery—had become grimy during their inspection.

Emmanuel said, 'Guido, I do not think that I have ever been more gr-reatly touched in my whole life. When I r-remember the dangers which you must have faced, the ingenuity which you have shown, I am filled with not only admiration, but deep, deep gr-ratitude. How long it will be before I can return here I don't know. I have many r-responsibilities in England ; my father is very ill, I do not think that he will live very long, but I shall keep in very close touch with you. Who knows, it may be possible for me to send Simeon here to learn from you, not only, my friend, the business, but to study from you all the beautiful and valuable . characteristics which you can teach him—so very easily.'

Guido ejaculated, 'Santa Maria!'

'Life isn't going to be very easy, Guido. It will never, in our lifetime, be what it once was, when we laughed easily, earned and spent money easily ; that time has gone, perhaps for always. But here we still have beautiful things, and there will be some people who will always be searching for beauty. Let's be certain that they find it here and that it is always "tr-rue" beauty.

'I am going to have documents dr-rawn up by which you will be a partner with me, you will be able to buy goods. I beg you,' and his voice grew deeper and more intense, 'never buy anything which is—unworthy, anything of which you cannot be *certain*. I would rather, if you found what you thought was a Mantagna, that you sold it as "believed to be . . ." and later discovered that it was real after you had sold it and lost money, than that you should swear to the authenticity of a picture when you were not quite, quite certain.

'I would r-rather that people wr-rote us down as something approaching fools than as something danger-rously near to being knaves. To be stigmatized as a "fool" may be painful, to be called a "knave" is degr-rading.' Emmanuel smiled. 'I can imagine you being called the one, Guido, never, never the other! I know that it is impossible for me to show my deep gr-ratitude, but tell me now, is there anything—yes, anything— I can do that will please you?'

Guido wiped his eyes, sniffed loudly, and considered. Finally he spoke.

'I am greedy—avaricious,' he stated. 'There are two things which will make this world for me like the Garden of Eden. Though I have met chaps who walked as soldiers over this famous spot and tell me that it is bloody terrible! One is that when once more we have the distinction notepaper I may have my name in very smallest letters—Moroni Guido—beneath your honoured name—that is the first thing.'

'That goes without saying,' Emmanuel said ; 'tomorrow we shall draw up the wording for the new letterpaper. Now—the next!'

Guido sighed deeply, then inflated his chest. 'I have always remembered the hats which you wore. There is such a hat for sale now in the Galleria. Tell me—is it right that Gollantz should walk about in a Mr.-Eden-Trilby hat? Maybe for London it is very—well—all—right ; here—*Puff!* It is stinkingly awful. I beg that now this instant moment we walk to the Galleria and buy this good, individual hat.'

Emmanuel sprang to his feet. 'Immediately! Wash your face, Guido. I also will wash the marks of honest toil from my own hands and we will sally forth to buy this prince among hats. Arm in arm the two great antique dealers of Italy shall be seen together in the Galleria.'

Guido caught his hand and pressed it. He said, speaking very softly, 'Oh, do you mean—really—walk arm in arm! This is the day for which I have lived. How people will stare, how their eyes will gobble—no, goggle in their heads.' He laughed. 'I can see them turning a bright but hideous green with envy. And,' he used the wheedling tone of a child, 'possibly a small drink at one of the tables at Biffi?'

Emmanuel gave him a push. 'A small drink! After trailing round your junk shop, my friend, I shall r-require a great number of drinks. All very long, very str-rong and very expensive. You—partner of Gollantz and Company—will pay for them all! Now—go and wash your face.'

Late that afternoon the people in the Galleria—tenors, basses, sopranos, contraltos, painters, journalists and the like—were able to witness the sight of two men walking slowly and with considerable dignity down the wide arcades. The one, very tall, wearing a broad-brimmed black felt hat, which seemed slightly out of place with his very typically British lounge suit, carrying a cane with an ivory knob; the other smaller and dressed extremely well, if a trifle ostentatiously, with his arm slipped through that of the taller man. His face was set into rigid lines, but his eyes darted hither and thither, and when he found someone he knew his greeting was slightly effusive.

An observer had the impression that the smaller man wished to be noticed.

Later the pair selected a table at the restaurant of Biffi, where the taller of the two stretched out his long legs and sipped with appreciation the various drinks of which they partook. Had anyone been sufficiently near they might have heard the smaller of the two whisper, 'This is the happiest day of my life. All Milano is watching me with envy. I am acknowledged as the friend of the great Gollantz.'

To which the other replied, 'Oh, what complete rot, Guido! By the way, this cognac is excellent.'

For three days Emmanuel worked for long hours at the Gallery, his satisfaction grew with every hour. Very few of the goods which had been hidden had suffered in the least, the most serious matter were certain small patches of damp which—he felt certain—would respond to treatment and disappear. Guido had done his work magnificently, and Emmanuel never ceased to congratulate himself on possessing such a friend, who, in addition to his complete loyalty, had resource, courage and ingenuity. On the afternoon of the third day on which he had worked at the Gallery, Guido entered with that air of studious unconcern which Emmanuel had come to know signified some momentous happening. He strolled in, his face impassive, his hands in his pockets.

Emmanuel glanced up and said, 'Now what is it? Come on, Guido, no mysteries!'

Guido snapped his fingers. 'Mystery! *Osteria!* I am not one to make them. All is for me in the work of the day! I am known as "Content and fortunate Guido"; in English you say, "Happy and going for a bit of luckiness." No, I have a telegram. Tonight arrives Louis Lara.'

'No! Louis arriving! That's magnificent. He'll stay at the flat, of course. Oh, telephone to Tommaso; this is a *festa!*'

That night the candles were lit in the long sitting-room. Tommaso—greatly daring—had opened the grand piano, there had been much rushing about, purchases made in unlikely shops, paying incredible prices for food—but Tommaso was satisfied and so was his immensely stout wife, Lucia, whom no amount of stress and strain seemed to have affected during the German occupation.

Lucia came from Bologna, and her ideas of food, of the manner of preparing food, were traditional, and not to be shaken by the advent of any number of Germans. She had, after receiving Guido's telephone message, not only sent the thin Tommaso scouring Milano, but she herself—vast, weighty and capable of doing battle with any shopkeeper who attempted to get the better of her—had sallied forth. Both had returned with marketing baskets which weighted them down. Both were sweating profusely, and both were cursing the *'mercato nero'* on which they had made their purchases.

Lucia, panting and fanning herself with the *Corriere della Sera,* said, 'This Black Market—what a disgrace to Italy!'

Tommaso replied, 'Ah! *Povera Italia!* Ma, ma! Men must eat.'

'Of a truth,' she replied, 'once Gollantz has gone then we shall return to eating simple things. Signor Moroni likes simple food, but for the moment—what will you?'

'Now,' announced her husband, 'I shall take out the fine glass, the silver, the dishes of English china. A lace-trimmed tablecloth. *Dio mio,* like the old days, no?'

Lucia began to check over her purchases, intoning as she did so the menu which she had planned; her voice seemed to have taken on the richness of pure olive oil, the ripeness of the grape,

138

and the complete satisfaction which is induced by good Italian wine.

'*Uove ripieno*—how fresh these eggs are, and how delicious they will be when stuffed—as only I know how to stuff them! Trout from Lake Garda—*al ferro!* This morning it was swimming about in the blue water! Then—ah, here they are! *Rognone trifolato*—yes, here is the Marsala in which they will cook, with good butter. With them *Zucchini ripieno*—my special stuffing. And truffles with a hot sauce! Biscuits from Novara and *Zabaione*. Fruit laid on fig leaves, and wine—that is the affair of Tommaso.'

At eight o'clock Emmanuel walked into the big sitting-room, to find two people waiting for him. His very distant cousin, Louis Lara, thinner than Emmanuel remembered him, and his wife, the 'superb' Olympia, who had grown stouter than it seemed possible. Together they had remained in Paris during the German occupation, together they had risked their lives in the underground movement; they had known danger, privation, hardship, and yet here they were—Louis as immaculate as ever, Olympia even stouter than Emmanuel remembered her.

Louis sprang to his feet. Emmanuel thought that he was like a steel spring which never completely unwound. He seized Emmanuel's hand, kissed him on both cheeks and cried, 'Now I know that the damnation war is ended! Observe—Olympia!'

Emmanuel thought that it would have been difficult not to 'observe' Olympia. She was seated on the sofa, her golden hair shining with a metallic brilliance, her immense arms and bosom bare, both heavily laden with jewels. Her elaborate dress was of purple—it began at the bodice as heliotrope, changed to a pale violet, from that to a deeper shade, then to royal purple, and finally for some inexplicable reason appeared to change its mind and became a brilliant and arresting orange.

Emmanuel, freeing himself from Louis' embrace, went forward; she offered her hand; he bent over it and kissed it, murmuring as he did so, 'My dear, dear, Olympia, how delightful this is!'

Her voice was rich and faintly husky, her eyes—and they were very beautiful eyes—were filled with affection.

'So long damn' time, Emmanuel! So much water runs away since we met last. The world is quite changed. My poor Louis is so thin. That is because of all his valoriousness in the war times. This man—what he did! Incredible!'

Louis interrupted, 'But, Emmanuel, my dear, when I begin to tell you of the exploits of Olympia! Could we make a film of this woman's life, her daring, her courage, all Hollywood would go like crazy men. How often have we returned, separately, you understand, to our apartment. She has found in me a dirty old ragpicker, I have found a fine, handsome *Bonne*, or maybe a lady no better'n what she oughter be, or an old hag! Together we take a bath. Later we embrace, and say, or, to be truthfully, I say, "Maybe this is the last time we're together, eh, beautifulness?"

'Always she answers with a gesture which your Churcheeil uses; they call it "Victory V" sign; it don't mean nothing to do with "victory signs" when Olympia makes it. She always says, "M——"'—and he used a word not accepted in polite society—'no Hun arranges my life for me. Now, like the *Nani*, "off to work we go". I'll see you soon! Emmanuel, her life is a great saga, a history which will make the blood to circulate more quickly, to make the heart beat faster.' He spread his arms wide, as if he embraced the massive form of his wife. 'The noble, courageous, steel-spirited Olympia, I am forever her slave.'

She yawned, showing her beautiful—and natural—teeth. 'Emmanuel, stop heem. I am sickened of this. All day I 'ear eet. They were all so damn dull! They are *simple*, their advances are rolling eyes—so! Patting arms—so! Laying fat hands on my bosom—so! What is zee word?—not first-class, but—babies' class?'

Gravely Emmanuel told her, 'Elementary.'

'That is right! Oh, the day ven the Breetish arrive! *'Ow* I laugh! Montgomery don't smile except to—everyone, then not such a hellova lot. Alexander—oh, I admire so zees man!—smile at everyone, an' nevair at no one particularly! I believe I vould 'ave left my adored Louis for zees Alexander!' She bunched her over-manicured fingers, kissed them and flung the implanted kiss to the winds. 'Now, do we get cocktail—or ees zees 'ouse Austerity 'All?'

Guido rushed into the room, kissed Olympia's hands with fervour, shook Louis firmly by both hands, kissed him with deep affection, then turned to serve the cocktails.

How they all three talked! Emmanuel, listening, tried hard to gather the full import of their stories. Together they had both faced risks, dangers, even privations; and yet their stories of their experiences were punctuated with bursts of laughter, and at times had to be discontinued because Olympia protested that her stays were new, and that so much mirth put an unfair strain upon them.

Only when dinner—to which both Louis and his wife gave unstinted praise, Olympia partaking twice of every dish, and at the end of dinner announcing that, 'Since the damn war, I have

140

no real liking for food'—was over, and they were drinking coffee, did the conversation turn to more serious matters.

The distant sounds of traffic in the main thoroughfare were dying down, the street lights glinted in through the open windows. Olympia lounged on the big sofa, little Guido sat with his hands clasped round his knees, Louis Lara leaning back so that the light of the tall candles caught his face, throwing it into high relief with deep shadows in the cheeks and under the sunken eyes.

Emmanuel watched them all in turn. The Frenchwoman, once a famous dancer, who had been the mistress of an Archduke—when the world indulged in such luxuries—whose lovers had lavished jewels and great wealth upon her ; and who in the time of her country's danger and disaster had flung aside the luxury, the extreme comfort, and the elaborate clothes which her soul loved, and had rushed into the underground movement.

She had forgotten to be Olympia the famous dancer, the wife —and a completely faithful wife—of Louis Lara ; she had gone back to being Sara Levine, the Jewess, born in the back streets of Lyons. Emmanuel did not doubt that her exploits had been fantastic, that she had braved every kind of danger, and that she had come through simply by reason of her innate courage and reckless determination.

Now she was the Olympia he had always known, elaborately gowned, her hair dressed in the latest mode, her hands manicured, her whole body massaged and perfumed to the last degree. Had her memory grown dim regarding the war years in Paris?

And her husband, Louis Lara, the successful art dealer, the man whose pronouncements regarding pictures, whose taste concerning everything in the world of antiques, were accepted as infallible? Louis, who loved luxury no less than did his wife ; Louis, to whom good food, good wine, admirable clothes, the finest shirts, socks and shoes meant so much. Louis, with his good looks, his charm of manner and his deep admiration for everything that was British, what had he done during those years of occupation? Plotting, spying, hiding, listening, changing from one disguise to another. His face had altered. His good looks were no longer of the obvious kind ; he was haggard, sunken-eyed, his lips had lost their fullness, they were compressed and the line of them was thin. Had Louis forgotten?

His eyes turned to Guido ; Guido with his grey hair, his eyes which might still dance but which at times looked heavy and retrospective as if he remembered too much. He had told Emmanuel that in camp he had been treated well, that he had more than sufficient to eat, and that his boots never let in water. 'But,' he added, 'it can never be real happiness to have lost your freedom.' Had Guido forgotten?

He himself, once 'Private Gollantz', who had appeared before a court-martial, who had been under arrest, who had—— He moved impatiently, oh, why remember it all! It was over, finished, done with.

No, not over, certainly not finished, and without doubt not 'done with'; a chapter had ended, the page had been turned, and the new chapter lay before them. None of them had forgotten, none of them could forget, however hard they tried to do so.

Again he thought, had they any right to try to forget? Were not their recollections, their memories, assets of the greatest value to them all? True they might all immerse themselves in their present way of living; he, Louis and Guido might go back to their antique dealing, their search for pictures, brocades, embroideries, old silver and gold, but their memories would remain, must remain, if they were to be of use in the building of the new world. Every individual had something to contribute, something which had been learnt—slowly, painfully, and with difficulty.

What had they learnt—the four of them, seated there in his room in Milano! An Italian—who knew that his country was laid waste, its government unstable, the whole social structure rocking and ready to totter; the French Jewess and her husband, another French Jew of different class, but imbued with the same spirit of real and true patriotism; himself—conscious that Britain, the country which with her Allies had—on paper at least—won the war, and now seemed in imminent danger of losing the Peace. The war had been fought that democracy might flourish and live, that Fascism and Nazism might vanish from the earth! Now Democracy was in as grave danger as it had ever been—the names Fascism and Nazism might have vanished from ordinary politics as names—but was their death certain?

Louis was speaking; his voice broke into Emmanuel's thoughts.

'. . . Somewhere there must be a saviour for each country. This I maintain! Where is he, who is he—French, British, Italian? How shall we find him? Answer me, please!'

Emmanuel said, speaking slowly, 'Louis, he is found already. He is—what is the name of your newspaper?—*The Ordinary Man*. He is everywhere, he is everyone. When each and every man takes upon himself, seriously and conscientiously, the task of saving his country, then we may begin to see nations standing firm on their feet again. The saviours of France are you, Louis and Olympia ; of Italy—my dear, Guido, of Britain—myself. We want armies—not to carry arms, but to carry determination as their banner. We're not sufficiently *concerned,* we're not sufficiently ready to shoulder responsibility. When we are, when men and women waken fully to a sense of their duty, when each one says, "I am the saviour of my country"—then we shall see the day dawning.

'This is what I feel. I may not be able to live up to this fully, because other things cr-rowd in, we have limited vision, we are occupied with our own small tasks, ambitions, hopes and fears. Is it only when a war is declared that r-real patriotism flourishes? Cannot we have patriotism when the war is over, and when tasks of gr-reat magnitude are waiting to be done?'

Louis nodded, 'Always you were idealistic, Emmanuel.'

Emmanuel retorted, 'This is not idealism, this is pr-racticality.'

Olympia yawned. 'Only peoples veel alvays pre-fair what is ideal to what is prac-ti-cal. For to most practical t'ings are dull! If only peoples remembaired zat death is not glorious—only life is zat! Men do not *zink*—not nationally, zey zink only politically. Some nasty old man wiz a beard puts on a teekeet and zey all shout—"Mon brave! Mon brave!" Ozzer men vear ozzer teekets and alls shout, "Go to 'ell, dirty ole dog?" Pair'aps bot' good fazers, nice sons, kind to animals! *Puff*, Emmanuel, men and women are alvays damn fools, zat is why ve arre in zees dirty mess. Good night, I go to my bed.'

CHAPTER THREE

EMMANUEL had been in Milano for five days—days filled with hard work, with making· plans, with long conferences with Guido. Scarcely a moment had been left for rest much less recreation. Louis and his wife had gone, returning to Paris; and with Louis, too, Emmanuel had held long discussions. Their two firms had always, before the war, worked together; if a good picture did not sell in Milano it was sent to Paris and one from Louis' collection was sent back in exchange. The system had worked very well, both men liked and trusted each other, both had ideals regarding their business, and both were specialists in their own profession.

The morning he was leaving, Louis sat in Emmanuel's office for a last discussion. Guido came in and out with his hands full of papers and documents, prices and changed conditions were argued out and arranged.

Finally Louis pushed the last document away from him and sighed. 'I am tired,' he announced; 'in the days when the world was still civilized, at this hour men—who were also gentlemen—used to say to me, "Louis, *mon brave*, this is the hour for a drink!" My reply was always the same. "Not half!" Like Guido, I admire these English expressions.'

Emmanuel's eyes twinkled, 'Did anyone ever give you—half?'

Louis shook his head, 'Not often; when that did happen I would say, "Tell me, am I dressed in yellow? No? Then please observe that I am not a canary bird!" It used to cause a great deal of laughter'

'I'm certain of it. Well, as this is an occasion, although I don't usually drink in the office—don't grin in that fashion, Guido!—I shall break my rule.'

Guido said, 'The expression is—we will elongate the pointer!'

'I generally use the less elaborate form,' Emmanuel said. ' "Stretch a point" is good enough for me. Right, Guido . . . cognac, seltz, glasses, and we'll drink to our combined success.'

He felt young, happy and confident. Things were going well, they would continue to go well. He had Moroni, with his com-

144

plete devotion and his considerable acumen and astuteness, he had the co-operation of Louis Lara working hand in hand with him.

There might be difficult times ahead—thin times, but if what he could judge of the present price of newly made and inferior furniture, there must inevitably still be people with judgment who realized that to buy good things—which were old—was a more profitable investment than to buy new goods which were bound to deteriorate rapidly. The complete luxury things might hang fire, but he had noted the prices of modern imitation jewellery, and decided that they were as high as many of the beautiful old trinkets which he offered for sale.

They could face a few lean years—if indeed there were any real likelihood of them being lean, which Emmanuel doubted.

Louis, sipping his drink, twisting the glass so that the ice tinkled musically, watched Emmanuel intently. His thin dark face was very serious, his sunken eyes puzzled.

'This man,' Louis thought, 'is growing old—if indeed he has not grown old already. I, too, have changed. I know when I look in my glass that I am changed, but there are often times when I feel quite impossibly young. I do not believe that Emmanuel ever feels young. Perhaps for a brief moment, as just now, when he sits with me and with Guido, and without speaking of it we—put back the clock. What is his life? His father who is dying, and never understood him. His mother—charming, but useless to help him. His horrible brother, and his own son. There is the other brother, but he never comes really into Emmanuel's circle. He ought to marry, to have a personal life ; not to live for nothing but old chairs and old pictures!'

He said with complete lightness, 'Emmanuel, my dear, you ought to marry. This is my advice to you.'

He noticed the slight coldness in Emmanuel's voice as he answered, 'My dear Louis, attractive women don't rush into the arms of elderly business men—unless they are very rich.'

Guido exclaimed, 'And he could never tolerate an unattractive woman!'

'There is no necessity,' Louis replied coolly. 'Emmanuel is not a poor man, he will—on the death of his father, and may this not happen for many years—be Sir Gollantz. His looks are—if not strictly handsome, at least arresting and unusual. He has a slight air of melancholy which really nice women find attractive.'

Emmanuel finished his drink and set down his glass ; he looked from Louis to Guido and back again to Louis. When he spoke his voice was very grave.

'You both know my life, you both know that I adored my

145

wife. What have I to offer to any woman—even if a woman would be willing to marry me—except the "second best"? That's all I can offer any woman.'

Louis frowned. 'There you are! Again these impossible ideals! Because I have tasted nectarines is it impossible that I can like a good hard apple? Because Giorgione painted very few pictures, and I have almost a worship for them, am I never to turn my eyes with any pleasure on a Titian or a Reubens! God forbid! "Second best!" Have you so little knowledge of women! All women believe that their men give them love which is the greatest in the world—the idea of "second best" never enters their heads.

'Even when a man—a married man—takes a mistress, his wife always believes that she remains his finest love. How often have we heard women say, "Pooh! That creature! He doesn't love her ; what she exercises is a physical attraction!" As if, listen to me, a physical attraction were such a pale, worthless thing. No, no, Emmanuel—marry. A woman not too young, not one so lacking in taste that she will have your teeth by their edges, not so rich that people will say you have married her in order to buy a Leonardo, and not so poor that the world will say that she married you to escape from poverty.'

Emmanuel smiled a trifle wryly, 'Continue your admirable discourse, Louis. Let us have another drink, no doubt your eloquence will induce consider-rable thirst. So!'

Louis recrossed his legs and swung a beautifully shod foot ; he was enjoying himself.

'Naturally—and rightly—at over forty, one does not find the intoxication which in earlier days meant that you had fallen in love. Looking back! Ah, how well I remember the times when I have known—with certainty—that my heart was broken!'

He hummed softly 'T'anks for the memoree,' then continued, 'Not by one woman, but by hundreds. How I have been tortured by them—many of whom I did not even know! Figure to yourself my adoration for a beautiful creature—I believe an Italian Jewess—or of that extraction. Her name,' he sighed deeply, 'was José Collins. No, I never spoke to her ; once—yes, I said, "Good evening—t'ank you!" as she left the stage door. She smiled. A smile which extinguished all the lights in London, which made all the stars seem like cheap candles! Ah, that was love! Again I felt the same for Mistinguette, for La Spero, the widow of Matot the actor. Also for my superb Olympia. Now—I no longer break my heart if Olympia smiles at another man—and she very often does, though it never goes further—if she is out and promises to return at five o'clock when we have English tea——'

Guido said eagerly, 'For this mealtime, do you wear the smoking as in evenings? Mussolini stated that this was so.'

Louis said impatiently, 'He lied! He had never taken English tea—which I still t'ink is quite horrible! I hope that he is now drinking litres of it—and Hitler also! As I said'—his tone held a faint rebuke for the interruption—'if Olympia is late for "five o'clock" which she always is—do I imagine that she is lying dead in a hospital, do I listen with aching ears for the telephone, do I imagine that she has betrayed me with a gigolo? No! I say, smilingly, "The damn' woman is late again!" Love in one's youth is a fever which consumes you, in middle age it is a charming and prolonged convalescence. The temperature is normal, the appetite returns—only one eats with taste and discretion—the eyes are calm and the heart tranquil.'

'But—the other women—the ones you loved with such devotion even though you never "told your love"?' Emmanuel asked.

'Ah! Always they remain, delicious memories, encased in my heart, their names written on a scroll of finest gold! I do not love my Olympia less because I still love them—for Mistinguette my heart still beats faster, for La Spero—though she has married—indeed, a most romantic affair—I still know that my pulses tick more rapidly.'

Guido, his eyes filled with interest and some emotion, said, 'And the Colleen—what of her?'

'*Collins*,' Louis corrected. 'How difficult you find it to speak English names, Guido. There is a tragedy! She, too, is married—to a doctor who also writes books!'

Guido said hopefully, 'And he beats her no doubt!'

Louis said, 'Indeed no! There is the tragedy—they are divinely happy! Emmanuel, if I am to assist Olympia to pack her clothes I must go. But remember this conversation—Cliquot is wonderful, but beer also sparkles! I shall come to London or you will come to Paris!'

Back in London, the recollection of his friends in Milano still remaining with him. Emmanuel drove to Heber Square. His thoughts went back to Guido as he had seen him last, alternating between intense pride that he was left as the manager and partner of the Gollantz Galleries and grief that Emmanuel was leaving Milano ; to Giacomo, Tommaso and Lucia, who had insisted that he must take back an immense basket of food, sundry packets of cheese, and olive oil and a basket-covered bottle. The long, thin face of his lawyer Tolino, always so grave and so apprehensive regarding the future; he recalled the ardent Catholic, Rosteeno, who believed that the salvation of Italy could only come through her complete obedience to the Church, and most of all he thought of Conte Boccolini, who had once been 'podesta' of Milano, and had been 'removed' from that post by the Fascist Government. Poor Casimiro Boccolini, with his quiet voice, his subdued manner and his obvious distress at the state of the Black Market, the numerous strikes, the general unrest existing in the country.

Once Emmanuel had passed, in the Corso, the ex-Fascist 'Chico' whose real name was Baruch. A Fascist no longer, coming forward to greet Emmanuel with outstretched hand and a smile on his evil face.

'Ah, Signor Gollantz, how good it is to see you again in Milano.'

Emmanuel had frowned, and disregarded the outstretched hand.

Baruch asked, 'You are surprised to see me, yes?'

'Surprised to see you enjoying obvious prosperity,' Emmanuel said, for the Italian was well dressed, and to be well dressed in Milano meant that you were also expensively dressed.

'But why? Tell me,' with an ingratiating grin. 'Why are you surprised? You know that I was never, never a Fascist!'

'Milano is full of surprises.'

'If there is anything that I can do for you, Signor Gollantz, please remember that I am,' with a flourish, 'your servant.'

'I am obliged to you. I have all the servants I require.'

'I trust that you found everything safe in your Galleries. What a disaster had anything happened—a bomb fallen, the Germans taken your treasures! All is well—that is good. I am happy.'

He stood directly in Emmanuel's path; the Englishman met his eyes squarely.

'Then allow me to be happy also, Signor Baruch. Allow me to pass. I dislike to breathe the same air as yourself. Good morning.'

There was something about the atmosphere of London which Emmanuel found soothing. The town might look shabby, there were still many traces of the damage done by the bombardment, but everywhere was an air of solidity. He knew of the labour troubles, he had his own views—shared by many of his friends— that possibly the wisest courses were not being pursued with regard to rebuilding and reconstruction, but the air of the people remained unchanged.

These English had enjoyed security for so long, their tradition was so strong, that it was possible they relied too much on these things. They had always survived, always become stable after waves of instability—had they, he wondered, come to rely too much on these traditional things? As they had fallen back on catch phrases during the war, were they falling back on shibboleths now during what ought to have been the peace?

During the war they had said, 'The British lose every battle but the last.' They had laughed that England always sent 'a lad to do a man's job—and he does it!' They had made jokes concerning 'muddle' and 'mess', they had laughed at their own inefficiency, and roared with mirth when things went wrong. Now—were they ready to apply the same methods to post-war difficulties?

Yet these British did contrive to 'come through', and he remembered what old Emmanuel used to say. 'T'ey veen t'rough not because of t'eir vise politicians, for t'ese t'ey hev not got! T'ey veen t'rough because in generally t'ey are such ver' magnificent fools t'ey don't know ven t'ey are beaten, und in spite of t'eir politicians!'

His own house seemed very quiet, very small, very intimate after the apartment in Milan. He looked with affection at his beautiful old furniture, so elegant and so beautifully made, and smiled.

Simeon appeared, and shouted a greeting. 'Father, how good to have you home again!'

'And how are things with you? Have you found me a masterpiece?'

Simeon flushed, his eyes bright, 'I believe that I've got one or two nice things to show you. Only small things,' he amended.

With his arm on the young man's shoulder, Emmanuel said, 'Splendid, this is the day of small things! Now give me a drink before dinner, then, and only then, will I consent to remove the stains of travel from my usually immaculate person. Now,' stretching his legs, and leaning back in his chair, 'tell me—what news on the Rialto?'

'Grandfather Max isn't awfully well, Father. He told me last night—yes, I went out there for an hour's riding—that he hoped you'd go to see him to-morrow.'

'That goes without saying—of course.'

'Max was there,' Simeon continued, then Emmanuel saw the way his well-shaped nose wrinkled a little. 'I don't really care a great deal for Max.' He laughed. 'Max doesn't care much for me, I gather.'

'Then there is, obviously, no love lost, eh?'

'Uncle Julian's very busy, he's selling a great deal of stuff. He told me that the market was bucking up marvellously. Oh, and there was a message from Arbuthnot's this morning. He would like to see you as soon as it is possible. Not at his place—at his house in Hampstead. He asked if you would telephone to him.'

Emmanuel asked lazily, 'Why does he want to see me, I wonder?'

'He didn't say—well, he didn't speak to me, it was his secretary, Miss Carnforth. She said it was rather important.'

'Probably found a rare primitive, and when we clean it we shall find a portrait of the Prince Consort underneath,' Emmanuel said.

Simeon answered, 'Did that ever really happen, do you suppose?'

'Frequently, I imagine. There, having refreshed the inner man, I will go and make the outer man slightly more agreeable to the eye. See you later, Simeon.'

. The next day he drove down to Ordingly, having called in at the Gallery for an hour. Julian sauntered in, and Emmanuel noticed that one of his hands, the left, was heavily bandaged.

'Hello, been knocked about, Julian?'

Julian nodded. 'A burn. Oh, it's healing but it's damned uncomfortable.'

'How did you manage to do that?'

'Box of matches caught fire in my hand.'

'You should use a lighter.'

'I do—generally—always in the future. I say, Emmanuel, I'm afraid that the Guv'nor's pretty ill. I saw him a couple of days ago. My God, he looked ghastly, like a death's head!'

'And Angela?'

'She looks tired, but she puts on an act of being bright and hopeful.'

Emmanuel watched the petulant face before him; how strange it was that Julian appeared to regard his father's illness as a kind of personal annoyance to himself. He had always hated illness, his brother remembered; except when he was ill himself, then he expected the whole household to revolve round his bed! Death, quite literally, filled him with terror; Emmanuel had never fathomed the reason—was it fear of extinction, a realization of the impermanence of things which he liked to believe stable and lasting?

He picked up some letters, and said, 'Well, I'll get along to Ordingly. Where can I find you—if you're wanted?'

Julian's eyes seemed to dilate suddenly. 'You don't mean that the Guv'nor's going to die—to-day, do you? I tell you I can't stand death-bed scenes.' His voice mounted higher; Emmanuel caught a note which was almost hysterical. 'I'm devoted to the

150

Guv'nor, you know that—but it won't help him to have me standing about watching him die. Far better let me keep out of it.'

Very coolly Emmanuel answered, 'I said nothing about dying. I only asked where we could be certain of finding you. Pull yourself together, Julian. It's not only what you want, there is Angela to consider. If she wants you there—you'll damn' well be there, if either Bill or I have to drag you there. Get that firmly in your head.'

Julian scowled at him, his face sulky and resentful. 'You damned hypocritical swine,' he said. 'Because you're completely insensitive you refuse to try to understand what anyone else feels! Get along to Ordingly and play the devoted son, you've got a few arrears to make up!'

As Emmanuel passed Hannah's office he stopped to speak to her.

'I'm apprehensive,' he said, speaking softly ; 'call it premonition, what you will—I'll telephone to you if it's necessary. Tell Simeon to be somewhere about.'

She nodded. 'I shan't leave here,' she said. 'Have courage!'

He drove out to Ordingly, allowing the peace of the country to soothe his frayed nerves as it never failed to do. Again and again he filled his lungs with the sweet, clear air, as if he were trying to store it away to use when he might need it badly. Queer, he reflected, that Julian should have accused him of being insensitive, when all his life his intense sensitivity was one of the qualities he had tried to overcome—how hard he had fought to school himself into a state of mind which did not allow people and things to hurt him unbearably!

He sighed, and reflected, as he did so often, that life was not going to be easy. Max might have virtually retired from any active part in the business, but he had acted as a restraining influence, both his sons had been fully conscious that Max Gollantz was still the Head of the House.

With Max gone that rôle would fall on Emmanuel's shoulders. He would be Sir Emmanuel, the senior partner, the owner of Ordingly. He smiled with twisted lip, as if the thought tasted sour. Julian would have liked the title—Emmanuel wished that he might have had it. Ordingly was different, Julian had never liked the place, his interest in it had been of the slightest. It was convenient ; to live there saved him the expense and trouble of a place in town, the tennis courts were useful because he could pay off social obligations by asking his friends to come down and play.

More than that—Emmanuel turned in at the big gates, and Mrs. Follie came running out.

'Eh, I'm glad you're here, sir. Sir Meyer's just arrived.'

'Is my father worse?'

'Well, sir, Hewson was down this morning early, and he said that he didn't seem so well. Losin' strength, that was what Hewson said.'

'Have they telephoned for my brother and my son, do you know?'

'Couldn't say, sir. Mr. Bill's bin here all night.'

'Very well, I'll get on.'

He drew up carefully, impelled to do so as quickly as possible. Bill was waiting at the top of the wide stone steps. Bill who looked heavy-eyed and dead tired.

'Hello, Bill—how is he?'

'Not so good, old boy. Meyer is with him now ; they sent for Julian and Simeon about half an hour ago.'

'Just after I left. Julian's son here?'

'No, they asked Julian to telephone to him in the City.'

'And—Angela?'

'Wonderful. Tired out, but being marvellous. Charles is here, came early this morning. Better go up, eh? Max looks terribly ill, but he's quite conscious.'

In the sitting-room upstairs, which was next to Max's bedroom, he found Meyer Bernstein, the little Jew doctor who had risen to such heights in his profession, who had attended them all in their various illnesses, and whose admiration for Max Gollantz was unbounded.

'Hello, Emmanuel—you've been qvick.'

'I left before you telephoned. How is my father?'

'He's going fast. Qvite sensible of the fact. Not in the least disturbed. Ve shan't see many more men like your father, Emmanuel.'

'Can I go in and see him?'

The doctor spread his hands wide. 'Can't make any difference ; yes, vhy not?'

Emmanuel opened the door, and saw his father propped high against pillows, his face drained of all colour, the skin seeming to be stretched too tightly over the bones ; only the eyes were very clear, very much alive. Angela was seated beside the bed, and somewhere in the next room Emmanuel caught the sight of a nurse moving about silently.

Angela said, 'Emmanuel, how quickly you got here.'

He stooped and kissed her, then said, 'You forgot that I had

152

an appointment with my father for this morning. How are you, sir?'

Max smiled. 'I've no pain, which is something, eh?'

'A very gr-reat deal, I should say.'

'Your Milan trip? Successful. Tell me about it, Emmanuel.'

Keeping his voice even, untinged with emotion, Emmanuel recounted briefly what he had found in Milan; once or twice during his recital he made some comment which caused Max to smile. The story ended, Max said, 'It sounds remarkably satisfactory. That Moroni is a trustworthy fellow. And Louis Lara—he's an astute man. I'm sorry that I was once sufficiently foolish to dislike them both. You might tell them that—I changed my opinion of them.'

'They will appreciate that ver-ry sincerely.'

Max held out his hand, and Emmanuel, moving nearer to the bed, took it and held it in his own. It felt cold, the skin so thin that is scarcely seemed to cover the bones.

'There are a good many things for which I am sorry, Emmanuel. We've all got a streak of it—"That wild lie, which men call pride." My father had it, I inherited a good deal of it. You have less but—enough. Thank you for many things. I learn slowly—but I have learnt to trust you and believe in you.'

The door opened and Sir Meyer came in.

With something of his old impatience, Max said, 'Yes—yes, what is it?'

'Collingsby Jackson is here, Max.'

Max turned to Angela. 'Another doctor! As if this Bernstein were not sufficient!' The smile which he gave the little man belied his words. 'Give me one moment with—my son, Meyer, please.'

He turned back to Emmanuel. 'I can say with complete confidence that I can leave your mother in your wise and loving —yes, loving—hands. Don't be disheartened. Don't let anything or anyone—pull you down. God bless you. Now let us have this new doctor in!'

The day dragged on. The great London specialist spent a long time with Meyer's patient; later he ate an excellent luncheon; Emmanuel thought how perfect were his manners. He obviously enjoyed his food, sipped his wine with grave appreciation, and yet always contrived to retain an air which implied that he could have wished that he was able to enjoy it fully, unhampered by the nature of his visit.

Simeon arrived, bringing Reuben Davis with him. Bill asked bluntly why he had not brought his uncle.

'He said that he was coming in his own car, Uncle Bill. He was telephoning to Max to leave the City at once.'

'Julian wasn't driving with Max, then?' Bill's questions came quickly with a kind of precision like a hammer descending.

'I don't think so. Uncle Julian was coming alone.'

Bill glanced at Emmanuel, his eyebrows raised, his lips compressed. Later, as they walked together in the terrace, Bill said, 'He won't come. It's a case of, "Pray God we may make haste—and come too late." Pah, what a detestable fellow he is, that brother of ours!'

At four o'clock that afternoon Max Gollantz died. His two sons, his grandson Simeon, his wife and his devoted friend Bernstein were with him. Emmanuel and Bill, their arms round their mother, half carried her from the room ; looking at her white face, Emmanuel thought, "This is the only time I have ever realized that she has grown old!"

Emmanuel turned his head to see his brother more plainly. They were driving back from their father's funeral, and before them lay the prospect of talking to the crowd of people who had come to pay their respects to Max Gollantz. The 'Foreign Contingent' were sadly depleted. True, there were members of the Baruchs, the Hirschs, the Jaffes ; but they were fewer than the crowd which had gathered to the funeral of old Emmanuel. Louis Lara had flown from Paris ; a strange old man who gave his name as Ezriah Habbemma had arrived from some place in Holland. No one knew him ; he was small, old and bent, with a quiet lisping voice, his English scarcely understandable. He looked dazed and half stunned, Emmanuel had thought, until the old man told him that he had been a prisoner in a Nazi concentration camp for Jews.

'Now,' he whispered, 'I am free. It is all so strange. I heard that the good Max was dead. I pay my respects. I am a ver' distant cousin. To-night I return to Holland. Excuse, please, if I am a little confused.'

Now Julian sat, his arms folded, his face set and immovable. He had shown no outward sign of grief. He had arrived at Ordingly two hours after his father died, and told Bill that his car had broken down "miles from anywhere". He had refused to stay at Ordingly, and had driven back to town that same evening, pleading that he had some business which even the death of his father could not delay.

Julian's face betrayed nothing ; if he felt grief at the death of his father, his handsome, rigid face showed no sign. He was, as always, immaculate, beautifully correct; he sat stiffly upright, his arms folded, staring straight before him.

Emmanuel had realized during the past forty-eight hours the great effort his father had made to—virtually—beg his pardon. It had been bravely and generously done, and Emmanuel's heart felt warmed and strengthened. The relationship between his father and himself had never been a close one, and Emmanuel had felt—with reason—that his father had judged him too harshly, and too often without reason. The fact that he had returned home, that Max had greeted him with some affection and a certain quality of regret for what was past, was, Emmanuel knew, due to the passionate insistence of his mother and the courage of Viva Heriot.

It had been Viva who discovered that the blame which had been shouldered by Emmanuel should have been laid at Julian's door. She had braved them all, she had bullied Max, she had shown her contempt for Max Gollantz's readiness to believe in Emmanuel's guilt, to judge him harshly on every possible occasion. Max had tried his best to atone, and Emmanuel felt now a real sense of loss, a feeling that had they been given more time he and his father might have become very close, with a complete understanding between them.

The last two days had been filled with work. He had dealt with everything, had granted interviews, scanned the obituary notices, made all arrangements, and talked endlessly with distant relatives. Julian had been in London, Bill admitted frankly. 'Anything I can do, I'll do; but I can't cope with these foreign people. I can't speak any language except my own, and that not too well. Give me a job and I'll do it; but I haven't your ability, your diplomacy, Emmanuel.'

Angela was prostrated with her grief. Emmanuel had visited her room and found her white-faced and dazed. He had spoken gently, with all the love and affection of which he was capable.

She held his hand, and said in a strange voice which sounded dead, 'Give me time, darling. We've been together for so long, nearly fifty years. I'm like a clock that needs readjusting. The readjustment is difficult—and very painful. Don't worry, I shall be all right. Just give me—time, that's all.' Once as they sat talking quietly of old Emmanuel, of Max, of people they had known and loved, she said impulsively, 'If only Juliet were here—she could help me.' Then very thoughtfully, 'Juliet—or Viva. Their methods would be quite different, but—it would be nice to have either of them.'

Juliet—or Viva.

In his pocket lay the cablegram which Viva had sent to him.

It was typical of her, extravagant, in reality more like a letter than a cable. He had read it with pleasure ; Viva had no inhibitions, and when her heart was touched, as it evidently was at the news of Max's death, she had no hesitation in writing what she actually felt. He could understand why his mother, in her grief, should have longed for either Juliet or Viva. Two women so completely dissimilar, and yet both possessing a great honesty, and both capable of deep affection.

He knew that at this moment he too longed—as he always did—for Juliet ; but that also he would have felt a real and deep content if Viva could have been waiting for him at Ordingly. At the end of her cable Viva had written, 'Shall I come home?' He smiled, that was so typical of her. She would be quite willing to fling herself into the first available 'plane and to return to England, throwing herself into any plans which might make Angela happier, or help Emmanuel over what promised to be a difficult patch.

The car stopped. Julian got out, his face still immovable. Emmanuel, turning to look back, saw other cars disgorging their loads. There were the men who had been associated for so long with his father. There was Marcus Arbuthnot in his outmoded clothes and incredibly high collar, the two sons of old Sir Augustus Morris—Joseph and Samson—and the oldest of them all, Jacob Lane, leaning heavily on the arm of his secretary, his lips purple, his breath coming in little difficult bursts. Here were his mother's people—Wilmots, Drews, and Heriots ; his father's relations, Baruchs, Hirschs and Jaffes ; Louis Lara giving his arm to the small timid Habbemma. He saw his own son, giving his arm to Lady Heriot, while old Sir Walter tottered in their wake ; Julian's son, like his father, seemed to draw aloof from everyone.

Charles Wilmot bustled forward, drawing level with old Bill Masters, who limped badly, leaning heavily on his stick. He caught sight of little Gilbert, who had been Juliet's accompanist for so many years ; Gilbert, who grasped his hand and said, 'My dear young man, I am so sorry, so very sorry.' Behind him lumbered 'Buster' Carteret, who, shooting out a hand like a ham, said, 'Didn't know your father. You were damned nice about poor "Toby" Tatten, I thought I'd come along. Hope you don't mind. My sympathy to your poor mother. Yes—well—heard from Viva, eh?' and then blushed deeply as if he had introduced a topic not sufficiently serious for the occasion.

Emmanuel said to Julian, 'I can speak the language, so shall I see to the "Foreign Contingent"? Will you look after Arbuthnot and Lane and old Augustus Morris?'

Julian glanced towards the little group of old men who were making their way up the steps to the house, his lip curled.

'What? Look after all the Sheenies? Good Lord! Lot of second-hand dealers. I loathe the lot of them!'

Struggling to hide his annoyance, Emmanuel called to Simeon.

'Look after the "Old Brigade", will you, Simeon . . . there, Arbuthnot, Sir Augustus and Jacob Lane—oh, and get hold of Reuben Davis. I don't want them to feel neglected.'

'Why, yes, Father, of course.'

He hurried off, having already escorted Lady Heriot into the house, and Emmanuel watched him speaking to the members of the 'Old Brigade'. Charles Wilmot said, 'Doesn't seem to have made a great deal of difference to the poor lad, losing that foot, does it? Nice chap, I like him. How's he doing with you?'

'Doing very nicely. I'm delighted. I believe that he has a real flair. Well—better go in.'

Hewson was waiting for him as he entered; he offered a salver on which lay a heap of telegrams.

'These have just come, Sir Emmanuel.'

CHAPTER FOUR

SIMEON GOLLANTZ had been deeply affected by the death of
his grandfather. In a queer, removed fashion he had admired
Max wholeheartedly. Possibly he had never seen him as a man
subject to moods and impulses. To Simeon he had been the
Head of the House, the follower of old Emmanuel whose
portrait seemed to the young man still to dominate the whole
house.

True, his own father—Young Emmanuel—had the looks of
the old man ; people assured him that his father was cast in the
same mould, that he possessed the same attributes and characteristics ; but to Simeon his grandfather had held the 'ball and
sceptre' ; it was he who had ruled the Gallery in Bond Street, it
was towards him men's eyes had turned when something
spectacular came into the market, some work of art which was
destined for America, but which must be retained for England.

He had seen Max Gollantz not as a rather tired, sometimes
irritable, man, but a man who possessed the knowledge for
which young Simeon longed. Often he had driven out from
London, ostensibly because he wanted to ride or play tennis—
which, in spite of his false foot, he still played remarkably well—
but in reality because after dinner he could sit and talk to Max
about those things which were so dear to his heart.

Simeon had all the passionate love of things which were old
and lovely which had filled his great-grandfather. To him it was
a real and great joy to sit in the big drawing-room at Ordingly
and persuade Max to talk of pictures, silver, china and furniture.

Max had never had such a pupil. His own apprenticeship had
been served under Old Emmanuel, who had been so gifted, so
well acquainted with everything regarding antiques, that Max—
always inclined to suffer from an inferiority complex—had
scarcely dared to ask questions of this man who was recognized
as a world-wide authority. Max had gained his knowledge
slowly and painstakingly, he had talked very little, he had
worked astonishingly hard, and his knowledge was founded on
a very safe and solid basis. Gradually, and with immense hard

158

work, he had wormed his way into the very front rank of the dealers, and had earned for himself a name for knowledge, taste, and what mattered most of all to him—complete integrity.

Julian had disliked the business, Julian had promised to be a very brilliant politician. Everything had come easily to him; he had personality, charm and intelligence of a very high order. Julian had proved to be a disappointment; then had come his accident and the injury to his back. Meyer Bernstein had shaken his head and told Max that there was not the slightest reason for Julian to adopt the rôle of semi-invalid.

That had been the only quarrel between the two men in over forty years! Max had defended his son. Meyer had shrugged and pulled down the corners of his mouth, had used obscure Jewish words to express his contempt of Julian, and for a time the rift between the brilliant Jewish doctor and Max Gollantz had widened. They had bridged it, they became again fast friends and their acrimonious discussion was forgotten.

Meanwhile, Emmanuel, possessing the flair of his grandfather, had been learning by his own efforts. Emmanuel had learned in a hard school, and when he finally returned to England, a widower with a small son, Max realized that while his own knowledge might be deeper, yet Emmanuel had that rare gift of being able to 'take a chance' and to be right in his ventures.

Max had once said to Angela, his tone half humorous, half irritable, 'I know what is right, I can give reasons, facts; my history is fairly profound. I am invariably right, and I can give reasons why I am right. Emmanuel—there is something very oriental about that boy—knows by instinct. I don't say that he cannot verify his instinctive reasoning—oh, he can. But what he relies on most is this strange additional sense which he has.

'My father had it. How often have I seen him handle silver or china, his eyes half closed, his fingers moving delicately over the surfaces, and then make his pronouncement. Those pronouncements were invariably right. Emmanuel has the same gift. He knows his books or rules, he knows his marks by heart, but he can trust his fingertips and his eyes! He has an unfair advantage over the rest of us!'

When Simeon had decided to enter the business Max had shown his pleasure. Not in a particularly demonstrative manner, but by his quiet—almost secret—smile, by the tone of his voice.

Simeon was greedy for knowledge, and Max was anxious to teach. Here at last was a pupil who was ready to learn, who absorbed knowledge as a sponge absorbs water. For hours Simeon would sit listening intently, his eyes bright with excitement. To him Max recounted the glories of the days which belonged to the years before the war. Forgetting to be restrained and rather self-conscious, the elder man had told of the great days in the sale-rooms, of the bidding advancing slowly, almost cautiously, until at a given point caution was flung to the winds, and Emmanuel Gollantz entered the bidding.

Then, Max told Simeon, men sat stiffly upright, their lips compressed, their eyes following every delicate movement of Emmanuel's hand as he signalled to the auctioneer. He told stories of the meetings of the great dealers after the sales. He told how old Jacob Lane had declared to Emmanuel, ' 'Tis time you are made a great fool of! T'ese vases are not wort' what you hev paid. I wantet t'em—yes, wantet t'em badly, but you rich men—pah!'

Old Emmanuel had replied, 'I hev no wish that ve compare benk belances. I hev vasted, it appears, an hour of my time at zee zale-r-room. My time iss von huntret pounds an hour. For vot is the r-right pr-rice of der vazes, plus von huntret pounds—hev them!'

Max chuckled, 'Lane didn't accept the offer!'

His stock joke had been when anyone—Max possibly—bought a picture the authenticity of which was doubtful. 'Let us hev it cleanet, if you please. I don't doubt zat underneat' ve find something r-really valuable—maybe a Bellini, a Mantagna —who vill know?'

From Max young Simeon had learnt a great deal. Max had enjoyed those evenings ; he had thrown off some of his lassitude, his irritability had vanished, he had been alert and very patient. Now, Simeon, wandering about the gardens at Ordingly, felt lonely, and conscious that someone who was ready to give him highly specialized training had gone. He could still hear his grandfather's quiet, measured tones, see the fine, thin hands, and see the sudden fire light in his eyes when some subject very dear to his heart was mentioned. They had been more than teacher and pupil, there had existed between them a real and actual friendship. There had been times when Max talked of Ordingly with affection and enthusiasm.

'You like the place, Simeon?' he had asked eagerly.

'Like it, sir? I love every bit of it!'

'I am pleased. It's a fine place, a place which has dignity.'

He had led a queer life, young Simeon. Born in Milano, of parents whose love for him was only exceeded by their devotion to each other. His mother had died when he was only a year old, he had been brought up with the great Jaffe-Gollantz Galleries as his playground, with Guido Moroni as his favourite playmate, and with Emmanuel Gollantz as his ideal of all that

160

was best and most splendid in humanity. He had returned to England at the outbreak of war, with his father, speaking English fluently but with a pronounced Italian accent. He had been sent to a typically English school, and although the boys had been sufficiently kind, he had been conscious that they regarded him as 'more than half Dago'.

From time to time, his father, wearing the uniform of a private soldier, had visited him, and he had known that boys looked with some surprise at the man of whom Simeon had swaggered and boasted.

One boy had said, 'What exactly is your father, Gollantz?'

'A soldier,' Simeon answered.

'Yes, but I mean when he isn't in the Army?'

Simeon had felt that the words threatened some hint of patronage. He was nearly fourteen at the time, and sticking his hands into his pockets and adopting an attitude which was slightly truculent, he answered:

'My father can recognize a Zaganelli; in the complete darkness he would know a Morone; dai Libri is an open book to him. Ingres, Boucher, Chardin—these, too, he greets without a mistake. *Per farla corto*—excuse me—in short, he is the great authority on pictures.'

The boy said, 'Those names—the ones you said—are they friends of his?'

Simeon replied, 'The greatest of friends.'

'Then why is he just a Tommy?'

'Tommy? His name is Emmanuel!'

'Gosh, you're slow! He's a private, not an officer.'

'He dislikes to exercise his influence,' Simeon said. 'His admiration for General Wavell is great. He would not wish to deprive him of his leadership. You understand?'

His affection for his father had remained, nothing had shaken it, and although he no longer rushed into the lists to defend some fancied slight levelled at Emmanuel, his deep love for his father burnt as strongly as ever. For his mother, whose memory had been made a living thing for him, he had a reverence which might easily have become a little artificial and completely sentimental. It was thanks to the care of Emmanuel, Guido and Iva Alfano that it had not done so. True, Emmanuel mentioned her very seldom, and when he did so Simeon listened to the deep, warm tones of his voice. It was not what he actually said, but the sincerity and controlled emotion which his words conveyed. Guido talked of her as someone who had only left them for a short time, as if, Simeon thought, she had gone for a tour to America or Australia. He had once said to Guido, 'You speak as if you expected her to come back any day. . . .'

Guido answered, 'Nothing is impossible. If she should, then I wish to be ready to meet her. This thought is what has made me try always to behave like a gentleman, like a good feller. If I'd been a bad lad, I would blush right down to my heels when I met her. That's like what she was.'

Iva Alfano—who was Signora Paul Mancini—sometimes played and sang to him in her beautiful, rich voice, and when he thanked her, when he said how wonderful it had been, she shrugged her massive shoulders, and replied, 'Poor leetle boy! You zink Alfano iss good. Ziss is bekas you neffer listen to La Forbez—your muzzer.'

On his twentieth birthday he had dined with the Mancinis, and Paul had produced a book of records, saying, 'Don't allow your father to hear these. I believe that he has them all, but maybe he likes to listen to them alone. Iva and I have managed to get them for you. They're your mother singing. Take care of them, young feller, they're very precious.'

Simeon had carried them home, and in his own room had played them very softly. German, French, Italian and English— lovely melodies of the great musicians, given to the world in the beautiful voice of Juliet Forbes. There was Taubau's setting of *'Ah, Mon Amour Est Comme La Rose', 'Das Lied in Grunen'* of Schubert, 'I Attempt From Love's Sickness to Fly' and 'When I Am Laid in Earth', *'Freundliche Vision', 'Es Ist Alles Wei ein Vunder Carer Garten'*, 'Morgan', and half a dozen others. Simeon sat entranced ; he had never heard such a voice, or realized that it was possible for the character of the singer to be made clear through her singing. The range was magnificent, the enunciation clear and exact, and the phrasing seemed to him to make each song into a splendid pattern, beautifully rounded, exquisitely balanced.

He took off the last record and laid it away gently and carefully. He was not a highly imaginative young man, but as he carried the album to his desk and laid it away he felt that he was not alone. With that music, music of many countries, of many types, he felt that the mother of whom he had heard so often had entered the room, and had sung to him with the desire that he should get to know and understand her.

That had been nearly a year ago, and since that time he had never again been conscious that he had lost his mother when he was too young to remember her. There were her photographs, a few very precious snapshots taken at Como, in the mountains, once entering the courtyard of their apartment in Milano. With these and those records, Simeon built up his picture of Juliet Forbes.

Emmanuel rarely spoke of her, and when he did it was to mention her briefly. Simeon was sufficiently perceptive to realize that his silence was due to the fact that the sense of her loss was too keen, always present, to make conversation about her easy.

He was content with his own conception of her. He knew the tones of her voice, and to him two people were in his world to whom he gave unstinted love, admiration and loyalty—his mother and Emmanuel.

Two days after his grandfather's funeral Simeon walked round the gardens before driving back to London. The great house still seemed hushed and silent ; he knew that his grandmother still lay in her darkened room asking only to be left alone, assuring everyone that she could 'fight it out better alone'. Sir Meyer said, 'I haff neffer doubted her courage ; now she herself hass proffed zat I vas r-right. A gr-reat voman.'

Last night Simeon had heard a long conversation between his father, Charles Wilmot, and his two uncles. They had been shut in the library, and from time to time the sound of his father's voice, temperate and controlled, had reached him ; later, Bill Gollantz's deeper and louder tones ; Julian's pitched higher, and rising on an ascending scale, brought down to earth it seemed by some remark of Charles Wilmot's, sharp and incisive.

Later, a door had slammed, and opened again immediately ; he had heard Bill's voice saying clearly, 'Make less noise—you'll disturb Angela!' and a few moments later his father, white-faced and hollow-eyed, had entered the small drawing-room with Bill and Charles Wilmot. Emmanuel had not spoken. Bill had asked, 'Anything to drink, Simeon?' and Charles, seating himself and hitching up the knees of his immaculate trousers, had said, 'How very unpleasant some people can be when money is under discussion!'

Simeon had given them the drinks for which they asked, he had stood watching his father, wishing that he could do something to take that strained expression from his face. Emmanuel looked up and smiled.

'Sorry that you should have heard the family at play, Simeon. Not particularly pleasant. Take my advice and keep out of it all.'

Bill nodded. 'Queer, everyone wants to grab! Oh, I expect that I do myself. Why the devil don't we let Julian scoff the lot? Then we might be spared these disgusting exhibitions.'

Charles said, 'You don't allow Julian to—scoff the lot, my

163

boy, because there is still such a thing as justice in the world, and I for one am going to see that it is administered. Poor Max's will is perfectly fair, he always gave Julian far more than he had a right to, the fellow's simply greedy, avaricious. Pah! Give me another drink, Simeon, and make it a little stronger. I've a nasty taste in my mouth.'

Now, on a beautifully fine morning, Simeon had breakfasted alone. One of the nurses had come into the dining-room and told him that his grandmother had at last fallen into a sound and natural sleep. He finished his breakfast with a better appetite, meditating upon how good home-made marmalade and fresh butter tasted on bread which was new and crisp.

He drank a third cup of coffee, then whistling to Max's old setter, walked round to the stables. He asked Mallet, the groom, for news of his horse. 'I've neglected him,' he said, 'I hope you've had him out.'

Mallet shifted his feet uneasily. 'Well, sir, I've not as a matter of fac'. He 'as bin out; in fac'—he's been let down. Narsty graze on the off fore leg, sir.'

'Let down! Let's see him! How the devil did this happen?'

'Well, sir, it were Mr. Max, sir. The fac' is Mr. Max has had him out once or twice, tole me as you didn't think he was gettin' enough exercise, an' as Mr. Max don't go up to the City till latish every mornin' he's bin takin' him out. This happened yesterday. I was prop'ly upset abart it. Mind you, the horse is all right. I've lurked arfter it.'

Simeon looked at the graze, nothing very serious, but most certainly it would leave a scar. He knew that his heart was beating very fast. He didn't like his cousin particularly, and for that reason dreaded to have any discussion with him for fear his dislike should make him lose his temper.

He nodded to Mallet, said, 'If it's well enough, I'll take him out in the morning, just something gentle. What do you think?'

'Not do him no harm, I don't reckon, sir.'

Simeon, still conscious that his pulses were hammering, walked back to the house. He tried to argue that after all Max might have taken Crusader out from a sense of kindness, and that an accident might happen to anyone; but in his heart he knew that he was angry and indignant.

He stood staring at the house, allowing its mellow beauty to soothe his nerves and delight his eyes. Strange to think that Ordingly belonged to his father, that one day it would be his. Strange, too, to remember that his father was 'Sir Emmanuel', for of all the great antique dealers Max Gollantz had been the only one to receive a baronetcy. Jacob Lane had been knighted,

Hannah Rosenfeldt said that Arbuthnot might be in the Birthday Honours, but Max had been given his title years ago, because he had given a Gainsborough to the nation and his services on some special mission.

Simeon heard a step on the gravel near him and turned to find his cousin Max approaching. Max was a tall, good-looking fellow, with a good figure and the same bright golden hair as Julian. He looked particularly well this morning, carrying himself with a certain air of jauntiness and certainty.

'Hello, Simeon. Nice morning, eh?'

'Very nice.' He paused, then said with studied evenness, 'Oh, Max, don't take Crusader out again, if you don't mind.'

Max flushed. 'Who said that I'd taken him out?'

'Mallet, when I asked who'd let him down.'

'Let him down! The brute let me down! I only took him out because he was getting out of condition through never getting sufficient exercise. The brute's as fat as a pig!'

'Mallet can exercise him——'

'Mallet's no horseman!'

'He's never let Crusader down, anyway!'

Max stared at his cousin, his dark eyes, in such startling contrast to his fair hair, were narrowed and very cold ; their gaze made Simeon feel vaguely uncomfortable.

'Very well, it's no particular pleasure to me to ride your wretched nag. You're getting into your stride very quickly, aren't you?'

'Stride?' Simeon asked. 'What—stride?'

'Walking about surveying the ancestral home. I was watching you just now. Playing the part of the young heir!' Max laughed. 'It's amusing.'

Again Simeon felt confused, clumsy and at a disadvantage.

He stammered a little when he answered, 'Don't talk—well, such rot. I wasn't thinking about—about being the heir. Good Lord!'

Max continued to watch him closely, his lips curved a little.

'That's just as well, isn't it?' he said.

'What's—just as well?' He was growing heated, he felt that he was arguing like a schoolboy, that Max was contemptuous of his inability to score verbally.

'You—really—don't know?' Max asked. 'Honestly?'

'Know—what? I don't know what you're talking about. Come on, Max, what are you trying to hint? Let me hear!'

Max traced a pattern in the gravel with the toe of his shoe, his eyes following the design intently ; suddenly he looked up. His face was less hard, he frowned as if something puzzled him.

For a moment he did not speak, then burst out, 'By Jove, I think that's a damned shame! You mean to say that—honestly —you don't know?'

'I've not the remotest idea what you're talking about.'

'You really believe that one day you'll have Ordingly?'

'I suppose so—I've never thought about it. Grandfather used to ask me if I was fond of the place—I never actually thought of it belonging to me. Now, it belongs to my father and——'

'That doesn't say it will ever belong to you, my boy. Look here, we're not particular friends, but I do feel they're playing you a dirty trick. That's the family all over. This God of Respectability they all worship! They're all full of it—no, I make two exceptions, my father and myself. But Uncle Emmanuel, Uncle Bill—the precious Wilmots and Heriots, Grandfather and Grandmother—it makes me sick! Everything, everybody must be sacrificed to their beloved Family, and its damned tradition. They don't care who suffers, what rows are involved, so long as the world looks at them and says what splendid upright people they are! They're not, you know! Never heard of the scandal about old Emmanuel's wife— Juliana? Phew! Or Grandfather's brother's son, Frank, who married Morrie Stansfield? Oh, there's a very pretty crop of stories about them all! Never heard of . . .' He paused. 'A man called Leon Hast? A collector, a millionaire?'

Simeon came nearer, his face had lost its colour, he shifted his weight on to his good foot; his breath was coming faster, his eyes shone bright and very hard.

'Look here,' he said, 'I don't like you, I never have liked you, right back to the days when you made fun of me because I didn't understand about English schools, and had been to a day school in Milano. Yes, it's rankled all these years. Now, let's hear what all this is about. How am I being deceived, who is deceiving me, and why is there all this rigmarole about the family and its love of respectability? I want to know, and, by God, I'm going to know!'

Max shrugged his shoulders. 'For Heaven's sake don't bawl like that! No, why should I tell you anything? The trouble with you is that you have too good an opinion of yourself. You're like your father! Uncle Emmanuel was well out of favour until he came crawling back and ousted my father. Neither my father nor I will ever forgive him for that. No, I'm not going to tell you anything. Go and find out for yourself.'

Simeon's arm shot out, and he caught Max's shoulder in the grip of his strong fingers. 'You will tell me,' he said, 'you will tell me; you've said too much and not quite enough. Out with it

166

—or I'll thrash you until you do! Why shan't I ever have Ordingly?'

His grip tightened, he shook his cousin backwards and forwards. Max bared his teeth, snarling; his eyes were like cold agate. Simeon could almost feel the hate which shone in them.

He repeated, 'Come on—out with it!'

Max shook himself free. 'Because,' he said, 'you're a bastard! They're trying to cover it up as long as they can. Your father never married this Forbes woman—who'd been Hast's mistress. —Viva Heriot divorced your father, and all your father did was to live with this singing trollop——'

Simeon struck him on the side of the face, whispering, 'I'll kill you for that! I'll kill you——'

Max struck back, and for three minutes the two young men fought there on the neatly raked path where for years there had existed only dignity and quiet. Simeon kept repeating, 'Take that back—d'you hear, take it back!' while Max reiterated what he had said, varying his statements with epithets which drove Simeon to fresh guests of fury.

It was Hannah Rosenfeldt who found them; she had come down with letters for Emmanuel, and, finding him in the middle of a conversation with Bill, had wandered out into the garden. Her thickset, clumsy figure came round the corner of the house, and her eyes were greeted with the sight of the two young men fighting with an intensity which held something grim about it. Simeon was fighting less wildly than his cousin; indeed, it seemed to Hannah that he delivered his blows with a coolness and precision which were particularly relentless.

Both their faces were streaming with blood, and from where she stood she could hear their heavy breathing.

She walked forward, and when within a few yards of them said, 'W'at is t'is, and your grendfat'er scarcely out of the house? Is this decent behaviour, to fight like wild dogs? *Mesbuggab,* is this what you are? Stop immediately, I tell you. Simeon—I speak! Now!'

Through his teeth, Simeon said, 'Go away, Hannah, go away.'

'If I go, it will be to br-ring your father. Hes he not enough to bear? Listen, I tell you, listen!' Her voice rose, and Max drove his fist against his cousin's throat. 'Your grandmother ill, a house where there is mourning. Shame on you both!'

Simeon gathered all his strength together, he led with his left and followed it up with a heavy blow from his right. Max swung on his heels, and fell on to the smooth turf. Simeon wiped his bleeding nose with the back of his hand, and turned to stare at Hannah.

She repeated, 'Simeon, shame on you! Help him up. What is all this about, tell me?'

Simeon shook his head as if to clear his eyes, then leaning down, seized Max's hand and dragged him into a sitting position. Leaning down, he said very distinctly, 'Now get up, and never let me catch you riding Crusader again, or I'll give you twice what I've given you this morning. And remember—keep your mouth shut, damn you—or I'll shut it for you! Get that?'

Hannah stared at Max as he scrambled to his feet. 'You've knocked out a couple of my teeth, you swine,' he said.

'I'll knock your bloody head off,' Simeon returned, 'if I hear another word from you. Get out of my sight, you damned scum!'

Max walked away, a handkerchief held to his face. Hannah watched him go.

'And because you find that he has ridden your horse, you behave in this way? I thought better of you, Simeon. To behave so in a house of mourning, over who rides a horse! I am filled with shame for you.'

Simeon, assiduously dabbing his cut lip and bleeding nose, muttered, 'All right, Hannah. Only I wanted to give him a lesson. He can have another whenever he needs one.'

She repeated, 'Oi, oi, oi—for a horse! Such a thing!'

He slipped his arm through hers. 'Look here, darling, leave this alone. It's something between Max and me, something that's going to be settled, and if it's settled—then, by Jove, he'll get another hiding! He's a liar and a dirty liar. Only just say nothing about it.'

She made a sound of protest. 'Tch, tch—say nothing about it! Will no one esk why your nose is like a cauliflower, why one eye is closed, why Max has lost a tooth——'

Simeon said, 'Two teeth, I fancy.'

'Say nothing! You imagine all people are blind! A fight for a horse! Such a yen!'

Simeon did not see Emmanuel, he met Bill Gollantz in the hall as he came down from his bedroom where he had repaired as much of the damage to his face as was possible. Bill stopped and stared.

'Hello, Simeon, been having an argument with the bedpost?'

'Something like that, Uncle Bill. Will you tell my father that I've gone up to the Galleries? If he wants anything, ask if he'll telephone to me. Can I give you a lift?'

Bill said, 'Well, I dunno. I'm nervous of driving with a chap

168

who looks like the heavyweight champion after a twenty-round fight. What's it been about?'

'Little argument about a—horse.'

'Umph! In my day it used to be about a woman. Times change. Still, make out your story and stick to it. I'll tell your father, and then we'll drive up together. Given another half hour, that eye should be a beauty. Good thing you're not dining out.'

Together they drove up to town, neither spoke, and Simeon could feel his bruised face rapidly stiffening. His mind kept going over and over what Max had said. 'You're a bastard' . . . 'to live with this singing trollop'. Ordingly would never be his, he had no right to it. He was a bastard. He frowned, and to frown hurt at the moment. Ordingly didn't matter, perhaps it didn't really matter a great deal if he were a bastard, but—what did matter was that Emmanuel had never told him, never given him any warning, had left it to Max Gollantz to tell him. He was a modern young man, he had never held those rigid beliefs regarding 'respectability' which, he knew, had been his grandfather's. He knew sufficient of human nature to find sufficient reasons for deviations from what were the accepted conventional customs.

That his father had loved Juliet Forbes deeply and sincerely he did not doubt. It was impossible to have lived with Emmanuel Gollantz and not to have realized that his devotion to Juliet had been—and, indeed, still was—something very great and very beautiful.

Carefully, young Simeon, with his bruised face and rapidly closing right eye, tried to examine the whole affair, tried to put himself in the place of the chief actors, and to arrive at some conclusion.

His father, Max stated, had never been married to Juliet. Viva Heriot had divorced him—was that because she knew of his association with the singer? Once that divorce was absolute, why then had they not married? Why had he, Simeon, been allowed to call himself Gollantz, why had his grandfather asked him—with ill-suppressed anxiety—if he loved Ordingly? Was it because, had he had sufficient time, strength or courage, he felt it incumbent upon himself to say, 'But it can never be yours, Simeon. It will one day belong to Julian and his son'?

Somehow, that didn't seem to tally with his knowledge of Max Gollantz, Max Simeon realized, had regarded respectability, and believed it necessary to conform to the rules of the rather narrow society in which he moved—and was completely content to move.

Simeon sensed, rather than knew, that his grandfather had not, until very recently, been completely in accord with Emmanuel. How he knew that he could not have said, but he had always felt a sense of strain, a certain coldness . . . His mind hesitated, then found the word for which he sought—a certain wariness in their conversations, as if they both watched intently for 'danger signals'. This being so, and his grandfather presumably knowing that his son's son was a bastard, why had he overcome his dislike for irregularities to allow Simeon to come and go as he pleased to Ordingly, to be accepted there as Emmanuel's son?

Again he frowned, and again he felt the discomfort of doing so. Then—his mother, 'Hast's mistress'—who the devil was this Leon Hast? 'That singing trollop'—the description did not tally with the picture of her which stood in his bedroom. He might have understood the description being applied to Olympia Lara, even—although he knew that he would have resented it —to Iva Alfano, but to that beautiful woman with the serene expression, the mouth which seemed ready to break into a smile, and the wide-apart dark eyes—no, it didn't fit.

He remembered how Guido had spoken of her, how Gilbert had mentioned her name with a kind of gentle reverence, and how often he had seen something which amounted to physical pain on his father's sensitive face when her name was mentioned. No, he couldn't believe that the word used by Max Gollantz fitted his mother.

He sighed, and Bill, glancing at him, said, 'I don't know what's on your mind, young Simeon, but take my advice and—give it up.'

'Unfortunately, I can't, Uncle Bill.'

'Some problem, eh? Then if you know anyone who knows the answer, go and ask them. Don't sit there frowning and biting your lips. If you haven't got the answer, you won't get it that way, believe me.'

'I don't know quite who to go to—for the answer, Uncle Bill.'

Bill shrugged his shoulders. 'I'm a lawyer, you might try me.'

Simeon thought, 'Uncle Bill! He's cool, almost detached. He's bound to know—he and Uncle Charles handle all the family affairs. I daren't ask my father—it would hurt him too badly,' and with that thought came another, 'He's had his share of being hurt!'

He said, 'Are you in a desperate hurry? Could you come to Heber Square and let me talk to you? There'll be no one there,

170

except Martha and Rachel. Hannah's never back until late. I'd be grateful.'

Bill thought, 'Either it's debt or a girl. Poor chap. He's worried to death. Let's get it straightened out.' He said, 'Well, I think I can. Right—Heber Square!'

As Simeon followed his uncle into the narrow hall and from there into the small sitting-room, he was struck with the pleasant impression of solidity which emanated from Bill's broad shoulders and thickset figure. He had none of the elegance of either Emmanuel or Julian, but there was complete reliance, an obvious ability to stand firmly on his own feet, which he seemed to radiate. The thought gave Simeon considerable comfort ; from Bill he would get no carefully tempered replies. Bill would give him the truth—however blunt and apparently brutal it might be.

Bill sat down heavily, and began to fill his pipe. The very ordinary action seemed suddenly to clarify everything in Simeon's mind. He stood there, watching Bill pressing down the tobacco with a rather thick finger, unmoved and immovable, displaying neither interest nor curiosity, immersed in the competent filling of his pipe.

That was the way to take everything, not to be caught in whirlpools of sentiment and fury, not to resent what might have happened years ago, but to face life as it came. All his life he had loved his father, given him admiration and devotion—very well, Emmanuel was the same person. He had trusted him for over twenty years, what right had he to doubt him now? If this thing were true, then doubtless his father could give him an explanation if one were needed.

He said, 'Uncle Bill, I believe that this is something I ought to discuss with my father. I don't believe that it's quite fair to talk it over with you.'

Bill, lighting his pipe with elaborate care said, 'Just as you like. Can I have some coffee? Is it a girl?'

'Good Lord, no!'

'Debts?'

'Nothing like that, it's more personal.'

Bill, his pipe burning to his satisfaction, said, 'Just order that coffee, will you? No, don't ring—shout! The house isn't so big as all that!' When Simeon returned, he said, 'This is something to do with the scrap you had this morning, eh? With Max—umph, I thought so. Now come on, let's hear all about it. Listen, Simeon. I know my brother Emmanuel, even better than you do. I don't tell people this, it sounds damn' silly, but he's been my hero since I was a small kid. He's all the things that I

171

should like to have been—good-looking, possessing infinite charm, brilliantly clever at his own job, and—what's he got out of it all? I'll tell you—blasted little! As a boy he was always preoccupied about our mother—he always adored her—he was rather a "worried" small boy. Then our charming brother Julian dragged him into some sticky mess, and slid out leaving Emmanuel to "hold the baby".'

Simeon asked, 'Don't you like Uncle Julian much?'

Bill stared at him blankly. 'Like him! He's a horrible feller.'

Simeon said, 'Go on, Uncle Bill.'

'Of course, this is all tiled in, Simeon. Not for outside consumption. Give me another cup of this coffee—whew, it's good! So Emmanuel went away, cleared out, because he didn't want his mother to be worried. What happened out there I don't know, except that he worked like stink. He came back and married Viva Heriot——'

'Mrs. Tatten?'

'Mrs. Tatten. That was all right, I don't say they were wildly happy, but they trotted along all right—until . . .' He looked up and frowned. 'This is the difficult part, Simeon. I've told you so much because I want you to understand that Emmanuel's had about as much as he can take. If there's any bother—bring it to me, don't go to him. He'll shoulder it, as he's shouldered most things, but—well, let's conspire to give him a break if we can.'

Simeon nodded. 'Uncle Bill—would you go on about my father? When he was married to Viva—what happened?' His face was pale where the bruises had not tinged it with scarlet and purple patches, his voice sounded tight and constrained.

'It's difficult. Juliet Forbes came to England . . . your mother . . .'

'She wasn't my mother then?' Simeon sounded suddenly breathless.

'Good Lord, no! Emmanuel had been in love with her for years—I've an idea that he fell in love when he was about eighteen. Well, the long and the short of it was that he and Viva talked it over. He left—no, not to go to Juliet, just to get away. Finally Viva fell for Toby Tatten and asked Emmanuel to let her divorce him. He did—he *would*!'

'Was—was my mother in the case?'

Bill stared at him coldly. 'I never heard so. Why on earth should she be? Anyway, it's no business of yours or mine if she were.'

'If Emmanuel—if my father—was so much in love with

172

her . . .' Simeon's words came more slowly, 'why—didn't he —marry her?'

For the first time Bill Gollantz sat stiffly upright and stared at his nephew; his face—always carrying a high colour—changed to a heavy red, even his eyes became slightly bloodshot; he scowled.

'Have you gone mad,' he asked, 'or are you modelling yourself on your poisonous uncle—Julian? What the devil do you mean by asking a question like that? Why didn't he marry her? What the hell are you saying? Of course he married her! Married her just as soon as she'd marry him—she had scruples, thought that because she was a little older than he was, because —oh, damn it, nothing that mattered a damn, that was Juliet all over. Too scrupulous for this world, bless her. Marry her! My lad, never let me hear you ask a question like that again; if Emmanuel heard you—even though you are his son, I believe that he'd kill you.'

'And I was born . . . ?'

Bill sprang to his feet. 'You were born—well, in the regulation time, and even if you hadn't been you'd have every reason to go down on your knees and thank God that you had such a father and mother! Great God, what do you think you are? Emmanuel's bastard? A by-blow? Who's been putting these damned ideas into your head? Come on, out with it!' He dragged out a handkerchief and wiped his forehead.

Simeon said, 'I've been told that I was a bastard—this morning.'

'Ah! Now we've got to the milk in the coconut. That's the meaning of your swollen nose and decorative eye, is it? And who said that?'

'That's my business, Uncle Bill. I'm sorry that I've made you angry, and thank you very sincerely. I wanted to—be certain, that's all. Thank you again.'

There was a dignity about the young man, with his puffed and swollen face, his quiet voice, and his self-control which made Bill Gollantz watch him with a certain approval. He lowered himself back into his arm-chair and, still wiping his face, said:

'Get me a drink, Simeon. Not the old brandy, with a thimbleful in a tulip glass. Get me a whisky-and-soda and make it strong. I need it. Then come and sit down and listen to me. I'll give you chapter and verse. Thank you.' He drank deeply, and set down his glass. 'Your father and mother were married in Milan before the British Consul. I fancy in some English church as well—of that I'm not quite certain. In my office

173

I have the papers relating to the ceremony. In future refer anyone to me, if you please, and for Heaven's sake never let Emmanuel know of this conversation. Your mother died in Milan a year after they were married—Emmanuel brought you up, and a very decent job he made of it.'

'Thank you, Uncle Bill. One more question, please—who was Leon Hast?'

'Hast, Leon Hast,' Bill repeated, 'a very noted collector, a patron of the arts, a connoisseur. He was at one time engaged to Morrie Stansfield, who was a cousin of my mother's—second cousin. She was killed in a motor accident—with Hast. Years and years ago.' With a return to his old irritable manner, he continued, 'If anyone is trying to couple Juliet's name with Hast's—refer them to me. If I were you, young feller, I should walk very carefully when you begin to ask questions which might possibly have answers apparently reflecting against your mother. There are a good many people who are apt to take umbrage at that kind of insinuation—I'm one, old Bill Masters another, Charles Wilmot and Gilbert. I'll only tell you that when Hast was broken to bits in this accident—blind, paralysed —Juliet was very good to him; probably the only person in the world, except Bill Masters, who would have stood by him. What are you going to do about this—person—who called you a bastard?'

For the first time Simeon smiled. 'I've knocked out two of his teeth—that is the first instalment. The rest—oh, I'll pay off the score—give me time.'

CHAPTER FIVE

SIMEON GOLLANTZ was not a particularly imaginative young man. He had a good brain, which he used to advantage, but he was not given to indulging in great flights of fancy. His uncle's conversation had impressed him deeply. When Bill had suddenly shown his indignation at the suggestion that Emmanuel had never married Juliet Forbes, Simeon had experienced a distinct thrill. Bill, to him, was a fine, rather stolid person, and to see him shaken out of his usual equanimity by the mere suggestion that Emmanuel had not married Juliet, and that in consequence Simeon was a bastard, proved to the young man the very high regard in which Bill held both his brother and his brother's dead wife.

In his own room Simeon went over the events of the day. He could remember the tones of Max's voice, could visualize his rather pale, but eminently good-looking face, its expression of surprise, which in its turn changed to restrained indignation. He could feel again his own anger rising, not—he admitted—primarily because it seemed to him such a terrible matter to have been born out of wedlock, but because the assertion was made, implying that it was shameful, that Emmanuel had hidden something from his son because he himself was ashamed.

Simeon had been brought up in an atmosphere where Emmanuel was regarded as someone who was slightly removed from other men ; as someone who was fashioned out of finer clay and was incapable of any action which was not completely just and upright. His mother—that woman of whom he had made a mental picture of all that was beautiful and kind—had been to him someone of almost incredible beauty and fineness, and to watch Max's face when he referred to her had been like a blow in the face.

Now, when Bill had talked to him with considerable frankness concerning both Emmanuel and Juliet Forbes, Simeon was filled with new fury against Max. In addition he felt consumed by a determination to prove to Max that his lies were dis-

175

credited, and that due punishment should come to him for the allegations which he had made.

His state of mind, as he sat in his bedroom, his long legs outstretched, his eyes half-closed, was far from Christian. He clenched his hands, the eyes beneath their half-closed lids were very cold and hard. Once he raised his hand and felt his bruised and discoloured eye tenderly. He was a young man who took a reasonable pride in his appearance, and the thought of arriving in Bond Street in the morning with a black eye annoyed him very much indeed. Someone would pay for that black eye!

He was just thinking that he might go to bed when Hannah telephoned that he was wanted on the telephone downstairs to speak to his father. Emmanuel had insisted on a system of house telephones; he disliked bells, disliked the ringing of them, and so each room had its telephone installed.

'Right, Hannah, I'm coming,' Simeon answered.

Downstairs, on taking the receiver, he heard his father's voice.

'Simeon—that you?'

'Yes, Father.'

'I don't know whether I shall be at the Gallery in the morning. Your grandmother is better, stronger, but I feel that it might be well if I r-remained here to-morr-row. I have word from Marcus Arbuthnot that he wishes to see me. Please go in my place. I have no idea what he wants, but whatever it is— handle the matter with care, and if possible'—Simeon heard his father's quiet laugh—'give him rather more courtesy than is usual. He is an old fr-riend not only of mine, but of my father's and my gr-randfather's. I can leave it to you, eh?'

'Of course. I'll telephone for an appointment in the morning.'

'R-right. Good night, Simeon.'

As Simeon hung up the receiver Hannah appeared and came nearer. Her rather sallow, heavy face seemed to Simeon to have acquired new lines during the past few days; her eyes looked heavy as if she had not slept; her movements were slow, ponderous.

She asked, 'Is everything all right?'

'Yes, my grandmother is better, but my father thinks that he had better stay at Ordingly for another day.'

She nodded approval. 'Always such a boy for his mother! Never will you know the devotion which he has given to her. Bill has always been good, but he is not capable of giving love as Emmanuel gives it. And Julian . . .' She spread her hands wide and shrugged her massive shoulders. 'This one!'

176

Simeon said impulsively, 'Hannah, it's not awfully late. We couldn't have a cup of tea together, could we?'

'Tea! Never have I known the time when I could not drink tea! What is time? Are we slaves to pieces of machinery called clocks? Many may be, I am not! Come to my room and we will drink a cup'; she chuckled, 'perhaps more than one cup, eh?'

Simeon followed her to her sitting-room; he had always thought it quite the ugliest room he had ever seen. How Hannah Rosenfeldt, who had lived among beautiful things all her life, who knew the value of fine furniture, china, pictures and glass, could tolerate this hideous room he had never understood. The floor was completely covered with a thick Turkey carpet in red and blue, the furniture was heavy and dark—a darkness, Simeon felt, obtained by an application of varnish rather than the passage of time. The walls were almost completely covered with pictures, among them standing out by their sheer merit were the two Brughels given to her by old Emmanuel Gollantz. Lovely in their colouring and in their beauty of design. One of Simeon's earliest memories was of when his father had first brought him to England, and he had been taken to tea with Hannah Rosenfeldt.

She had pointed to them and said, 'Look, presents to me from your grandfather—the first Emmanuel Gollantz. They are Brughels . . . "Blue Velvet" Brughels! The rest—the Family!'

He remembered how his father had laughed and said, 'Hannah's Rogues' Gallery!'

She had replied, 'To speak of a Rogues' Gallery implies the existence of more than one rogue! The Family only possesses one!'

Emmanuel had laughed, but said, 'Now—Hannah, my dear, now!'

While she busied herself with making tea, which for Hannah was a long and formal ritual, Simeon wandered round the room, looking at the photographs and pictures. There was a copy of the portrait by Sargent of old Emmanuel. There he sat, his fine hands resting on the ivory knob of his stick, his elaborate black stock rising high, above it a narrow line of white linen; the stock was held by his famous black pearl pin. His handsome, arrogant face was tilted a little backwards, as if he stood at a height greater than that of ordinary men, and so was forced to tilt his head to get the right line of vision. Still staring at the portrait, Simeon asked:

'Is my father like him, Hannah?'

177

She continued to make her elaborate preparations.

'Umpa! Sufficiently. In looks, very much, in character—no. The old Emmanuel was kind with a hard core; Emmanuel lacks that hard core. Emmanuel—your grandfather—found reasons for men's failings; Emmanuel—your father—finds excuses!'

Simeon moved on. There was his grandmother in her presentation dress; his grandfather Max wearing Windsor uniform; there was Bill—even then stocky and undistinguished—dressed in khaki, taken as a boy in his school O.T.C. He found a picture of his father wearing the uniform of a private soldier, another wearing an officer's tunic; there were numbers of himself taken at various ages. A grave little boy wearing clothes which might conceivably have been English, but did not seem to be completely so. A large picture of his mother, lovely, serene and smiling a little.

'Hannah, was my mother very beautiful?' he asked.

She replied, 'That picture is exactly like her. You've got eyes!'

'She looks marvellous.'

'That's not surprising—she was.'

'You've got pictures of all the family—except my uncle Julian.'

She turned towards him swiftly. 'I need no picture of this one. I carry one in my mind—always! Come and have your tea, please.'

He sat down and stirred his tea. 'You don't like him?'

She shrugged. 'I know him—this one!'

'Tell me.'

'Not yet. Sufficient to say that always I am watching. One day I shall find what I am looking for! One day I shall have a great deal to tell you, Simeon. But it is not time—yet.'

He said, 'My father wishes me to go to see Arbuthnot in the morning.'

Hannah sat suddenly upright. Simeon thought that her eyes held both expectancy, curiosity and—fear. She said, 'Ah, Arbuthnot, eh?'

'Yes, he told me to be very . . .' he laughed, 'very civil.'

'Do you know what he wants?'

'Not a clue, neither has my father.'

'Then be very careful, do not commit yourself in any way. I wish that your father could have been with you. Ah! well—we shall see.'

Simeon sat watching her as he drank his tea; this queer, elderly, completely shapeless woman with a devotion to his family, and without conceit, he believed to himself, which was completely selfless and unquestioning. It was as though, he thought, in her early youth she had been taken into their service, and that for the rest of her life she would regard them as her liege lords, to whom she owed obedience and service.

Not that there was anything in the least servile in her attitude towards them; in all her life she had never fawned nor cringed to any of them. She had accepted such confidences as they offered to her, had locked their private affairs and their secrets in her heart, never to divulge them to a living soul.

It would have been so easy, Simeon reflected, for Hannah to have asserted herself, to have assumed an attitude which demanded the acceptance of her value and loyalty. She had asked for nothing. She had been perfectly content to work—honestly and with meticulous care—for many years. She had fallen in with Emmanuel's wishes that she should take care of his son while he was in the Army without protestations, without any sign of regret for the house at Northwood of which she had once been so proud. Here in Heber Square she lived her life with them, but never intruded. Her two rooms were her own, she valued the sense of privacy which they gave her; when Emmanuel asked her to come and talk to him she came as a guest—glad of his hospitality, but conscious that she was giving him the benefit of her ideas, her conversation and her knowledge.

The running of the house was left entirely to her; both Martha and old Rachel were obedient to her wishes and orders. She never asserted her authority, never inferred that she was of a higher social position than they, but their respect for her was complete.

Simeon knew that old Rachel was 'frome', that she kept her fasts and feasts, that she never allowed her own food to be mixed with that of his father's and his own, yet—miraculously —there was no friction.

Hannah's own religious beliefs were unknown to him. There were certain days when she did not appear at the Gallery; apparently she had some understanding regarding these absences with his father, but he had never heard them discussed.

He realized that she knew everything concerning his family, and that she had rejoiced, suffered, and been happy with them. It was as if she had sunk her whole life in them, and that this fact contented her.

Now, unexpectedly, she looked at him with her queer agate-coloured eyes, with their heavy lids, wrinkles and puffiness beneath them, and said, 'Tomorrow you must tread very carefully. I know Arbuthnot—he was born Abrahams but he is a good man—he is very smart, very knowledgeable. He is good

179

enough, honest, and he will expect honesty from you. You have had various things to do for the firm, you've done them well. I have a feeling that tomorrow is an important day. Now go to bed. The young need plenty of sleep. God bless you.'

Marcus Arbuthnot nodded. 'Very well. Show him in here.'

He was an old man and tired; he hated to remember that he was growing old, that his figure on which he had lavished such care was getting flabby—and flabby in the wrong places too. After his bath he would look at himself in the long mirror, and wrinkle his nose with disgust at the muscles which had become slack, at the skin which seemed to have grown too big for the bones which it covered.

Then he would submit himself to the ministrations of his valet; be massaged and rubbed with harsh gloves to improve the circulation, and then sit down enveloped in a huge towel to be shaved. He knew that he winced a little as the narrow shoes were pushed on to his feet; he knew that his collar was too high, that it hurt his wrinkled neck, that he would have liked to wear easy, loose-fitting clothes and well-worn shoes. But he also remembered that he was still Marcus Arbuthnot who in the 'nineties — 'The Gay 'Nineties' — had been one of the best-dressed men in Town; he would continue to hold that title!

Now, seated at his desk, perfectly shaved, his linen very glossy, and his clothes beautifully brushed and pressed, he looked like some outmoded figure, carefully preserved but growing brittle and lacking any ease of movement. He caressed his lean jaw with long, thin, perfectly manicured fingers.

Simeon entered, and Arbuthnot looked at him with interest. The grandson of old Emmanuel, the son of Emmanuel the younger. A nice-looking boy, good eyes, well turned out. His collar might be soft, but it was well laundered and his tie was tied very well. His voice was pleasant, well modulated. Arbuthnot, who was growing a little deaf, liked clear voices with a distint enunciation.

'I bring the regrets of my father, sir,' Simeon said. 'He is detained at Ordingly, my grandmother has been very ill—the shock of my grandfather's death was very great. My father thought it better that he should remain with her for another day. He hopes that you will understand and forgive him.'

Arbuthnot nodded. 'Sit down, my deah boy. Very sad business. I've known Max Gollantz for morah years then I care to count. Great shock to me. Yer father's quite right. Always had a great devotion to yer grandmother. Why not, eh? Charmin' woman, charmin'. But . . .' He paused and again caressed his jaw. 'I dunno if you can be of much use in this mattah. Know anything about chinah, eh?'

'I'm just beginning to learn, sir.'

'Silvah?'

'There again, I am just learning.'

Arbuthnot chuckled, 'If yer wise you'll go on learning all yer life. I've been in this game for years. I still make mistakes. Well, it's a very true sayin' that the man who never makes mistakes never makes anything, eh? Now, touching the mattah of this silvah. Can you tell me the Irish markings for the time immediately before—before—the Commonwealth?'

Simeon frowned, thought for a moment, then said, 'The date 1638, for example. Crowned harp, decorated "A" set in an arabesque.'

The old man nodded, ejaculating, 'Ah! And now—the Commonwealth?'

Again the young man frowned, then answered, 'Date about 1658. . . . Harp in greater detail, with the crown slightly detached. The "A" in Arabic form, in an undecorated shield.' He laughed. 'I hope that I'm right, sir!'

'Specializing in silvah?'

'No, that's my Uncle Julian's side.'

'Ah! And chinah?'

'I buy a little, sir. But that, too, is his province.'

'Um! Well, my deah boy, I think that I must see yer fathah. I'm pleased with yer. You'll do! Carah for a glass of sherry and a biscuit, eh? Ring that bell, will yer?'

Later Simeon returned to the Gallery and went into the little office where Hannah worked.

She looked up and asked abruptly, 'Well?'

Simeon shook his head. 'Upon my word I don't know. He asked me about silver marks on Irish silver. I managed to give them. Then he said that he was afraid that he must see my father. Hannah, he's a quaint old boy, isn't he? Gave me a glass of very good sherry and a dry biscuit. He's like something—historical, isn't he?'

She nodded. 'That's exactly what he is. Silver marks, eh? What silver marks, if you please?'

'Pretty old, rare pieces they'd be, I imagine. Cromwellian and earlier. Does he specialize in that stuff?'

She did not reply, but repeated, 'Cromwellian—and earlier, eh? Now, get along, I have work to do.'

Later in the day Hannah Rosenfeldt walked through the Gallery and stopped to speak to one of the young salesmen.

'Have we got any Irish silver at the moment? I'd like to see it.'

'Sorry, Miss Rosenfeldt, you're too late. We had about a week ago. Very good too, I believe. At first Mr. Julian believed that it was 1717, but later he discovered that it was much earlier. Cromwellian, in fact. It sold immediately to a Mr. Lloyd Ferrers. He's clever, Mr. Julian, isn't he?'

Hannah nodded. 'I'd like to have seen it. Never mind.'

The young man was delighted to show off his knowledge; he began to talk rapidly and eagerly. 'Miss Rosenfeldt, I believe that he's got another marvellous piece. Birmingham—1779—with the duplicated king's heads. I've not seen it, but I heard a whisper about it. Marvellous, isn't it?'

She nodded, her heavy face impassive. 'Some people have a flair for finding good pieces.'

That evening Hannah Rosenfeldt made her way by bus and tube to the house of her friends, the Salamans, who lived in Hampstead. They were people with a deep love of music, and from time to time held small parties at which music was the entertainment offered. On this particular evening a violin, cello, viola and piano played the music of Mozart. Hannah listened rapt and entranced. She had arrived at the Salamans with her mind in a turmoil, her brain felt tired and incapable of working properly. They greeted her very warmly, for not only was her knowledge of music profound, but she had been generous to many struggling musicians who had suffered in Europe owing to their Jewish nationality.

She sat there listening to the music which she loved, her heavy face growing more and more tranquil; her eyes half-closed, her whole figure relaxed. The lovely sounds seemed to envelop her, and when the musicians came to the close of the work which they had played she smiled.

The violinist, a little dark-eyed man with a tired, lined face, said, 'Tell us, Miss Rosenfeldt, what amuses you?'

She opened her eyes wider, the smile still touched her lips.

'I could not help thinking what fools we are to concern ourselves about trifles when there is still—Mozart. Please play once more, and I shall go home practically cured.'

Mrs. Salamans asked, 'Cured, Hannah? Cured of what, please?'

'Allowing myself to grow too egoistic, Rachel. Imagining that I am really a rather important and very intelligent person. Now—please, music!'

She took a bus as far as Oxford Street, then descending, walked slowly down Bond Street. She loved London at night,

182

when the lights were reflected on the damp pavements, when the streets—so full of noise and movement during the day—became silent and still.

It gave her a thrill of pleasure to pass the Gollantz Gallery and remember the treasures which lay behind those well-barred windows, that locked metal gate. She even crossed the road, so that she might let her eyes travel over the whole building, the wide windows, the closed entrance, and the small steel door through which old Emmanuel had always entered the building. It was never opened now ; young Emmanuel, Julian and the rest of the staff entered by the main entrance. Hannah stood watching, allowing her mind to indulge in fancies and memories. How often had Emmanuel stopped at the door of her office and said, 'Hannah, eet is time—und past time—for you to vork. Kom, I shall send you avay t'rough my leetle door.'

She remembered the glint of his gold chain as he drew out the small intricate keys, and inserted one in the lock, saying 'So! Von key—now here is his brudder key—and lastly—the smallest of all, a verry Benjamin among keys!' as he turned the three separate locks. Who had that set of keys now? she wondered. She had one set, locked carefully away among her most private treasures. The old man had given them to her many years ago, saying, 'Now, I am going to giff you the Freedom of the City—my leetle city in Bond Street!' He had weighed them in his hand, smiling as he did so.

'Such small 'tings, eh? But important. That is vhy I giff them to you, to prrove my complete trust and faith. They veel be useful if at any time it might be necessary for you to vork late. Only,' he chuckled, 'you must make friends mit the policeman, or maybe he'll arr-rest you for burgling my prroperty.'

As she stood watching, her mind filled with memories, she saw the little door swing open and a man emerge from the darkness of the long corridor into the street. For a moment she blinked her eyes, almost convinced that her recollections were so vivid that she was imagining that she saw old Emmanuel. Then, craning her neck, and staring out from the shadow in which she stood, she saw that the man was young and slim, tall, and wearing a long, light overcoat. He carried a parcel under his arm, glanced right and left, then without haste slipped away, keeping in the shadows of the houses.

In considerable agitation, she hesitated as to what she should do. Slowly down Bond Street came a police constable. Hannah went forward quickly to meet him, saying, 'Constable—quick —that man, look—walking in the shadow by Finnigan's—he's just come out of Gollantz Gallery! Through the little side door. He's carrying a parcel!'

The constable looked down from his superior height at the stout elderly woman. 'That's correct, madam. He's got every right to go in and out if he wishes. We know all about it. That's Mr. Julian Gollantz ; comes back for some special work or other.'

Hannah, suddenly shaken, exclaimed, 'Julian!'

The policeman laughed, 'Bit familiar, aren't you, madam! Very well-known family. I heard that their father was just dead.'

She nodded. 'Well, good night.'

She walked on, into Piccadilly, and turned towards Knightsbridge. A few moments before she had absorbed in her thoughts of a man she had loved and admired ; now those thoughts were centred on the one member of the Gollantz family she had always distrusted and for whom she had felt not a mere dislike but a deep and constant loathing. She forgot the lateness of the hour, the fact that she was tired, and trudged on past the Park, taking no notice of anything, completely absorbed.

Mechanically she turned from the high road into the quiet and completely silent streets which Emmanuel always said were like a backwater. Automatically she stopped before the house which was her home. Heber Square was very still, in the distance she heard the hooting of a taxi-cab, somewhere a dog barked—a high, nervous sound—a cat slipped past her intent on its own business. She mounted the wide stone steps, and taking out her key, opened the door. The little hall was lit brightly, she remembered that Emmanuel disliked dim lighting. As the thought came to her, the door of the sitting-room opened, and Emmanuel stood, his figure looking, to Hannah's excited imagination, immensely tall and dignified.

'Hannah! I had almost given you up! I can tell by the look on your face that you have been listening to music. Come in, and talk to me for ten minutes before—like r-respectable people— we go to bed.'

Her voice sounded strange in her own ears as she answered, 'I thought that you were staying at Ordingly.'

'I was, but my mother—thank God—is so much better. To-night before dinner we sat and talked of many things, many people. Then because Simeon had telephoned that Arbuthnot wished to see me urgently, and because she was so much better, I decided to come back here. I have spoken to her on the telephone, she is r-resting, very tr-ranquil.' He took her hand and led her into the little sitting-room. 'What a br-rave woman she

184

is, my beloved mother. Hannah, it would seem that as the years pass we grow closer. That all those small—what shall I call them?—misunderstandings which once came between us, disappear one by one. Now, sit down and let me give you a drink.'

She sat down heavily, and placed her hands on her knees.

'Was Julian at Ordingly?'

Without turning as he poured out the drinks, Emmanuel said, 'No—you know his str-range fear of death; he has his own small flat in Town, and it was obvious that he was gr-reatly relieved to get away from Ordingly. There, Hannah, drink that. You're tired—music always tires me, emotionally.'

She nodded. 'Yes, I am tired—emotionally.' Then abruptly she asked, 'Emmanuel, what happened to the keys of the little steel private door at the Gallery? The one your grandfather used——'

'The little steel door?' he said. 'I had almost forgotten its existence. As for the keys—I have no idea. Pr-robably they are somewhere at Ordingly. Possibly my mother might r-remember. Why?'

'I only wondered. Emmanuel, be very prudent when you have this conversation with Arbuthnot.'

He shot a quick glance in her direction. 'What do you mean? Do you know something?'

'I know nothing.'

'Suspect something, then?'

She did not reply, but setting down her empty glass, said, 'Good night, sleep well.'

Marcus Arbuthnot stretched his thin neck to ease it in its high collar. His secretary, watching him, thought that he looked even paler and more desiccated than ever on this bright morning. He said, 'Colonel Grahame is calling to see me at 10. Gollantz will be here at 10.15. While either of them are with me I do not wish to be disturbed. If I need you, my deah, I will ring through to your office. Is the sherry therah? And the biscuits? The last lot were, I thought, a trifle soft. I detest soft biscuits. Will you be so good as to see about them? Thank you.'

She stood watching him, her expression affectionate. She had been his secretary for so many years that she had come to take a kind of pride in his small affectations of speech and dress. She knew that physically he was failing, only his brain was as alert and clear as ever.

'There is some '75 cognac,' she said; 'you know that it is better for you than sherry. Shall I put that out?'

He nodded; it was evident that he was scarcely listening to her.

'Yes, yes—why not. certainly.'

Five minutes later Colonel Carey Grahame was admitted. A tall, thin man, with a scarlet face and small angry blue eyes. He barked his words rather than spoke them.

'Ha, Arbuthnot! Good of you to see me. Obliged. Nasty business. Not only this affair of the Coleport, but my good friend Lloyd Ferrers has grave doubts concerning a piece of silver. Dublin. Sold as 1638. Nothing of the kind! 1658—in his opinion and mine. Oh, that's good enough, it's the fact that he was sold something which wasn't all it set out to be. You've always told me that these people were honest. Without wishing to be offensive, I can't say that it looks like it. Damn, I've not been collecting for years without knowing a defect when I see it. Cleverly done, I'll grant you. That's not the point. Repaired stuff is repaired stuff, look at it how you like!' He paused for want of breath, for the whole tirade had been delivered at great speed, and as he took the chair which Arbuthnot indicated he was panting a little.

Arbuthnot said, 'First, the Coleport. Sold to you as perfect?'

'With the exception of one small plate—yes.'

'And you found——'

'The teapot had been repaired.'

'Have you brought it with you?'

'Left it outside with your secretary. It's in a small case.'

'And the silver—oh, a salver, I see—the property of Mr. Lloyd Ferrers?'

'That is outside also. He'd have come with me, but the poor feller is crippled with arthritis.'

'Very sad. Well, shall we have these—er—exhibits in?' He rang and followed the ring with a telephone call; a moment later his secretary entered carrying two small cases. Arbuthnot rubbed his hands, they made a faint crackling sound, as if the skin were very dry. 'Now, shall we have Phillips in to open them?'

Grahame barked, 'Not necessary. Cases both hinged. Allow me.'

Arbuthnot took the teapot, and turned it in his white beringed hands. Then taking a magnifying-glass he examined the piece carefully. Grahame said, 'Found the repair, eh?'

The old man did not answer; he set down the teapot, and took up the salver, murmuring, 'A nice piece—ver-ry nice. Charmin', in fact Ah—herah we are! Yes, quite. Umpha!' He laid it down and sighed. 'Would you carah for a cup of tea, Colonel Grahame? I am addicted to tea at this hour. Yes, and surely, my deah, Emmanuel Gollantz is herah? I've nevah known him late, nevah.' He chuckled, 'If you please—Sir Emmanuel Gollantz and tea for three—four, if you will join us.' Emmanuel entered a moment later. Arbuthnot held out his hand, and murmured a greeting, then turning to Grahame, said, 'Colonel Grahame, Sir Emmanuel Gollantz. Now, Emmanuel, me deah feller, I want you to straighten out this unpleasant business. Coleport teapot, part of a service which with the exception——'

Emmanuel said, 'With the exception of one small plate and the spout of the teapot, was perfect. Am I right?'

Grahame exploded, 'Look at the spout of the damned thing!'

'I am doing so,' Emmanuel said very calmly, 'and I congratulate you on the admirable r-repair. It is beautifully done. May I borrow your glass, Mr. Arbuthnot, if you please? Yes—r-really beautifully done.'

Grahame almost shouted, 'Repair be damned, sir! Sold to me as a perfect piece! D'you hear that? A perfect piece with the exception of the plate! And you're Gollantz of Bond Street!'

'Tut, tut!' Arbuthnot reproved. 'If you please, Colonel Grahame.'

Emmanuel smiled. 'Most certainly I am Gollantz of Bond Street. If this was sold as perfect, then there must be some error—which I shall lose no time in correcting. I offer my sincere r-regrets. I beg that you will accept this set—this r-repaired set—with my apologies and compliments. Another set' —he spoke more slowly—'which shall be perfect, will be found for you at the very earliest possible moment. Is there anything else?'

Arbuthnot pointed to the salver. 'This is the property of Mr. Lloyd Ferrers. Also sold by—your representative.'

Again Emmanuel picked up the magnifying-glass and examined the piece of silver.

'Irish, of course,' he said. 'Very nice, very nice indeed.'

'The date,' Grahame demanded, 'what's the date?'

'I was coming to that. Shall we say about 1660?'

'My deah feller, no! That's a "c" on the mark. This is "A".'

'To be sure. Oh, you specialists! This is 1658 surely.'

'It was sold to my friend Lloyd Ferrers with a guarantee stating that the date was 1638!' Grahame snarled.

Emmanuel set down the salver. Arbuthnot saw that there

were beads of sweat standing on his forehead, his fine hands shook a little.

'Forgive me,' he said to Arbuthnot, 'we are both wrong. The crown and harp misled me. The difference in the decoration of the shield containing the letter. I am afraid,' he smiled with difficulty, 'that in spite of the sterling mark, we must date this salver as 1747. Would you be so kind,' to Arbuthnot, 'as to examine that sterling mark? Colonel Grahame, to offer my apologies to your friend is simple, to admit that Gollantz's have ben guilty of giving a guarantee for silver—which pr-roves to be incorr-rect, is anything but simple. To me, it is a disaster.' He turned to Arbuthnot. 'I am at a loss. You see what has happened, of course. The crown and harp have been left, the "A" has been altered. And then not even altered to the corr-rect date.'

'Inserted,' Arbuthnot replied ; 'very well done, but—tampering without a doubt. Most distressing!'

'Colonel Grahame, I can only offer to make reparation to Mr. Lloyd Ferrers in the same way which I have pro-romised to make it to you. I am more distr-ressed than I can say. Will you ask him to tear up his guarantee, and with the 1638 salver— which I shall find for him—I will send one which I shall wr-rite myself.'

'Very right and proper,' Arbuthnot said. 'Ah, join me in a cup of tea, Emmanuel. Colonel Grahame, I take it that you are satisfied?'

'I admit that Mr. Gollantz——'

'Sir Emmanuel Gollantz, Colonel Grahame.'

'That Sir Emmanuel Gollantz has behaved in what I consider a most proper manner. At the same time I should like to advise him that if this kind of thing continues, the reputation of his firm is going to suffer considerably.'

Speaking very smoothly, Arbuthnot said, 'I think that we can safely leave the — er — reputation of his firm in Sir Emmanuel's hands. Sugar, Colonel Grahame?'

Later, when the Colonel, somewhat pacified, had taken his leave, Emmanuel turned to Arbuthnot. His face was even paler than usual, his voice seemed to have lost its vigour and colour.

'My God,' he said, 'that this should have happened to us! It's terr-rible. What am I going to do?'

Arbuthnot pointed to a pair of candlesticks, highly decorated, which stood on a side table. 'Look at those,' he said.

Emmanuel walked over to where they stood and began to examine them. Arbuthnot watched him closely. 'Well?' he said. 'Well?'

'London, I fancy, about 1730. Yes, here's the mark. What? This can't be right—Arbuthnot, what is all this? Is this some new piece of horror? Tell me, tell me!'

'An example of a little knowledge being a dangerous thing, my boy. The actual mark is concealed among the decorations . . . let me show you—look, therah, and on this one—herah. Those fools imagined that therah was no mark, because they didn't know where to look for it. They therefore insert anothah where it can be seen! Now, put them down, and let me ask you a question or two. This must stop. The reputation of your business will crumble like a pile of sand if this continues. Answer me truthfully—have you any idea who is doing this— faking?'

'Yes,' Emmanuel said. 'Yes.'

'Can you find out how and when and wherah?'

'I think so—I must.'

'You *must*. Now take a cognac, and we'll talk of this anothah day. You're shot to bits, my boy.'

CHAPTER SIX

EMMANUEL left Arbuthnot's office conscious of a sense of physical weakness. He felt that he might have been recovering from a long and serious illness; he had suffered a shock which had left him shattered and deeply distressed. All his life he had been proud of the reputation of his father's firm, and although he realized now that again and again he had felt sudden spasms of uncertainty with regard to Julian and his activities, he had fought against them as something unworthy in himself.

Arbuthnot had sent Colonel Grahame to the Gallery; Grahame had recommended his friend, this man with the double-barrelled name, to seek there for the silver in which he was interested. Both these clients had been disappointed—more than disappointed—defrauded!

Emmanuel had suffered many humiliations in his life, but never such humiliation as he had experienced this morning in Arbuthnot's office. His pride has been shattered, he had felt that no longer would he be able to face other dealers in the great sale-rooms! Stories such as the one which had been recounted this morning were never really silenced. A whisper here, a hint there, and the whole of London knew that Gollantz' had been selling stuff which was—he felt his muscles contract at the thought—faked!

His figure held stiffly erect as he made his way to the Gallery. That he knew where the blame lay was very little solace to him. He understood his brother Julian's mentality. Julian had seen an opportunity to make a little money here, a little more there, and to make money was his one aim in life. To make money in a manner which entailed as little actual hard work as possible! He frowned as he considered the character of his brother. Julian was, quite literally, incapable of 'running straight'. Given two paths, the one straight and narrow, the other broad and more amusing—there would never be the slightest doubt which Julian would take.

Added to that fact, there was to be taken into consideration his brother's inordinate conceit. He believed that a knowledge

190

—as for example of antique silver—which took other men years of their lives to perfect, could be obtained by him in a very short time. His estimation of his own intelligence was enormous!

These things Emmanuel knew; through them he had suffered more than most men. Julian had done his best to drag him down in order to save his own skin. Emmanuel, for the sake of the mother he adored, and who he knew adored Julian, had taken the blame not once but several times.

Now he had come back to England to take over the reins of the great business; he had been working at various plans which he believed might bring back the complete prosperity of the firm. He had organized, put his theories into practice, and already the Gallery had recovered something of its old atmosphere. Where there had been a certain attitude of 'go-as-you-please', he had restored order and discipline. The whole place looked better, the office was run in a completely businesslike way; only the two 'lines' which Julian had reserved for himself had still been open to certain elements of slackness.

Again and again conversations had occurred when faithful little Reuben Davis had been heard expostulating, 'What's happened to that Rockingham service? Where is it?'

'I heard Mr. Julian say that it was sold, Mr. Davis,' young Watson would answer.

'Then why is there no record of it? What was paid for it? Where is the cheque? This is intolerable!'

Then Julian, suave and completely at ease, would come and give explanations and reasons, and the matter would blow over; Davis, still scarlet in the face and frowning, would accept Julian's statements.

'That Rockingham service? Good Heavens, man, don't be so tedious! The customer paid in cash. I found myself short of that useful commodity. I paid in a cheque to the firm. It's so simple! They paid £74. I paid a cheque for that sum. It's there! What is there to make a fuss about?'

'Listen, Julian,' Davis would argue, 'that's not the way we've always done business. I'm not imputing anything——'

'Good Lord, I should think not! You're going too far, Reuben!'

'I'm only saying that—we have our methods, and I see no reason why we should change them!'

Julian had answered, his voice lazy and insolent, 'My dear man, times change and we change with them; your methods have long been as antique as your—furniture!'

Julian—this man Seber, who had left the firm, and was—in

some capacity or other—working for Julian. What were they doing together? The answer was damnably simple. Faking silver, repairing china, selling stuff, charging a little more than the sum with which the firm was credited. Emmanuel's lips curled in disgust—ten pounds here, fifteen there, an odd fiver—and for sums such as those Julian was ready to sell the reputation of the firm which had been held in complete respect for nearly three generations!

He entered the Gallery, and for a moment his own worries were submerged in the sense of satisfaction which he felt. The place looked magnificent, cared for, tended and made as perfect as was humanly possible. That old refectory table, and round it set six admirable Cromwellian chairs; the two pieces of excellent pewter standing on the fine polished surface of the table, their dull lustre reflected in the shining wood! This side table, where lay half a dozen rare and beautifully bound books. That cabinet where today only rare Meissen china was shown. How attractive it was, and what a sense of pride and pleasure it gave him.

He beckoned to young Watson.

'Yes, Sir Emmanuel?'

'I only wanted to tell you how very much pleased I am with the appearance of the room. You're doing ver-ry well, Watson, ver-ry well indeed. My compliments.'

The young man flushed with pleasure. 'Thank you, sir. I do think that I'm—well—getting the hang of it. Just a little at any rate.'

'You've learnt one of the first and greatest lessons,' Emmanuel said, 'never overcrowd. A few pieces—and in good taste, well displayed. Tables filled with all kinds and sorts of things will never attract anyone except the buyers who are out for cheap bargains. I am very much pleased.'

He walked on into his own office, and rang for Hannah. She came and stared at him anxiously.

'There are two gentlemen to see you,' she said. 'Is everything all right?'

Emmanuel pressed the palm of his hand against his forehead.

'I shouldn't think that everything could be more—wr-rong.'

'Tut, tut! Put it from you. I have something to tell you, but later. Will you see these gentlemen? One of them says that he is anxious to return some property of yours. A table, he said.'

Emmanuel looked up, and repeated, 'A table! No—it isn't possible. It's the table, my table! What's his name? Don't tell me that it's "Reggie"! Good Lord,' as he took a card which she handed to him, 'it is "Reggie"! There can't be two Major Reginald M. W. Sinclairs. Send him in, Hannah, this means cham pagne!'

She nodded, 'Very well,' thinking how a sudden happiness changed him. 'He isn't really growing old, it's only that his youth is getting smothered. Now he looks young and eager! Oi, oi, if only he could always look so!'

A moment later two men were ushered into his room, the first a small fair man, wearing a single eyeglass, with curly hair which was beginning to recede a little from his broad forehead, the other a tall man, much younger, with a long thin face and large intelligent eyes.

The former held out his hand. 'Hello, Gollantz, I've brought your table. How are you?'

The other man said, 'Nice to see you again.'

Emmanuel, smiling, his face a little flushed, stammered, 'Reggie—and—"The Quiet Lad"! This is wonderful! Sit down, and here's the champagne! Hannah, these are two very good friends of mine—Major Sinclair, and—damn it, I don't even know your name!'

Reggie said, 'His illustrious name is the Honourable Wilfred Godstone. And allow me to inform you that my card is slightly out of date, my rank should be "Brigadier". There's glory for you!'

Emmanuel said, 'Good Lord! Now, Hannah—this is Miss Rosenfeldt—you may realize the kind of people I hobnobbed with when I was in the Army!'

'Hobnob my foot!' Sinclair said explosively. 'I had no wretched private soldiers "hobnobbing" with me, m'lad. Get that straight.'

'Sorry, sir.' His heart felt suddenly lighter, it seemed that he had been transported from Bond Street and its worries to another country, where there might be endless sand, numerous discomforts, even sporadic dangers, but where life had been simple and easy in comparison with the one which he lived now. 'And the table?'

'The table, my dear Gollantz, is carefully packed in gunny sacking. It has travelled, it has known vicissitudes, and even a moderate amount of danger. It reposed in the loft of an Italian peasant's house for months. I was fully occupied and it was some time before I could return to claim it. It has been the cause of considerable altercation between my honourable self and various officials—who, like all officials, were completely lacking in any finer feelings. I could write lyrics about it—beginning with desert sand, and ending with England in the piping times of peace, though up to date I have heard no piping and seen few indications of peace.

'Godstone and I—he is not one of my officers—are going forth to examine what is left of the Empire, in the hope that we may find some—what was the nice phrase in the "White Company"?—small advancement. In other words, we are leaving immediately for Trieste.'

Godstone said in his pleasant, quiet voice, 'Trieste isn't exactly —part of the Empire, sir.'

Reggie returned airily, 'With the world in the melting-pot, God knows what it may be in six months! Gollantz, your very good health! Congratulations on your brand of champagne!'

Godstone murmured, 'All the best, Gollantz.'

'Now, let's have your news. I was sorry to read that you'd lost your father. Bad show. How are you? Married? Godstone here is married! Lovely girl, shocking business for her and her family, who are nice, respectable people—earls or something of the kind. Not that I actually hold that against them.'

'No, I'm not married,' Emmanuel said, and as he spoke realized how much he would give to be married to some 'lovely girl' even if her people were not 'earls or something of the kind'. 'I live with my son, Simeon.'

'Didn't know you had a son!'

'Nearly twenty-one. Was in the R.A.F. Lost a foot in a crash, but he manages all right. He's in this business with me; he does very well.'

They sat together, smoking and drinking their wine, and slowly the load of misery which had lain on Emmanuel's shoulders seemed to lighten. How good it was to talk to these two men again; how little either of them had altered! Reggie as ready as ever to talk about anything and everything; Godstone smiling gently, speaking rarely, but radiating a quiet and kindly serenity.

It was Sinclair who glanced at his watch and started to his feet. Emmanuel noticed that he still smelt faintly of good scented soap.

'At this moment various Poo Bahs at the War House are shrieking for my blood. We shall in all probability be sent hot foot to the South Pole! Can we always find you here? We're only going on a mission. What the mission is precisely we have no idea, but as no one else has either, that need not trouble us. Various people have been over-zealous—in a variety of ways; others have not been sufficiently so. Our old friends the "Jugs" must be taught to cultivate the friendship of the Italians, the Italians must bury a number of hatchets which they have kep.

bright and shining for use against the said "Jugs", The British must learn to smile on both nations impartially. How we shall arrive at this "consumation devoutly to be wished" neither of us has the faintest idea.'

Godstone interpolated, 'It's possibly as well, sir. We shall arrive with open minds.'

'I don't approve of open minds, my lad,' Reggie returned; 'if they are too open, everything they ever contained is liable to have taken wings and flown away! No, I am completely biassed, and the mission will be a tremendous success. S'long, Gollantz, take care of the famous table. Let's all dine when Godstone and I get back, eh?' He shook hands warmly and hurried out.

Emmanuel whispered to Godstone, 'He hasn't changed, has he?'

'Never will—and thank God for it. Goodbye.'

Emmanuel returned home feeling that, after all, difficulties could be tackled and that, given time and sufficient courage, he could tackle them. His sense of outrage and dismay remained, but the visit of Sinclair and Godstone had, in some way, given him fresh courage and determination. As he entered Heber Square his step was almost light.

Again and again he smiled, as he walked home, at the thought of the little table, which he had found in North Africa, and when he had been sent home, after being wounded in an air raid, Sinclair had taken charge of it for him. How like Reggie to cling to that table, through long voyages, dangers and almost insuperable difficulties! He had examined it before he left the Gallery; and as long as he could remember nothing had given him greater pleasure than the sight of it as he saw the sacking removed, and was able once again to see the beautiful lines, the graciousness of the shape, and to touch again the well-matured wood. Once polished—and he had insisted as he always did, 'No French polish remember!'—it would become a thing of real beauty again.

Old Peters, who had come down from the workshop to take charge of the precious table, had stood looking down at it, caressing his large nose with his finger and thumb as was his habit.

Emmanuel said, 'Nice little thing, isn't it?' much in the tone of a fond mother who speaks almost slightingly of the child she loves and believes to be a miracle of beauty.

Peters nodded. 'Bit o' orlrite. Mind yer, nothink ter set no sale-room rockin' on its 'indlegs—but a pretty little piece. I'll see as it's treated rite. Goo'. nite, sir.'

How pleasant it had been to see Reggie and the 'Quiet Lad' again! To find Reggie exactly the same, and best of all to know that he had been sufficiently interested to keep track of the little table. That fact was worth more than the table itself. Emmanuel's smile widened; one day both Reggie and the 'Quiet Lad' should come to Milan, and—what a wonderful time he would give them both!

Godstone—the Hon. Wilfred Godstone—was married. Reggie had said to a 'lovely girl'. It must be very pleasant to be married to a 'lovely girl', Emmanuel reflected. To have someone to whom your comings and goings were matters of importance; someone who liked to be with you, as you liked being with them. Never again, he knew, could he hope to recapture the ecstatic happiness which he had known with Juliet. Never could he hope to hear the sun and the moon and the stars shouting together! To know what it meant to feel that the coldest day, the greyest sky, became suddenly warm and the canopy of the sky blue and clear, because the one woman who really mattered came walking towards you in one of Milan's busiest streets.

These things were over; irretrievably lost; past recall. These things had ended with—Juliet. Never could he give to any woman the adoration which he had given to her; never again love with the intensity which he had experienced for her.

Second best; his sensitive lips curled at the phrase! Second best. And yet, life was full of 'second bests', which were in themselves very, very good, even very precious.

Because the world had held only one Leonardo, only one Michael Angelo, only one Valesquez, was that to infer that no other painters or sculptors were worth while? Even in the class which came below the one which followed on the heels of the giants, there were many things which were charming, beautiful and possessing a lasting beauty. The Ca'd'Oro was not the only lovely palace in Venice, the great door of Pisano at Florence was not the only masterpiece of its kind. Again and again he had visited small—even obscure—galleries in Italy, France and Germany and found to his delight pictures by painters—almost unknown to him—possessing real and actual beauty.

There could never be another Juliet. Emmanuel knew that he disliked even trying to imagine such a thing! For the rest of his life she must stand apart, and having known and loved perfection he could never hope to experience it again. But— into his mind came a picture—he saw it very plainly—and yet

196

for a moment could not give it a name. The picture was that of a head and shoulders—a woman—where had he seen it? Not Milan, not Venice, yet somewhere in Italy! Suddenly he snapped his fingers!

Of course! The National Museum at Florence! A woman—not still very young, but lovely, very lovely. Calm and aloof, yet giving the impression that fires smouldered, that at any moment she might throw off her calmness and become vital, eager, interested in everything. Who was she?

The name evaded him; and still frowning and puzzled, he entered the house, to find his brother Bill waiting for him.

'Hello, Bill—nice to see you. Have some tea?'

'Thanks. Any news? I had a letter from Viva this morning. She sounds pretty bored—that means she'll come home, I suppose, eh?'

Emmanuel stared at him, the frown still between his eyebrows. Suddenly it disappeared; he smiled and said, 'Thanks, Bill. I've got it! Battista Sforza!'

Bill stared at him. 'Have you gone dotty?'

'No, I don't think so. I was trying to remember the name of a bust—it eluded me. Now I've remembered. I never realized before that Battista Sforza was the image of Viva!'

Bill ejaculated piously, 'Good Lord! Never heard of the lady. However, I didn't come here to chat to you about art. I've heard something pretty serious, and it's got to be settled once and for all.'

Emmanuel sat down, while Martha poured out the tea. When she had gone, closing the door quietly behind her, he said, 'Yes, what is it?'

'I dropped into Killick's sale-room this afternoon. I do sometimes when I've half an hour to spare, and think that I might light on some odd book or other. The sale's tomorrow. They're selling the whole collection of——'

Emmanuel said, 'All right, Bill, skip that part. I'm going myself.'

'Well, there were a couple of fellows talking. I was turning over some books. One said—now listen to this: "If Gollantz makes a statement, gives a guarantee, then—you can take it as correct." The other chap said, "Um, I wonder. Used to be the case. It may have changed lately. If what I hear is true, it *has* changed!"'

'The first man shrugged his shoulders. "Poor Max Gollantz; he's out of it now, but I've always believed that Emmanuel was dead straight." The reply to that was—listen to this: "Was

197

possibly. I fancy that he's picked up some very slick bits of dealing lately!"

'Maybe I ought to have told them who I was, made a scene, but I funked it, only, Emmanuel—if that kind of thing is going round, it's got to be squashed. It's pretty stinking, eh?'

His brother nodded. 'Distinctly. Yes . . .' He lifted the house telephone and asked if Hannah had returned. 'Will you ask her to be so good as to come here? Thank you.' He turned back to Bill. 'Something is going to be done. And done—once and for all.' Hannah entered, and he motioned her to sit down, then slowly and exactly recounted what Bill had told him. Hannah sat, her hands folded, her face impassive.

'Now let me tell you what happened this morning at Arbuthnot's.'

With the same exact care, speaking in a voice which held no trace of anger or passion, Emmanuel told them of his interview, and of what he had found. That ended, he looked from his brother's flushed and furious face to Hannah's pale and impassive one.

'That,' he said, 'is my story, and my story accounts for what you heard, Bill, in Killick's this afternoon.'

Hannah nodded, then said, 'Now let me tell you what I saw last night. Here is the reason for both your stories!' She recounted what she had seen on the previous night, her sight of Julian and her short conversation with the constable.

Bill said, 'It's pretty evident that he goes there regularly, eh?'

'I suppose that he uses the little office which is always kept locked,' Emmanuel added.

Hannah replied, 'He not only has the outer, but also an inner office. Don't you remember, it used to be kept as a store for paper, boxes and wrappings? Julian took that when he first came —before you were out of the Army. He must have taken your grandfather's keys from Ordingly, no?'

Emmanuel mused, 'If only we had another set of keys——'

She said very calmly, 'We have. Your grandfather gave me a set many years ago—he said that he was giving me the Freedom of his City in Bond Street. I have never used them—here they are.'

She handed to Emmanuel three small and beautifully made keys, strung on a thin gold chain. He took them and weighed them in his hand, meditatively, without speaking.

The room was very quiet. Bill shivered suddenly. The silence oppressed him. 'Gosh, it's all sufficiently ugly,' he said harshly. His brother sighed ; it seemed that Bill's voice had roused him from the mood into which he had fallen.

198

He said, 'I'll keep these, if you don't mind, Hannah—for a night or two. I'm going to use them.' He slipped the keys into his pocket and rose, standing very tall and upright before them both. 'This has gone on long enough. I've been foolish, probably culpably weak. I have known in my heart that something was wrong—very wrong. I did nothing because I really hoped that Julian and I might work together. I know that my father wished for that greatly, with an intensity that was almost fanatical. We never have been able to, we never should be able to. We might as well realize that and take steps to prevent the complete loss of the reputation which has been built up with such meticulous care. You agree, I am sure?'

'Certainly,' Bill said, 'but what are you going to do?'

'Wait in the Gallery for Julian. If he doesn't come tonight, he'll come another night. Whenever he comes I shall be waiting.'

'You're right.' Hannah nodded her head. 'Quite right. Only be careful. Cornered rats are apt to bite!'

He smiled at her, 'Oh, be ver-ry sure I shall take every precaution.'

That night he left Heber Square and walked to Bond Street. He had no doubt that he would find all his suspicions were correct, that Julian—probably working in partnership with Seber—was tampering with the sterling marks on the old silver, charging a higher price than the one quoted by the firm's valuer, and retaining the profit in addition to his own commission. At first Emmanuel had been filled with horror, that had changed to fury, and later to a cold contempt. Now his mind felt very clear, limpid as a still pool and as cold.

Slipping his hand into his pocket, he felt the chill of the keys to the small steel door which his grandfather had caused to be made. Because he was not actually cast in a completely modern mould, he sighed.

Those days . . . Days when there was still dignity, and better still—essential kindliness. Old Emmanuel, often working late on the close examination of some work which had been sent to him, or waiting to have a talk to old Peters about some repair which was needed, disliked to feel that his whole staff was kept waiting, doing nothing but hang about until he left the building. He had evolved the idea of that small door, he had caused an elaborate lock to be made, and if he decided to work until hours long past those which were ordained for the staff he could do so with a quiet mind.

Those were the days of consideration. Emmanuel did not doubt that very frequently wages were far too low. He had always paid his employees well and had felt that he had the right to demand good and faithful service from them. His grandfather had probably paid wages which were substantially lower, but—quite apart from the fact that the cost of living was proportionately smaller—those employees knew—he repeated that word to himself—*knew* that their welfare and well-being were something with which Emmanuel Gollantz was intimately concerned. With him a case of sickness, a family disaster, had not been something which merely touched his sympathy ; these things had been something concerning which he felt it his duty to occupy himself. With him there had been no question of 'doling out charity', no question of 'doing this or that for poor Tom, or Dick or Harry', the whole reaction had been instantaneous and sincere.

Admittedly there must have been very many bad employers, people who regarded their work people as machines—machines which, when they broke down, were relegated to the scrap-heap. On the other hand, common fairness demanded the admission that his grandfather—and father—could not have been unique.

The world was changing, a new spirit was at work ; a spirit which regarded all 'bosses' as suspect, as greedy, avaricious creatures seeking only to use the brains, the muscles and the strength of their people to the very greatest advantage to themselves.

He sighed ; somewhere there was gross unfairness. He admitted that the stories of the old employers of labour, in whatever form, had roused his indignation and his horror. He regarded these people who had exploited the capacity for work in their fellow-men as monsters ; but there had been others, surely?

Old Emmanuel Gollantz, his son Max, even his grandson, the second Emmanuel, had ideals—ideals which they attempted to put into practice. He wrinkled his fine nose in disgust when he thought of men who had talked to him of their magnificent canteens, their medical services, their holiday schemes and the like! He had listened, and had assessed these things at what he sincerely believed to be their proper value. They were, he felt, plasters! They were not kindly concessions ; they—in the main —proved no real interest in the workers ; in most cases they were an attempt to 'dress the window', and in many other cases they were an attempt to evade certain modes of taxation.

The whole trouble, so it seemed to him, in the unrest which existed in the industrial world was a lack of understanding between masters and men. What was needed was a realization of each other's problems. Reasonable discipline did not mean oppression ; orders given and accepted did not imply a lowering of self-respect on the part of the person who was given instructions. He himself had served as a private soldier, and never felt that to show respect, to salute his superiors, had lowered his own character or tacitly admitted an inferiority. In these days too much importance was given to small, insignificant things. Peters—for whom Emmanuel had the greatest respect—had never found his character degraded by answering 'Yes, sir,' and 'No, sir.' His own son, while in the Gallery, never used the word 'father'; it was quicker, more impersonal, to reply, 'Yes, sir.'

He turned into Bond Street, his mind still absorbed with his ideas.

He had fought for England in the firm belief that he, in common with millions of others, was fighting for freedom, fighting a fixed determination to prevent Britain ever being subject to the rules and laws of Nazism and the horrors of the Gestapo. He, again in common with thousands more, had looked forward to an England which should be a model for the whole world; an England where men and women, having been victorious overseas, having won the greatest war of all time, were ready to make a final effort to fight their last great campaign—that of successfully winning the Peace.

Instead of finding a united nation, a nation marshalling its forces for a final and great effort, he had found petty arguments, long and futile discussions, ill-digested plans, and general discontent.

'A house divided against itself'—he mused, 'how right the old slogans of all the political parties were, if only they could be welded into one. "Unity is strength", "Equality of opportunity" and "Liberty, Equality and Fraternity". So admirable, so practical, so beyond the range of argument! Well!' he shrugged his shoulders, and took the keys from his pocket. 'Well—for the sake of a few just men the city may, still, be saved.'

Carefully and without fumbling he unlocked the door, and found himself in the long narrow corridor, heavily carpeted, which led to the main showrooms. The door closed, easily and silently, behind him. He walked along the corridor and made his way to his own office. He did not switch on the light; the windows were heavily barred and the light of a street lamp made the room comparatively well lit. He sat down and prepared to wait. Glancing at his watch, he found that it was half past ten. He leaned back in his chair, closed his eyes and let his mind wander.

Strange where your mind wanders when you allow it a free rein. He saw the long Gallery in Milano, with Guido coming forward, a little excited, to tell him of some new treasure which had been found ; he could hear his excited, rather high-pitched voice ; then came the slower and heavier tones of Casimiro Boccolini, speaking of weighty and important matters, his face grave, his eyes always very kind. He saw his little shop in Milano, which had always looked rather dirty although it was kept scrupulously clean ; a chicken-skin fan, and—a woman who came to ask that she might see it. Juliet—Juliet and Como, where he devised the decorations for her villa. Little Gilly, two Americans who had called there in passing—he had forgotten their names ! Yet he could see them so clearly.

Ordingly and the shadows thrown by great branches of the trees which his mother loved. The desert, with its stones and boulders, a German patrol, bursts of gunfire which hung on the air like handfuls of cotton wool. Reggie and himself in Egypt, an air raid, houses suddenly leaning sideways and falling. England—so green, so neat ; the great cathedrals with their storehouses of beauty—stately Lincoln, sturdy time-resisting Durham, the grace of York, the complete loveliness of Canterbury, the glory of Westminster and the chapel of Henry the Seventh, the comfortable intimacy of Ripon, with its beauties in carved wood and its choir stalls. Fountains—even in retrospect he caught his breath, when he remembered the smooth green sward, the little talkative river, and the grandeur of the cloisters and the great East window. The Moses of Michael Angelo, the pathetic loveliness of his Pietá in Saint Peter's, the Fountain of Trevi—how often had he flung small pieces of money into that fountain so that he might be certain to return —one day—to Rome ! Florence and its old bridge, its splendid bronze doors, and—Battista Sforza by Laurana.

He opened his eyes. Why did that particular work keep recurring to him? He smiled suddenly. Why? The reason had come back to him. Battista Sforza might have been Viva—Viva Heriot, who had once been his wife. There was the same tilt of the head, the same slight arrogance, and the complete self-assurance which never degenerated into conceit or self-satisfaction. 'One day,' he thought, 'I must go back and see it again, not once but many times. I dislike copies, but I might be able to find someone who could make me one which was not completely— unworthy.' In the distance he heard the click of a lock, heard someone whistling very softly a tune of Noel Coward's—what was it?—'Some day I'll find you' . . . Yes, from *Private Lives.* Emmanuel sat upright, his eyes straining through the darkness ; a light was switched on, another door opened and closed. Julian had come and gone into his room.

CHAPTER SEVEN

EMMANUEL sat stiffly upright, every muscle tense. He waited, wondering what he was going to find. Were the solutions to his problems hidden behind that closed door, or was he merely going to lay himself open to a charge of spying and interfering? At that moment his dislike of his brother Julian and his works and methods was less than his eagerness to put an end to the derogatory comments, the suspicions and the distrust which were slowly growing in men's minds concerning the firm of Gollantz.

The place was very still ; it seemed that London slept soundly and peacefully. Once he saw the sudden flash of a policeman's lantern through the round hole which was cut in the heavy shutters which covered the main door. There was no sound ; the light might have come from a shooting star and passed as silently on its way. The room in which he sat was dimly lit, but the great Gallery was in complete darkness. Leaning forward, his hands clenched on the arms of his chair, he strained his eyes peering into the velvet obscurity. It was as though a great void of space separated him from his object. He shivered. He knew Julian's temper, knew how keenly he resented the slightest opposition to whatever he chose to do.

Emmanuel disliked violent arguments, he disliked watching tempers being lost and their owners forgetting the value of control. Then, straightening his shoulders, he rose and, stepping softly, feeling his way among the furniture and showcases, walked through the Gallery.

A light was burning ; he could see the thin thread of orange light beneath the door, could hear the faint hissing of something, as if a small kettle were boiling. For a moment he hesitated, then, stretching out his hand, found the handle, turned it, and entered the little room.

Julian was bending over some piece of silver, his fingers holding a small fine instrument, a small burner hissed beside him ; on the table near him lay various small objects—Emmanuel saw a tiny mallet, pliers, various minute dishes of

203

metal. Julian had not heard him enter. Emmanuel stood, his hand still on the door-handle.

'Good evening, Julian,' he said ; 'you work late.'

Julian started, obviously brought his fingers into contact with some hot metal, used a word which was more forceful than polite, and then spun round to face his brother.

Without rising he asked, 'What the hell are you doing here?'

'Like yourself—working,' Emmanuel replied. 'That's a very fine tankard you've got there.'

'I've learnt what's good.'

'And studied how to make it—apparently—better, eh?'

'What the devil do you mean?'

Emmanuel pulled forward a chair and sat down astride it, his arms folded on the back. He was using every ounce of self-control which he possessed to fight down the desire to open fire, to speak directly and frankly. He knew his brother, knew that such a method was bound to fail ; indeed, he doubted if any method which he could employ would have the slightest chance of success. The first was doomed to failure, the second might, at least, make some small impression.

Julian stared at him. 'Make yourself at home, won't you?'

'I should like to ask you what you are doing,' Emmanuel said, 'and at the same time supply the answer. That tankard which you have there is very typical—the twist at the back of the lid, the heart-shaped piece at the bottom and the general solidity are sufficient to give me at least an indication of its date and origin. I imagine that you are—very foolishly—attempting to insert a hall-mark of an earlier date. You're wasting your time ; that particular design is too individual. You made a mistake over the salver sold to Lloyd Ferrers, another in the case of some candlesticks which you eventually sold to a very great authority on silver, and into which you, I imagine, had inserted a *second hall-mark,* because you could not find the original. You don't know enough! You've tried to learn about silver in the "easy way". There is no easy way! Then again, this question of the r-repairing of china. I admit that it is done admirably, with gr-great skill, but—it is still repairing.'

Julian rose to his feet. His face was white, his eyes faintly bloodshot, his voice, when he spoke, sounded muffled.

'I don't know what you're talking about. I've brought a great deal of trade to this antediluvian place ; you're all out of date, years behind the times. I like—progressive methods!'

Emmanuel's quiet voice answered, 'So do I—when they are compatible with honesty.'

The atmosphere of the room was charged with anger—

Emmanuel's cold and still under control, Julian's ready to blaze into a flame at any moment. As his brother ceased speaking Julian watched him, his face heavy with anger, his eyes narrowed, his jaw protruding. Nervously his fingers closed and unclosed on the handle of the splendid tankard.

'I was dragged into this damned business,' he said thickly. 'I never liked it. I wasn't fitted to be an old clothes man, a junk merchant. I was meant for something better! Only—thanks to you, you bastard, I got flung down some steps in Milano and I've never been a really fit man since. You precious Puritan, you smug-faced swine—if your own life was exposed what pretty reading it would make! I've brought new business to this blasted firm of yours, a thing you never contrived to do! Instead of being grateful, you come here with your confounded high and mighty airs, and your bloody superiority, and try to trap me into making—statements! How did you get in?' His voice rose higher. 'How did you get wind of my being here? Come on, let's hear!'

'I heard, indirectly, from the police that you were using the side door,' Emmanuel answered.

'From the police!' Julian's voice rose still higher. 'What have the police to do with it?'

'Nothing at the moment. Nothing at any time if you will be wise, Julian. You have got to—get out. You've married an American wife——'

'One of the family at least married a woman who was not "no better than she should have been", eh?'

His brother's lips closed more tightly ; they looked like a thin scarlet line in his face, the bone of his jaw showed white, but his voice was even when he answered.

'Your father-in-law made a gr-reat deal of money during the war. I suggest that he might find a place for you in one of his various enterprises. I suggest, too, that you leave England as soon as possible. Under our father's will, you have a certain amount of money——'

'Less than I should have had if you'd kept your damned nose out of everything!'

'That is beside the point. The fact r-remains that you will leave England, and leave it ver-ry soon, and—for good.'

Julian flung back his head and laughed, 'How likely!'

'If not——'

'Well, and if not ...?'

'I shall make a public statement that nothing sold by this firm is guaranteed unless the guarantee is signed by me. I shall add the facts which have come to my knowledge, they shall be stated ver-ry plainly and ver-ry fully. One of the best-known antique dealers in this country, possibly in the world, will add his testimony to mine. That is what will happen, Julian.'

'Nice for the firm you're so proud of, eh?'

'Better than the firm being slowly discredited. This is not the first time these matters have come to my ears. There was a candelabra sold to Aunt Beatrice. For all I know to the contr-rary there may be hundreds of other pieces—falsely marked, repaired and sold as perfect—up and down the country. My r-reputation does not exist only in London. I have a partner in Fr-rance——'

'That pansy Louis Lara! Very pretty!'

Emmanuel disregarded the interruption, and continued to speak. 'I have my own place in Milano——'

'Where you keep another pretty little bit of work, Guido Moroni!'

'I have my son's future to consider——'

'The family bastard!'

Emmanuel took a step forward ; his long fine hands closed on his brother's shoulders, he leaned forward so that his face was within a few inches of Julian's. His face was distorted with passion, his lips curled back showing his teeth. All the gentleness had vanished, the control was flung to the winds ; he looked —what he indeed was—a man in the grip of passionate loathing.

He said, 'Julian, I'll kill you for that, you liar!'

Julian's fingers closed on the handle of the tankard, his muscles tightened, his arm swung up and the heavy silver tankard came down on Emmanuel's head. Emmanuel staggered under the blow. Julian heard his gasp of pain, and raising the tankard brought it down again and again on his brother's head. The hands which clutched his shoulders lost their strength, the fingers relaxed, and slowly Emmanuel's body sagged and slipped to the floor, where it lay, the blood from his head slowly staining the dark linoleum which covered the floor of the little office.

Julian turned swiftly to the desk. He extinguished the hissing burner, he picked up various small strips of silver which bore curious marks—a lion, three castles, an initial and so forth— and crammed them into his pocket. He opened several drawers, moving very swiftly, and taking out various packets, small boxes and several letters, pushed them into the small brief case which stood on the floor.

Then he stood and stared down at his brother. Emmanuel lay very still, his eyes closed, his face white as bone ; it was

206

difficult to say whether he breathed or not. Julian seized the tankard, and with his handkerchief rubbed its surface violently. Once or twice he breathed upon it and continued his rubbing. He pulled on his gloves, and gave a last polish to the object. Then, switching off the light, he went quietly and swiftly from the room, leaving the door a little ajar.

Bill Gollantz sat waiting for his nephew in his very respectable and eminently comfortable club. Several times he glanced at the clock which stood on the tall dark marble mantelpiece, and then compared the time which it showed with that of his wrist-watch.

Five minutes to eleven. Emmanuel had planned to arrive at Bond Street at a few minutes after ten. Simeon had gone off to run Seber to earth. Hannah—that invaluable woman—had discovered his address, a flat in Notting Hill. Simeon was to meet Bill at the club. The time was growing late. Where was the fellow? Where, for that matter, was Emmanuel? Then he saw Simeon enter, and, watching him, thought, 'Poor lad, when he's tired you can see that he limps a bit. Hard lines to lose a foot at his age.'

He said, 'Hello, Simeon. Any news?'

Simeon sat down, and again Bill noticed how he eased his foot.

'Um, I found him. He's going—going pretty quickly. I told him that I was reporting to you, and that you were ready with a warrant for his arrest.'

Bill said, 'Bluff, eh?'

'Mostly, I admit. A nasty piece of work, our Seber. Clever, mark you!'

'What's he going to do?' Bill asked.

'Anyone and anything he can find, I imagine. No need to worry about that kind of rat! He'll land up somewhere. D'you mind, Uncle Bill, if I leave a very large suitcase in your club? I borrowed it from Seber, and it contains all the "incriminating evidence". I went through his place with a small-tooth comb, believe me.'

Bill said, 'Strictly irregular, of course. Yes, leave it here. I fancy that we might manage a drink. I'm wondering where your father is. It's getting late.'

Simeon, his voice sharpening suddenly, asked, 'He's not back? Was he going to meet you here?'

Bill said, 'Oh, he'll turn up, imperturbable as usual. Drink this, and we might indulge in a stroll up Bond Street together unless you're too tired. Good. Here's the best of luck! We were just in time.'

They sat in the huge empty room, each allowing his own thoughts to wander. Bill was tired after a heavy day, Simeon was conscious that however well a false foot might be made, it had certain disadvantages. He was worried concerning his father ; he had been going to the Gallery at ten, it was now half past eleven.

'I think we'll stagger along,' he said to Bill, 'it's getting late.'

For the first hundred yards they both talked with animation, then conversation grew more and more desultory, and finally they walked along in silence. Simeon was conscious that his heart was beating heavily, and that sweat had gathered on his upper lip. Bill, walking slowly and steadily, puffed slightly. He was putting on weight, growing, in so far as his figure was concerned, like the Jaffe branch of the family. In another five years he would be immense!

They reached the Gallery and stood trying to find a glimmer of light. Everything was in complete darkness. The iron shutters were closed, the great steel gate over the entrance was shut, and looked strangely grim and forbidding. The small door was firmly locked.

Bill said, 'I suppose that he's gone. We might as well get along home.'

Simeon shook his head. 'I'd like to get in somehow. Hello, here's a copper.' The measured tread drew nearer, and the policeman stopped when he reached them.

'Nothing wrong, I hope, gentlemen?'

Bill answered briskly, 'Been along here before this evening?'

'I have, sir. About half past ten.'

'Notice any lights? Oh, by the way, my name is Gollantz. Wilmot and Gollantz, solicitors. Nothing unusual, eh?'

'Nothing, sir. Mr. Julian Gollantz left—as usual—about ten-thirty.'

'Ah, my brother, eh? Hard worker, my brother.'

'Works here most nights, sir.'

'No one else—he was alone? You didn't see anyone else go in?'

'Not a living soul, sir.'

Simeon stooped suddenly, sought about for a second or two, then said :

'Just shine your torch here, will you?' He pounced again, and in the light of the torch found a small bunch of three minute keys, strung on a steel chain. He stood upright, holding them in his hand. 'He's dropped them,' he said. 'Julian's dropped them. Let's go in.'

The big constable looked doubtful. 'It's not strictly regular, sir. I mean, I don't actually know who you gentlemen are. If you know what I mean, it's a delicate situation, in a manner of speaking.'

Bill, apparently unmoved, slipped his hand into his pocket and extracted his pocket-book. His movements appeared to Simeon to be so slow that he could have screamed at him, 'Be quick, be quick!' Bill took out a card and handed it to the policeman.

'There you are,' he said, 'and come in with us if you wish.'

'More regular, sir, if I do.'

Simeon was fumbling with the keys swearing softly, trying one after the other. 'No! Curse it! Ah, that's right. No—this is it! Now, here we go!' The little door swung open and Simeon walked ahead of the others, down the long, thickly carpeted passage. His fingers sought for the electric switch and found it ; light flooded the big showroom.

'No one here, sir. Apparently, at least.'

Simeon moved swiftly forward. 'This is Julian's office. Here, damn, where is the light! Let's have that torch again!' The rays of the torch flooded the room, rousing it into light again. Simeon almost fell over something which lay on the floor. He shouted, 'God, it's my father! Look! Look!'

Emmanuel lay where he had fallen, his arms outstretched, his head covered with blood, and a great wound in his temple. His eyes were closed, and to Simeon's excited fancy it seemed that he had ceased to breathe. The constable set down his torch and went down on one knee, heavily and stolidly, to make a closer inspection.

'Coo,' he murmured. 'Someone's caught him a nasty bash.'

Bill leaned over his brother. 'Emmanuel! Emmanuel! Simeon, go to his office, there'll be brandy there. Constable, better telephone for an ambulance. I'll stay here. There's a telephone in the showroom.'

The constable rose. 'Looks to me like a burglary,' he said.

Bill assented. 'That is undoubtedly what it is. Not a doubt.'

Simeon returned with the brandy and tried to open Emmanuel's lips.

'Don't worry too much,' Bill said. 'I'm not certain that brandy's the best thing with head wounds.'

'Do you think that he's—still alive?'

'Good Lord, yes!'

'He's very cold.'

'Sling that rug on the settee over him. Bound to be cold.'

The constable came back. 'Amberlance on its way, sir. Charing Cross Hospital. Always very prompt. I'd better take a few particulars.'

While Simeon, white and shaken, knelt beside Emmanuel, Bill gave the constable his impressions. His firm, heavy voice seemed to bring reassurance and a certain amount of comfort. The sound reached Simeon, though the actual words evaded him.

'As I see it,' Bill said, 'my brother Julian—working late, as usual—left at his usual time. Sir Emmanuel also had a set of the keys of the side door, and probably returned immediately afterwards—that is, either before my brother Julian had left or immediately after. The dropped keys which we found were not Sir Emmanuel's, his are on a thin gold chain. Probably Sir Emmanuel disturbed the thieves at their work. Here, without a doubt, is the weapon which they used when he interrupted them. This tankard. I think we may assume that Julian left a few moments before my elder brother arrived, and in the interim the thieves entered. Unless they had been hidden in the building. Ah! What's that? The ambulance.'

Uniformed men, skilful and careful, entered. Emmanuel was lifted on to the stretcher. He made no sound, gave no sign of life. Simeon followed. The time which came after was a wild and horrid nightmare to the young man. He felt that for the rest of his life he would visualize long, rather stark corridors, see swiftly moving figures in caps and aprons, smell the odour of disinfectant. He was very tired, conscious that he limped a little—how he hated to limp! Bill walked beside him, silent, watchful and stolid. Once he laid the tips of his fingers on Simeon's arm and said, 'He'll be all right, my boy.'

Almost fiercely Simeon answered, 'I don't believe it! I believe that he's dead!'

It seemed that they sat for hours in a little waiting room, rather bare and completely impersonal. A clock ticked faintly; the time was half past one.

Simeon said, 'It's not a good time—now until three. The heart's at its lowest strength.'

Bill shook his head. 'Don't you believe it.'

'If my father dies I'll kill Julian.'

'He won't die, and you won't kill Julian. Julian had nothing to do with it. Remember that. The thing was a planned burglary. Get that straight.'

'I don't believe it.'

'I didn't ask you to believe it.'

210

The door opened, a man in a long white coat entered followed by an elderly woman in nurse's uniform. The man said, 'Mr. Gollantz?'

Bill said, 'We're both—Mr. Gollantz. My brother's son, and I'm Sir Emmanuel's brother. How is he?'

'Pretty desperately ill. He's lost a good deal of blood.'

Simeon asked, 'Is he going to die?'

'That I couldn't tell you—even if I knew, which I don't. I advise you both to go home. We have your telephone number. You can come back in the morning. As early as you wish. Or we will telephone to you as to the patient's condition.'

'Can't I stay all night?' Simeon asked.

'Frankly, it is much wiser not to do so. You can't do anything, and he is unlikely to recover consciousness.'

'If he dies, won't he be conscious first?'

Bill Gollantz said testily, 'Simeon, for Heaven's sake, how you harp on about dying! At this rate you'll have the poor chap buried by tomorrow. I'm going home.'

'Very wise, Mr. Gollantz, very wise.'

Together they walked out into the silence; as they went through the entrance an ambulance swung through, moving silently and swiftly. Simeon shivered. Bill plodded along stolidly, unmoved.

The deserted Strand, only the odd late individuals making their way home, sometimes a little unsteadily. Neither of them spoke, Simeon absorbed with thoughts of his father, with speculations regarding him, with ideas as to what had actually taken place in the little room in Bond Street, Bill trying to work out some plan of action.

As they passed the end of the Haymarket he said, 'Listen. I'm going round to Julian's flat. If he isn't there, he's gone to Ordingly. We can find him. Go home, tell Hannah, and wait for my telephone call.'

Simeon, breathing hard, answered, 'I'd like to come with you.'

'Frankly, I don't want you. That's not being unkind. It wouldn't do any good. Go home, tell Hannah, wait to see if they telephone from the hospital. Look, there's a taxi!' He waved to the crawling vehicle. 'Drive me to Hay Hill, then on to Heber Square. That's all right. I know it's late, we'll see that you're well paid.'

The driver repeated, ' 'Ay 'ill, eh? Orlrite.'

At the entrance to the flats Bill climbed out. He turned to Simeon and smiled. 'Damn it, I'm a good deal more clumsy with

211

two feet than you are with one. Right! Keep your heart up. It's going to be all right. Heber Square, driver.'

The lift had ceased working, and Bill climbed the stairs swearing gently. He hated stairs, he hated violent exercise of any kind. Once he had loved it, had taken a pride in being hard and fit ; now there was so much to do, he hadn't time for rackets and fives, for tennis and the like. Gosh, what a mess this all was! Emmanuel lying half-dead, young Simeon with his white, drawn face and his heart full of fear. Wretched business for everyone. Young Simeon, he would come of age in a month or so. Better go through the papers and documents relating to his inheritance tomorrow—he mentally corrected himself—to-day. He stopped, panting a little. A light showed through the fanlight of Julian's flat. Bill hesitated, then lifting the little highly decorative knocker, gave five knocks alternating in strength.

'Ta—*ta*—*ta*—ta—*ta!*'

He waited, his head cocked on one side, like a listening terrier. Somewhere he heard a sound ; someone was moving.

He saw the letterbox pushed open, heard a voice ask, 'Who is there?'

Julian's voice!

He answered, speaking quietly, 'The law. Open the door.'

Slowly the door swung open and Julian stood staring at him.

Bill said, 'Hello, let me in, will you? I've got to talk to you.'

Julian, his mouth slipping open, whispered, 'The law!'

'That's all right,' his brother answered, 'I do represent the law. My hat, you've done it this time, Julian! This is where you've landed yourself, you damned fool!'

They walked down the passage into a room which was in a state of the wildest disorder. Bags were in the process of being packed, papers were scattered everywhere ; a small table held a decanter, syphon and glasses ; the air was thick with tobacco smoke. Bill looked at his brother ; his hair was disordered, his face the colour of chalk, his eyes staring and rather wild.

He breathed, 'Is he dead?'

Bill shook his head. 'Not yet. I've just left him.'

'Any hope—oh God! I swear that I didn't kill him!'

Moving to the table, Bill poured himself a drink, added soda, and sipped it. 'They don't hold out—much hope. What are you going to do?'

The last phrase was uttered in a voice so crisp, so impersonal, so detached and yet so authoritative, that Julian's white face quivered.

212

He said, making a vain attempt to recapture his habitual poise, 'Going to do? Oh, of course you don't know. Old Van der Hoyt wants me immediately in America. Amanda's there; business is booming and he offers me a magnificent opportunity. That's why I went to Bond Street, to clear up certain private papers. Then my precious brother came in and accused me of the most incredible things—the rest you know. Yes, I'm going to America.'

'And your son?' Bill's voice was persuasive.

'Max? Oh, I shall send for him. This potty London Stock Exchange is no good to him. His grandfather can find him something much better. Clever lad, my son.'

Bill sipped his drink reflectively. Julian had almost recovered his old swagger and certainty. He had lit a cigarette, and was busy mixing himself a drink. Only his hand trembled slightly.

'What about your defence?' Bill asked. 'If Emmanuel dies you'll need someone to defend you at the trial.'

Julian set down his glass. 'Trial!' he repeated. 'Trial—you mean if Emmanuel dies? They couldn't touch me. How could they? I did nothing. He insulted me, he threatened to kill me!'

Bill gave his deep chuckle which held no trace of amusement. 'There's a lot of "threatening to kill" in the air to-night. Simeon swears that if his father dies he'll kill you! By God, they can be ugly, these RAF types! It's their training, I suppose. They're taught to hold life—their own or the other chap's—pretty cheaply. I asked him how he proposed to kill you. He just held out his hands! "These will do," he said, but the expression on his face! Phew! I've never seen anything more coldly murderous. That's where the real terror lies, I think. They're so damnably *cold* about it all. Honestly, I believe if Emmanuel does die—and he's perilously near doing so—young Simeon will find you! Ugh! Not a nice prospect, is it? Makes me go quite cold! But this defence, Julian. If you're in America you must have someone.'

Julian wiped his forehead. 'I suppose you and Charles couldn't brief someone?'

Bill's bushy eyebrows shot up into his fair hair. 'My dear man, we're a very respectable firm! We shouldn't even consider it. No, you must get your son to make these arrangements.' Again that unpleasant chuckle. 'I should like to see myself proposing such a thing to Charles! He's never liked you very much, you know.'

'None of you have ever—liked me very much,' Julian said. 'You've always admired Emmanuel's play-acting, his "keeping

213

up the old tradition", his magnificent impersonations of his grandfather! At one time my mother understood me——'

'You mean that at one time she *didn't* understand you, surely?'

'She's changed. My father tried to give me a chance. I was making good. I was bringing far more business to the firm than had come to it for years——'

Bill interpolated, 'By what devious routes!'

'I loathe the lot of you!' Julian's voice was quiet, but his face—that dead-white face—seemed to glow with an intense fury. Bill could almost feel the hate which emanated from him. 'A lot of smug, self-righteous Jews from the Viennese ghetto! Covered with a veneer of culture——'

'Excepting myself, they have more than a veneer,' Bill murmured.

'What are they really? Sellers of junk! Mixing with the rest of the blasted tribes of Judah. The Gallery crammed with smarming, handwashing Yids! Hating me, because I don't subscribe to their carpet-selling acts! Because I don't look like a Jew, don't think like one, don't behave like one! Because I have more brains in my little finger than they have in their whole body!'

'But—it is such a crooked little finger, isn't it?' Bill said.

'You! A damned solicitor. Filled with the same smugness, the same—love of playing for safety! My whole life, my career, was ruined when Emmanuel's little pimp of an Italian knocked me down. I've never known a day completely free from pain since. I had to watch all my hopes, ambitions, aspirations—go! I had, virtually, to live on charity at Ordingly. During the American slump, when my wife's father lost a fortune, I was made conscious——'

'That you could no longer live on her,' Bill said. 'Julian, don't go on. It's too pathetic! I can't bear it. I'm tender-hearted and easily touched. You damned poseur! Pain—you don't know what pain is. Living on charity! Gosh, you did pretty well out of it, didn't you? Your hopes, ambitions and the rest of it—damned rot! Anyway, let's have done with all this play-acting. If Emmanuel "play-acts", he'd have to give pride of place to you! You're getting out? Good! When do you go? Your papers can't be in order, this only happened to-night. You'd better leave me your passport and other documents, I'll arrange matters.

'Get as far as France, by the earliest possible means. Telegraph an address to me. I'll arrange something. Clear up this mess here, burn everything that is incriminating. If Emmanuel dies—well, we'll wait until that happens. Otherwise, clear out

214

to America. Cable old Van der Hoyt to make an application for you. Tell him to reply to me. I'll put this through for you, Julian, and it's the last time I ever want to see you, have any communication with you. I suppose that you're not going down to Ordingly?'

'God, I haven't got time! Will you see my son for me?'

'I'll do that. Don't make a mess of this, Julian, or if Emmanuel dies they'll make such a very nasty mess of you. Hanging's a barbarous business,' he added reflectively.

Julian drank his whisky-and-soda noisily, then sat down suddenly as if he were a puppet and someone had let go of the strings. He covered his face with his hands, and Bill heard the long shuddering sobs which shook him.

He stood watching him coldly, yet with a certain interest. Then, shrugging his massive shoulders, he said, 'I'll be getting along. Get busy as soon as it's possible. I shall expect to have your address in Calais. You can trust me to get everything through. Good-bye.'

He walked out, locking the door behind him. As he walked towards his club he thought how strange it was that once before a Gollantz had left his country in a hurry and never returned. His father's younger brother Algernon had died somewhere in Switzerland. He had hated his elder brother Max—so recently dead. History repeating itself.

'Only,' Bill said softly, 'Emmanuel's not going to die. For all his ideals and fantastic notions, his romanticism and sentimentality, Emmanuel's made of tougher stuff than Julian. Pah, what a nasty little room! Hideous furniture! Carpet full of dust! Even the soda-water wasn't really cold! Whew! I'm tired.'

hich necessitate
He knew that he
nd why he had co
ired, his hair, w

BOOK THREE

CHAPTER ONE

EMMANUEL lay very still. He had no particular wish to move. His head ached intolerably, and when he tried to open his eyes the lids felt terribly heavy. From time to time he thought that he slept, and yet what he experienced was not like sleep, rather it was a sort of letting go of whatever held him to consciousness. A drifting away rather than sleep.

From time to time he was conscious that people came and stood near his bed; vague shapes and forms, voices which were either quiet and completely unintelligible or else which boomed so that the words they uttered were incomprehensible. There were cool hands which touched his head, hands which—however kind they might intend to be—sent knives stabbing through his brain. There were dry, rather brittle hands, curious hands, explorative hands, mechanical hands. They didn't actually belong to anyone in particular, they were simply—hands. Usually they smelt of something astringent, and the smell seemed to pierce his senses.

Then, over and under everything else, was this pain, which never seemed to cease for a moment, except when he managed to evade it by slipping away. Where did he go? That was something which he was too tired to fathom. He only knew that he did, from time to time, contrive to make an escape—to get away from the pain, the hands, the astringent smell, the cold touch of metal or china against his lips, the intense weariness of having to swallow something which trickled down his throat, and which necessitated his making the effort to swallow.

He knew that he was Emmanuel Gollantz, but where he was and why he had come there he had no idea, and he was far too tired, his brain worked too slowly for him to attempt to discover.

A queer affair that brain of his. Dimly he remembered things which had become imprinted upon it—the blue of a robe— some picture—trees with spreading branches—a woman called Battista. He moved his head wearily, and the pain stabbed him violently. No use trying to think. Thinking must wait. Once or twice he thought that he must be dead; the idea excited him, and made the pain worse. Then—he drifted away.

He had been there for days, months, years. There was a faint light a little to his left, as if somewhere a lamp was burning. Sometimes he thought that he heard footsteps, coming towards him very quietly, someone who trod softly. Once he heard a voice, a great distance away, call loudly and insistently, 'Father.' He imagined that the voice was familiar. It belonged to a young man called Sebastian—no, not that; Samson—that again was wrong. He was too tired to go on thinking, he let go his hold and drifted away into darkness.

Once he awoke in an express train, he was being whirled along. There must have been an accident, for his head was worse than ever. Later someone helped him into another train which moved less quickly. Some little local train he supposed.

The train stopped, he was helped out, into an hotel and put to bed. Voices reached him, but the words were not clear. He must have been to some sale in the country. What had he bought? He couldn't remember. Only one thing—a tankard, splendid, heavy, with a twisted top to the handle, and—a heart. Where was the heart? There was a heart somewhere! He was saying, 'The date? The date? Seventeen . . .' The rest faded, and someone held something which was cold to his lips, and said, 'Drink this.' Everything was like watching a bad film; a film which had been broken and mended imperfectly. There were pictures, then a blank. Not that he cared, he only wanted the pain in his head to cease, and sometimes he thought that if it got worse he would try to kill himself. Then, just as he was planning how to manage to do it, he felt a needle stuck into his arm, and his thoughts dissolved.

One morning—he had learnt when it was morning, because the light on his left glowed more brightly—he opened his eyes and knew that the weight of his eyelids was less. It was almost a pleasure to open them; they felt light, as if they were made of air! He moved them slowly. He couldn't see very well, shapes became merged into each other; what he saw first as a table became a wardrobe. That in turn became a chair and then a small fireplace. Something large, round, pinkish loomed above him; a voice boomed, 'You'rrrrre betterrrrr!'

Irritably he replied, 'Oh, be quiet!'

Days, weeks later another voice, a voice which lacked a face, said, 'It's me, Father—it's Simeon.'

He answered with a sudden sense of satisfaction, 'That's the name! I couldn't recall it. I said, Samson! Samson. How are you?'

The voices became more frequent, he began to recognize them, even to find names for them. This gave him great satisfaction, for surely very few people could think of the correct names for voices! He was mildly interested.

There was a voice which said, 'My deah boy, how are yer?'

He said, 'Ah, you come from Rome. Welcome! Welcome, Aurelius!'

The voice replied, 'Wanderin'—wanderin'.'

Much later he remembered that of course he had not meant to say 'Aurelius', he had meant to say 'Marcus'. It didn't matter, they both came from Rome.

Two people argued; one said, 'How can he possibly make a statement?' The other replied, 'Given time, if we handle him gently, he might.'

'And destroy all that we've done. I shan't allow it.'

Emmanuel said loudly, and very distinctly, 'Quite right! Quite right!'

More people, one whose voice was very light and rather high, the other heavier and lower—it went 'boom, boom' all the time. Like some great bumble-bee. The light voice was very attractive, he liked to listen to it. He'd heard it somewhere. He tried to turn his eyes but the effort hurt too much and he closed them and listened.

'Physically—yes, but we should like to keep him under inspection.'

The lighter voice said, 'You have been very, very kind; most skilful. But don't you think that he might come home now.'

The voice went on, 'An ambulance—most careful—nurses.' It grew indistinct, then cleared again, and the words came to him like music. 'He has always liked Ordingly.'

He made a supreme effort and said, 'I do like Ordingly. I'm going there. At once, d'you hear? At once!'

The light voice became possessed of a face—a face which he could see quite clearly. His mother spoke to him, he could hear every word she said.

'I'm going to take you to Ordingly, Emmanuel. Not to-day. You mustn't be impatient, darling. But very soon. Go on getting well, and then I shall come for you. I promise, my dear.'

'When?' he asked. 'When? Why can't I go to-day?' He heard himself whimper a little.

'As soon as I can get an ambulance. There are some poor men want it to-day. And to-morrow. After that—I'll come for you.'

His voice sounded sulky. 'What's the matter with them?'

'They've hurt their heads, as you have.'

'All right, I'll wait.'

'That's my kind boy.'

He slept a great deal, and dreamed once or twice of Ordingly, he saw the big trees and their widespread branches, the clipped lawns, the big portico, and the long stretch of buildings. He even heard the stable clock, and felt his feet treading the worn flagstones of the stableyard. An old setter came out to meet him, waving a tail like a plume. He snapped his fingers at it—and woke.

He lay in his own room, quiet, almost free from pain though his head was still bandaged. He could see the bright fire, with its leaping flames. He thought, 'Apple wood! Those old trees were past bearing any longer. Angela has always liked apple wood.'

It was delightful to be able to string thoughts together, thoughts which 'fitted' and did not go wandering about so that you found it impossible to follow them. Someone came to see him every day, real visitors, as well as Hewson, who brought him food, and nurses who came and went. One of the nurses was very pretty. Young, with fair hair, and a mouth that was always ready to smile. He wondered what her name was, but it was too much trouble to ask, so he called them both 'Nurse'. The other was older, with a leathery face and beautiful even teeth. She had big, cool hands ; hands which could unfasten the bandage without hurting—at least without hurting too much. She never said, 'That doesn't hurt,' but 'I'm afraid that hurts.'

He gritted his teeth and answered, 'No, not a bit.'

Angela came every day ; he liked to watch her, admired her clothes. She smiled a great deal and laughed softly, a laugh which did not hurt his head. She brought flowers sometimes ; perhaps only one rose, and held it near him, saying 'Smell that! That's called "Mrs. Max Gollantz", called after me!'

He said, 'It's lovely, but you're lovelier.'

Bill, big, broad-shouldered Bill, muttering, 'Gosh, you've given us all a fright, confound you!' Simeon, looking thinner and rather tired, who stood looking down at him, blinking his eyes very hard.

Emmanuel said, 'Hello, Simeon, nice to see you.'

Simeon gulped, and replied, 'Last time you called me—Samson!'

'No! What an unnatural father you've got! How's the Gallery?'

The young man's eyes brightened. 'Grand! Sold a pair of George the First candlesticks at Sotheby's for five-sixty ; and a tankard for eight hundred.'

220

Something stirred in Emmanuel's brain, his lips curved into a smile.

'Not . . . the . . . tankard?'

'Not likely, Father. I'm having a special case made for that!'

'I remember it all quite clearly, you know. I didn't at first, but it's all coming back to me now. A very, very good tankard that!'

'I shouldn't think about it if I were you, Father.'

'Believe me, I shan't—unduly.'

Lady Heriot visited him ; she swept into his room bringing a perfume of 'Soir de Paris' with her, her bracelets and bangles jangling, her gloves—in the Edwardian fashion—far too tight.

She obviously tried to lower her voice, and almost whispered, 'Manny, my dear boy. Walter sends his love. Y'know Viva's back? I expect she'll be along to see you some time. Looks wonderful. Y'know, Manny, old "Buster" Carteret's making the running there. Sticks like a leech! What a knut he's turned into! Must have spent a fortune on new clothes, and bought coupons on the Black Market! Well, let 'em all come! Got to do it in these days. My word, Manny, I could say to you—get your hair cut, old boy. You look like a child musician! However, what about it! You're better ; that's what matters. We've been worried to death. Get well soon, and we'll have a "getting better party" eh? Oh, I can always get the stuff! Trust your Auntie Bee!'

A darling but just a little exhausting. So Viva was back, and old 'Buster' Carteret was 'making the running'. Well, 'Buster' was a good fellow, perhaps he'd suit Viva. He lay back and wondered what would suit Viva? Dances and gay suppers— though suppers weren't particularly gay in these days! Visits to Paris, for the races, then Ascot, Goodwood and the rest. And yet—was that really all she wanted? He frowned, and decided that it was no business of his, that Viva knew her own mind, and probably knew where to find her own happiness. Several times during the evening he repeated to himself, 'I like Carteret ; a very good sound fellow. Very fine fellow.'

Hannah came, stepping heavily, and, seating herself at his bedside, remained impassive and monumental. He stretched out his hand, she took it in both her own.

'Tell me about everything,' Emmanuel said.

'That would take too long. I can tell you that Simeon is doing more than well. This boy works like ten niggers, he has gained the admiration of all. He will make a great antique dealer, mark what I say. Also young Watson, begs me to bring his deep respects. That, also, is a good boy. A reliable boy. Reuben Davis, Fred Hooper—this one found a carpet last week—

twenty-eight by seventeen—Eastern—very beautiful. It sold this week for five hundred and twenty. Peters, too, and young Joseph—all asking after you, wishing you well again. We miss you badly, Emmanuel.'

'I shall soon be back again.'

'But,' anxiously, 'not too soon, please. Do not imagine that you are indispensable, this is a mistake. We all manage very well.'

He laughed. 'I know that you all long for the moment when I shall enter the portals of the Gallery once more! You have all conspired to make me conceited.'

As he grew stronger and was allowed to sit in the big chair by the fire Angela came more often and stayed longer. Emmanuel liked to watch her, as she sat with a piece of her exquisite embroidery in her hands, or sought among her silks for the exact shade which she required, her pretty hands, hovering, he thought, like butterflies above a flower.

Slowly and at various times she told him of Julian. She had not seen him before he left, though he had written affectionate letters to her on his arrival in America. Bill—dear Bill—had arranged everything. He had not consulted her, and he was right in not doing so. It appeared that old Van der Hoyt had long wanted Julian to join him. Business was booming, and he had given his son-in-law a very fine position. Julian had sent for Max, and he too had left for America. She drew a long scarlet thread through her work, and said, without raising her eyes:

'I don't think that I, at any rate, am likely to see Julian again. Don't imagine, my dear, that it distresses me too much. A little, I admit, because I am a very conceited woman, and I should like to have felt that my whole family depended upon me to a great extent, and flattered myself that none of them could have been perfectly happy if they were not in constant touch with me.

'That is foolish, of course. There are many people who grow up like young birds, puppies, kittens and the like. While they are very young and dependent they cling to their parents; after they leave the nest, or whatever it is they happen to regard as "home", their parents become incidental. It may be very right and proper—I don't know.'

Emmanuel, who still felt that discussions were beyond him, contented himself with saying, 'Oh, I don't know, darling.'

Angela, her eyes still on her embroidery, said, 'Funnily enough, I have never been really *in* any of your lives. Julian always lived his own. When he was going in for politics he liked me to go down to his constituency, liked to take me round with him, but I was a kind of "decoration", never part of the structure. Bill rather made his own decisions, and after all no mother can be intimate with her son's affairs if he is a solicitor, can she? Bill is so completely—satisfactory, it would be wrong to wish him to have been different in the smallest way.'

'A great fellow, Bill,' Emmanuel assented, 'and me? What about me?'

For the first time his mother looked up from her work, and smiled at him.

'You,' she said ; 'Max and I made so many mistakes over you. We were both so stupid. Possibly I was not quite so stupid as my dear Max, and yet—I don't know—I was so blind ; I relied on what I was told, instead of relying upon what I *knew*. I was always getting facts—when it was just too late! No, Emmanuel, neither Max nor I have been much help to you, and yet now, you're the person we're—because wherever he is I know that Max feels the same—looking to to—"take over".'

He smiled back at her. 'I'll do my best.'

'That will be no change, my dear.'

Emmanuel began to speak quietly, almost as if he only spoke his thoughts aloud, without realizing that he was speaking directly to another person. His eyes were half closed, the leaping flames of the wood fire lit up his rather gaunt, thin face, showed the hollows in his cheeks, and the clear line of his jaw from ear to chin. Angela thought that his thick dark hair, even though it was greying at the temples, seemed too heavy for his face. His voice was low, and very musical ; she thought that she had never realized before what a very beautiful voice Emmanuel possessed.

He said, 'I'm glad that Julian writes to you ; glad that his letters are affectionate and kind. If he ever loved anyone, he loved you. To me, to Bill, to my father it might seem to be a love which lacked strength, but people can only give—what they have to give. Julian never had a great deal of love to offer anyone, you know. He has more charm, when he cares to exercise it, than any man I know, and he's come to rely on it. More, he has never had scruples. He looks on my father's ideas, on mine, as something outdated, old-fashioned and very limited.

'Somewhere—ages ago—a Gollantz must have been a pirate ; must have sailed the Seven Seas plundering, taking whatever he wanted. I imagine that he wore magnificent clothes and cut a tremendous figure. Julian is the reincarnation of that pirate.

'I'm not ; Bill's not ; we're ordinary, hard-working, r-rather plodding merchants. He despises both of us, because he can, if he wishes, make so much more money than we can. We earn what we get, he plunders gaily and pits his brains against those

223

of other men. He's got plenty of courage; it's more r-reckless than such courage as Bill and I possess. We're cautious; he may sense danger, but he only laughs at it.

'Had I read of Julian in a book of adventure, when I was about fourteen, he would have seemed to me to be a hero. Now, I know that he's wr-rong. It is not Bill and I who are old-fashioned—but Julian! Men can no longer sail over the oceans with the "Jolly Roger" flying at the masthead for ever. The world is too well organized, and eventually machinery is set in motion to lay them by the heels. I don't wish to see him again. I don't wish him any harm—why should I? I only hope that we never meet; that he does what he has never been content to do in his life—and that is, leaves me alone.'

His mother nodded, 'He'll—leave you alone, Emmanuel. After all, if he did come to England on a visit, you have always Milano to which you can go.'

'I am to bolt to Milano when he signals his arrival, eh?' but he laughed as he said it, and his words were sufficiently light to convey no sense of resentment. 'Very well, we'll arrange it like that. And Bill—where shall Bill go to?'

Angela answered, her eyes dancing. 'To shoot pheasants or grouse with Charles in Scotland—if it's the right time of year.'

'And if it's the wr-rong time of year?'

'Oh, there are winter sports, or bathing, or fishing. Our Bill is easily disposed of, bless him!' There was a long pause. Emmanuel began to wonder if he were not a little tired, if he would not welcome the arrival of his attractive young nurse, with her ready smile and her suggestion, 'Don't you think, Sir Emmanuel, that perhaps you're getting a little tired?'

He had discovered her name, a name which he thought as charming as her face—Daphne Conroy. She had even talked to him a little about herself. Her father was a doctor in Newquay; they were not rich, but they liked their home, and she loved her brothers and sisters. She told him stories of their various amusements, of their various ambitions. Colin was in the Navy; George was going to be a doctor and eventually take over the practice; Mary was studying music at the Royal Academy and hoped to win a scholarship; and Barbara, the 'baby'—'only seventeen' but so pretty—was engaged to a very clever young man who was working for the B.B.C.

He liked the 'sound' of her family, imagined them all at home, indulging in very simple amusements—which did not necessitate the spending of too much money. He thought that the house would be comfortable, rather shabby, with a garden filled with flowers in the front and vegetables at the back.

His mother's voice interrupted his thoughts. 'Emmanuel.'

'Yes, darling.'

'I know that this is wrong of me; I know that it's time that you went back to rest, but we don't often get the opportunity to talk without interruption, do we? Tell me, what did actually happen—that dreadful night at the Gallery?'

Emmanuel said, 'Didn't Bill tell you?'

'I'm asking you, Emmanuel.'

He frowned. 'Well, a gr-reat deal of it is supposition. Julian was working late—I wanted to see him, and I was waiting in my own office. He came in, went into his room, I followed him. We had an argument, and finally he left in a fur-rious temper.

'Now whether the thieves had followed him in, whether they had made their entrance before he got there, possibly even before I got there, no one can say. It's sufficient that they made a r-rush at me.'

'Didn't you see them?' Angela's voice was very calm.

'No, they must have come up to me from behind. I was examining a tankard which Julian had just bought. I imagine that they thought Julian and I had heard them and that he had gone for the police. The r-rest isn't clear. Anyway, Julian had left his keys in the door, for Simeon found them, and after giving me a few but well-chosen and very-well-directed blows on the head, they got away. That's the story.'

She said, 'Well, it's a very good story. I didn't know that Bill had so much imagination. That's what is called "reconstructing the incident", isn't it? Did they take much—these thieves?'

'I really couldn't say. Naturally we wanted to hush it up as much as possible. The insurance people don't take too good a view of people like ourselves who have burglaries, you know. I believe that Bill—with Charles' help—hushed it all up ver-ry well indeed.'

'And Julian left the following morning?'

'Oh, he'd been expecting to go for some time, only he didn't confide in any of us.'

She rose and folded her work carefully, then came over to where he sat and kissed him lightly. 'Bless you,' she said, 'you may both be very clever, but you're damned poor liars, my child! Ah, here's Nurse Conroy to blame me for allowing you to talk so much. I'll come up for a moment after dinner.'

The attractive young woman came forward. 'I'm a little late, I'm afraid. I forgot the time. I'm so sorry.'

Emmanuel said, 'I'm sorry that you were late. You've just missed hearing my mother using violent language towards me!

I'm disappointed that you should not have been here to defend me.'

Angela, turning back as she opened the door, flung at them, 'Take not the slightest notice, Nurse. He's a cad to repeat private conversations.'

Emmanuel was up and dressed for the first time; he stared at his thin, white face in the mirror, and said meditatively, 'What a devil of a wreck!'

Daphne Conroy laughed. 'Nothing of the kind! How wise we were not to give you a mirror six weeks ago! Then—you really did look terrible.'

He leaned forward, staring into the mirror, and settled his tie to his liking.

'Thanks to you both, I'm on my feet again.' He added, 'You don't know how gr-rateful I am.'

She answered gravely, 'You've been a very good patient. This is the first time I've ever nursed an—important person.'

'Important! What rubbish! An elderly antique dealer!'

'I'm glad that you're better,' she continued, without heeding his interruption, 'but I shall be sorry to go. It's so lovely here.'

She saw his haggard face light up. 'You like Ordingly?'

'Could anyone help—liking Ordingly?'

'But you love Newquay, don't you? You'll be glad to be back.'

'Only for ten days, and then I come back to London. I'm going to nurse Lady Heriot; she wants massage and someone to generally look after her, and Lady Gollantz recommended me.'

Emmanuel said, 'Now that is pleasant! Aunt Beatrice! My favourite aunt! But she's not r-really ill, is she! Nothing serious.'

He watched the girl's face break into one of the smiles he liked so much; her eyes lit up and seemed, he thought, to dance. 'Well, not really ill,' she admitted. 'She does want some massage, and—only don't tell anyone I said this, will you?'

'Not a soul!'

'I think that she's rather bored, and she is putting on weight, and hates it. She wants someone who will "regulate her diet". And—I shall. She'll be almost slim when we've finished with her.'

'We? Who are—we?'

'Sir Nathan and I.'

'Ah, good old chap! Now, can I go into the other room?'

'Yes, and there's a visitor waiting to see you. She's been waiting for nearly ten minutes. We kept it as a surprise for you.'

Walking very slowly, for his legs still felt that they were ready to be disobedient to his wishes, he went into the sitting-

226

room which led from his bedroom. Someone rose from the big chair by the fire, someone who came forward with outstretched hands, and said, 'Emmanuel!'

'My dear, dear Viva, how charming to see you!'

She said, 'I've been before, when you weren't able to see me. Sit down and let me look at you! What have they been doing to you? You've lost stones and you were never fat, Heaven knows.'

He leaned back in his chair and watched her, allowing her to talk to him but making no attempt to interrupt her. How attractive she was! Possibly scme of the youth which he had known had gone, but in its place there was a vivid maturity. Her voice seemed deeper, more full, her whole attitude held poise and certainty. Emmanuel found that he was enjoying listening to her. He was not yet sufficiently strong to find conversation easy, but to have someone like this ready to talk to him amusingly was a joy.

She said, 'There, I imagine that someone will be coming to rout me out. They take great care of you, Emmanuel?'

He answered, 'They almost kill me with kindness.'

'And Julian's gone to America, eh?'

'Julian has gone to America,' he assented.

'Small wonder the Americans dislike us,' Viva said, 'if that is the way we repay their loans to us! What was the real truth. Tell me.'

He made his queer characteristic movement with his hands as if he tried to brush away something unpleasant. 'Viva dear, let Bill tell you. He knows the story—so far as any of us know it —far better than I do.'

He watched the sudden tilt of her chin which he remembered so well. 'Which means that all this Gollantz gallantry and Knights of the Round Table still persists! Really, my dear, you are all of you slightly ridiculous, you know! All right, keep your story locked in your hearts. That's the right phrase, isn't it? I must go!'

Emmanuel held out his hand. 'Will you forgive me if I don't get up? My head is still a little apt to play tr-ricks. Where are you going to live, Viva; with Aunt Beatrice?'

She was busy with lipstick and a tiny mirror, and did not reply for a moment, then putting both back in her bag, closing it firmly, she answered, 'With Mama? Oh no, I don't think that's a very good idea. I—well, I might get married again.'

'Married again!' And to Emmanuel's disgust he caught a faint note of dismay in his own voice, and felt suddenly angry. What had it to do with him? Viva had a right to find what happiness she could. He said again, with slightly overdone warmth, 'Married again—good! Nice fellow? Of course he must be, or you'd not want to mar-ry him.'

Her eyes met his very steadily, as she said, 'Well, old "Buster" has been a very good friend to me, hasn't he? Kind, attentive, thoughtful.'

'Carteret, you mean? Oh yes, very.' He wanted to say that she couldn't possibly marry that fat man, with the scarlet face, who obviously drank far too much, however kind and thoughtful and attentive he might be. Wanted to say that he'd bore her to death in a week! Viva Tatten to marry 'Buster' Carteret!

Viva said, 'I don't believe that you approve, Emmanuel.'

'My dear, I have no right to appr-rove or disappr-rove. If I seemed a little suprised it was because he didn't seem quite— not quite your type, that was all.'

'Make a suggestion then as to who is my type?' She flung the words at him like a challenge.

'Frankly, I don't quite know. R-really I have no r-right. . . .'

She laughed. 'All right. Think it over, and if any suitable names suggest themselves, send me a note, will you? Good-bye, Emmanuel. Go on getting well.'

She was gone, staying for a second to leave a very light kiss on the top of his head. He sat very still, his hands hanging between his knees. Viva to marry 'Buster' Carteret? Slowly the realization came to him that he didn't want her to marry Carteret ; he didn't want her to marry anyone except—his mind halted and seemed to shy away from what he knew to be facts, as a nervous horse might shy at a piece of paper fluttering in a country lane.

He sat very still, the room was slowly darkening, only the small, bright fire danced and sent flashes of light into the dusk. He had not made such a signal success with his marriage to Viva ; they had been unsuited, she had resented his gravity, his persistence to regard his business as having more importance than dances and theatres.

Then he had realized that he had given his heart so completely to Juliet that there was nothing left for him to do except—go away. Well, he'd known complete and absolute happiness for a year. Viva had been ideally happy with poor Tatten—now, were they both older if not actually wiser? They were more tolerant, possibly seeing things in truer perspective, both more adaptable. Would Viva listen to him, or would the thought of 'Buster' Carteret with his high spirits, his love of laughter and 'good times', outweigh anything which Emmanuel Gollantz might have to offer? What right had he even to think of asking Viva to marry him? Imagine if she laughed—as she had laughed at him so often—and said, 'What, marry the man I once divorced! My dear, what fools people would think us!'

And yet, Emmanuel mused, no other woman attracted him as Viva did, no other woman amused and interested him as she did. More than these things, there was a deep and profound love for her in his heart. Not, he admitted, the same wild adoration which he had given to Juliet, but did men of nearly fifty love in the same way as they had loved at twenty-five? Or women, for that matter? Even if Viva would consider marrying him, would she ever feel for him what she had felt for 'Toby'?

He remembered something which his grandfather had once said to him, years ago. He could hear the strong old voice speaking clearly, see again the man for whom he had always had an especial reverence. 'The spr-ring, my dear boy, is exquisite. Alvays the colours are so new, and fr-resh and clear. Tr-rue, there may be storms, but t'ey pass and again the sun shines. But r-remember also, the autumn is a good time, a kind, tolerant time. Some people t'ink it is a sad time. T'ey are fools! Autumn is time of fulfilment. Please r-remember.'

The door opened and Daphne Conroy came in.

'Why, you're in the dark, Sir Emmanuel!'

'Yes, I am rather.'

'You're tired; it's time you came back to rest.'

'There again,' he said, 'I believe that you are r-right.'

CHAPTER TWO

IT seemed to Emmanuel that after the first day he was allowed to get up, dress, and walk into the next room to sit there by the fire, life took on a quicker tempo. More people came to see him, and with each day he found that he could talk more easily, and with less fatigue. Louis Lara came from Paris to talk of his 'peerless Olympia'. Paul Mancini came bringing Iva Alfano. Iva was growing too stout; she admitted it, and declared that she did not care.

'What is opera to me?' she demanded. 'To sing at Covent Garr-den in Eengleesh! *Dio!* Not that this ter-rible language is not easy to me as kiss the 'and, but to seeng in eet! It may be that I do a concert tour, but Paul and I have made moniee—ver' mooch moniee—and why must we then—now, wait, I hev the express-i-on so good—why must we then wear out the guts of ourselves to work like 'orses? No, I shall buy a 'ouse at Cheeping Camden——'

Emmanuel said, 'Why Chipping Camden, Iva?'

She threw back her head and roared with laughter. 'Eet is sooch a comic name theese—Cheeping Camden! Imagine eet! Or the ozzer—h'Ashby de la Zoo-ooch! England is filled with sooch names.'

And finally Guido came from Milan. He entered Emmanuel's room as he might have entered a holy place, walking on tiptoe, scarcely daring to breathe. He took Emmanuel's hand, and falling on his knees kissed it repeatedly.

Emmanuel said, 'For Heaven's sake, Guido, my dear fellow, get up!'

Guido rose; tears were pouring down his cheeks; he wiped them away with a beautiful handkerchief.

'My beloved Master,' he said. 'Dante believed that he knew some'sing of the Inferno! Pah! This Dante! He knew nossing, but nossing! I, Guido Moroni, have forgetted more t'en Dante ever knew. Pagliacci shouts about his breaking 'eart. Anosser *imbecile*. I have had a broken-ing 'eart for weeks. Still I live, for my courage cannot be broken. Lions, tigers, airmen, and so

230

forse—they are wretched cowards when comparisoned with Guido! News came, ver' badly news, desperate news. News which 'eld no 'ope. I walk in the Galleria, my head held 'igh an' proud. "Please," they esk, "the noble Gollantz, what news?" I smile, a drawn-away smile, secret and knowing! I bang on my chest with my closed fist. I say, "Ah, have no fear! Gollantz cannot die! Gollantz will live to return to Milano to bring joyousness to our 'earts!" you like my latest clothes? Quiet, suitable for gentleman, eh? Dark, but not as *lutto*—what is it—mourning is dark, eh?'

Emmanuel said, 'Quite admirable. How long have you been in England?'

'For nearly ten days. I have reposed in the sharming house of our leetle Simeon. I have seen your Galleries. Business is first rate. Simeon is bloody fine dealer ; his manners are damn' good! To old trouts he is polite, to all he is polite. I have also been to Tower of London, and to raise my hat to the King who I watched driving out from Buck House. Here I find it is called that—Buck House. I learn so quickly all words, there is great astonishment everywhere. Again not Varr Offus, but Varr House. I don't say "Pardon", I say, "Come again, chum!"'

Emmanuel pressed him to say at Ordingly for the remainder of his visit. They had much to discuss, and often Simeon joined in their talks. Emmanuel said to Guido one day, 'That's a good lad, never minds trailing out to Ordingly to talk business with us, does he?'

Guido narrowed his eyes for a moment, then said, 'No, certainly not. Your veesh is his pleasurement. Maybe there might be one ozzer small reason, per'aps no?'

'What other reason could there be?'

Guido shrugged his well-padded shoulders. ' 'Ow would I know? Esk me anozzer!'

'His grandmother? He's devoted to her.'

'Pal, you maybe got it!' Guido returned, and burst into laughter.

Emmanuel said, 'You and your damned silly slang! Where the deuce do you pick it up?'

'Theatres—music 'all. Last night Simeon took me to see an American play, gangstaire play. Miss Conroy gave us pleasure of her company. She is very prettie, eh?'

'Nurse Conroy! Good ; it must be pretty dull sticking around here all the time. Nice girl.'

Guido frowned, as he always did when he wished to look highly intelligent, then said, 'I did not get the impression that Mees Conroy found Ordingly dull. Quite differently I imagined.

T'ere, we have talked an enough long time. I shall make a noise like a bee. Do you comprehend zat ver' funny remark?' He laughed without restraint. 'It signifies—Buzz off. T'is means to —get cracking. How much I like t'is Eengleesh language.'

'You are certainly en-r-riching your knowledge of it,' Emmanuel said drily. 'I have never heard more slang in my life than I have done in the past ten minutes. All right, Guido, we'll get down to business later. And you'll stay out here at Ordingly—yes, please do.'

Guido clicked his heels together, bowed and said, 'What Saire Gollantz orders, Guido is ready to do.'

Emmanuel, left alone, stretched out his long legs before the fire and let his thoughts take possession of him. They seemed to run round in circles, always returning to the same place—Viva, Carteret, himself. Of one thing he was certain, that he did not want her to marry 'Buster'. What, then, did he want? He asked himself if he would be able to think of her marriage with any other man with equanimity?

Mentally he ran through a list of his friends and hers—good fellows, men who could give her everything she wished for. Anyway, Viva was a rich woman in her own right. What did she really want? Emmanuel frowned. There had been a time when he would have answered, 'A good time—what Viva regards as a "good time".' Now, he wasn't certain.

He tried to put the question bluntly to himself—'Do I want to ask her to marry me, and if I do what earthly right have I to imagine that I could make her happier than "Buster" Carteret could?' Was he merely playing with the idea as a kind of gratification to his own self-conceit, or did she really mean so much to him?

He passed his hand over his forehead, as if he tried to sweep away his doubts and perplexities. Perhaps his attitude was merely that of the 'dog in the manger', and yet when she had married Tatten he had not resented her doing so. Admittedly— he sighed—life had all been different then; it was not possible to make comparisons. Now for over twenty years he had been alone, slowly recovering from the blow which Fate had dealt him. Juliet had died, he had been left with Simeon.

Did life really renew itself, could you make fresh starts, rebuild a sound, noble structure on the ruins of the old? Yet life was a lonely business, and might well be even more lonely. Simeon would marry; Angela—he shivered suddenly—was no longer young; his brother Bill had his own life, his own interests. Hannah, good, faithful, and completely devoted, was growing old; it was only her determination which kept her still working at the Galleries. Guido was an Italian, they didn't transplant well, and Guido loved his Milano.

His frown deepened, he knew that he was avoiding the real question. Did he love Viva sufficiently to have the right to ask her to marry him? That was the crux of the whole business. Not his own fear of loneliness; not the fact that he wanted companionship—all that mattered was that he must decide how much he loved her.

He took out his watch—he had never worn a wrist-watch; his grandfather had always said, 'T'ey are for boys, t'em watches. Men should vear a vatch, kerry it in a pocket!'—and flicked open the cover. Holding it so that the firelight caught it, he stared at the picture of Juliet which he always carried inside the case.

'Can't you help me?' he whispered softly. 'You always did, you always have. Can't you assure me that you understand, dearest?'

Was it some trick of the firelight or did the eyes actually light up and the beautiful mouth soften into a smile? Emmanuel stared at the picture, his face drawn and intent. Then slowly and carefully he closed the watch-cover and slipped it back into his pocket.

'You understand,' he whispered, 'you don't mind; don't think me unfaithful to you. The love which I gave you will last for ever, the love I can give her won't be the same—I don't wish it to be. But it is very real, very good, and completely sincere. Thank you, Lovely Juliet.'

He was lying in bed reading that evening; he felt tired, but pleasantly so. Guido had been to talk to him of Milano and the work which was being done in the Gallery there; his reports were reassuring and very satisfactory. Louis Lara was their best customer, and goods were constantly being sent to Paris and also large consignments to America. Their exports before the war had been large, so that even with the present restrictions they could sell and despatch a considerable amount. It was evident that Guido was developing into a very good business man. When he left to go to play some two-handed card game with Angela the smile of content lingered on Emmanuel's lips.

Angela had said earlier in the evening, 'This little Italian man! But—charming, Emmanuel, quite charming. He's made me feel years younger! I shall give a dinner-party for him.'

Strange how ideas changed, Emmanuel reflected. Ten years ago, how both Angela and Max would have disliked Guido Moroni! To have brought him to Ordingly would have been to commit the gravest solecism. Now here was Angela hailing him as a delightful guest.

The door opened and Simeon came in. Emmanuel glanced up, smiling, and said, 'This is nice! How are things at the Galleries?'

'Very good, Father,' Simeon answered. 'It seems to me that in these days you can sell almost anything. Oh,' quickly, 'I don't mean that we're unloading rubbish, we've none to unload, but people are very keen. They're not exactly struck on this utility furniture, and they don't mind paying a higher price for something they do like, and can be proud of. Hannah sent you her love, and would like to come over on Saturday to see you. Will that be all right?'

'Delightful. Tell me more.'

Simeon moved over to the fireplace, and stood staring down at the fire in silence. Emmanuel could see his grave, young face, note how the firelight caught the warm brown of his hair. What a nice-looking fellow he was!

Emmanuel asked, 'The foot all right?'

'You mean the new one? Magnificent. I scarcely know that I'm wearing it. Father, I wanted to ask you something rather important. Are you sure that you're not too tired to listen?'

'Most certainly I'm not. I'm hoping to be back in harness in a couple of weeks. I might even take a t-r-rip to Milano with Guido when he goes back. Fire away—what is it?'

Simeon moved back to the end of his father's bed and laid his hands on the foot of it.

'Well, it's this, Father. I want to get married. Would you mind?'

'Ma-r-rried!' Emmanuel ejaculated. 'Simeon, you're very young!'

'I don't know, Father,' Simeon said; 'you know the war did knock a lot of the "youngness" out of us. We learnt to think for ourselves, to rely on ourselves, to make quick decisions. Some of us don't feel too happy about the future, and if there is going to be another show, well, we might as well get as much happiness as we can while the going's good. I've plenty of money to keep a girl properly. I was talking things over with Uncle Bill. I was astonished to find out how much I had got! It was rather frightening really.'

Emmanuel said, 'A good many people have worked p-r-retty hard for that money, Simeon, among them your mother.'

'I know, oh, I know.' eagerly; 'don't think that I want to just fling it about. I want to work too, work hard. I don't think that work is any real fun if you don't work hard. But—you'll be living out here, won't you, and Heber Place would be ideal for——'

'You've got it all worked out, eh? Tell me about the girl. Who is she, one of Aunt Beatrice's debs? Don't d-r-rag the family forcibly into the higher strata of the aristocracy, Simeon. I could never live up to it.'

'Her father is a doctor,' Simeon told him. 'Oh, it's no use beating about the bush. You do like her, and she likes you ; it's Daphne Conroy. I've asked her to marry me, and she said that I must come and ask you. Aunt Bee likes her awfully, so does Grandmama, so does your friend Guido. He says that she is like an English rose.'

'One of Guido's more o-r-riginal remarks,' Emmanuel commented. 'This is a pretty business, Simeon. You take advantage of my lying at death's door to make love to my p-r-rettier nurse! How do you suppose she can give her full and undivided attention to me when she is longing to get away and read your latest effusion?'

Simeon grinned. 'There haven't been many, I've been here practically every day, Father.'

'Making love to my nurse under p-r-retence of playing the dutiful son! What a snake in the grass!'

'I didn't let much of it grow under my feet, Father.'

'Snakes don't possess feet! Well, what do you expect me to say?'

'Only—"yes, and bless you, my children". That's the usual formula, isn't it? She's leaving here on Saturday, and I thought that I might go down and see her father, get to know the family. They live at Newquay.'

'I know all about where they live, my lad, and her sisters and brothers and what they all do for a living, and who they're going to marry. She told me all that weeks ago!' He held out his hand, and Simeon came round to take it in his own. The two men's eyes met, Simeon's suddenly grave and thoughtful, Emmanuel's dancing a little. 'Good luck to you both, Simeon. I want nothing but happiness for you both. She's a nice child, a kind one too. I'm not certain that I didn't cherish faintly sentimental feelings with r-r-egard to her myself some time ago. Little did I know that I was forestalled! Good luck to you, my dear Simeon. I shan't see her again to-night, but bring her to talk to me in the morning, please.'

Simeon, his face flushing, said, 'Thanks, Father. I'm awfully glad you like her. She's a wonderful girl.'

Emmanuel nodded. 'I'm sure of it. One moment, I want a last word with you. Do you r-r-emember when you were quite a small boy, I asked you how you'd feel if I married again? You said that you thought we were very well as we were. Is that still your opinion? Would you r-r-esent it? Dislike the idea very much? Tell me honestly. I don't say that your r-reply will actually affect my decision, but—well, I admit that I should like to know that the thought was not offensive to you. There are many things which I might say to you, may say some day, but now all I want is your answer to this question.'

'And the lady, Father?'

'That I don't think I can tell even you—at pr-present. It is possible that she may have other ideas, that her affections may be alr-ready engaged elsewhere. Sufficient to say that she is ver-ry charming, and—but I won't bore you with a list of her qualities.'

Simeon still held his father's hand, and looked down at the thin face, with its hollow cheeks, at the sensitive mouth, and the fine expressive eyes. He was not a demonstrative young man, but some sudden impulse made him stoop down and kiss his father. 'When you said that to me—I was just a kid ; kids are selfish. I suppose I felt that if you married I should lose you— or part of you. Now, I've got a little more sense ; I shan't ever lose you, because we've grown to be very close, and we trust each other. I'm in love with Daphne, and I realize how lonely you must be, must have been very often since—since my mother died. I'd be glad if you got married, and—I believe that my mother will be glad too. Now it's my turn to wish you luck, and I do honestly and sincerely.'

'Then good night,' Emmanuel said, 'and my gr-r-ateful thanks, Simeon.'

Angela gave her dinner-party for Guido ten days later. Simeon was back from Newquay, eager to talk of the Conroys, and praise their kindness to him. Emmanuel listened, his mouth touched by a smile. The boy was happy, that was evident. Guido grew sentimental, and recounted stories of Simeon's childhood.

Angela said, 'Signor Moroni, he seems to have been a very brilliant child!'

'Of a brilliance which was incredible!' Guido replied. 'He was the talk of all Milano!'

Bill Gollantz said, 'Moroni, make it all Italy, can't you!'

'That is not possible,' Guido returned, 'for eet would not be the trut'.'

Viva sat on Emmanuel's right at dinner. He watched her whenever it was possible, and thought how charming she was, and how attractive she looked. She talked well, and with a certain wit as well as fluency. Later, when they stood together in the big drawing-room, she turned to him, and said, 'Imagine Simeon going to be married! Makes one begin to fell how time is slipping past, Emmanuel.'

'Not when I look at you, my dear Viva.'

'Emmanuel, I don't really believe in your compliments!'

'Tr-ributes, not compliments,' he corrected. Then, with something of an effort, he asked 'And your engagement?'

'Oh, it's not announced yet. But I've made up my mind.'

'R-regarding Carteret?'

She nodded. 'Quite.'

'I hope with all my heart that you will be ver-ry happy.'

She gave him one of her sidelong glances, and repeated, 'With all your heart, eh? That's very sweet of you, I hope that you mean it.'

'But of course——'

Viva retorted, 'Oh, don't stand here discussing my engagement all night. I want to talk to Signor Moroni. It's time you went to bed, Emmanuel. You look all in. You ought not to keep such late hours.'

'I'm going back to Bond Street next week. Nathan is quite willing; thinks that it will be good for me.'

'He's a fool. I shall come in next Monday to see how you are. Incidentally, do I have to remind you what next Monday happens to be? You've forgotten, Emmanuel. It's my birthday. Mama insists on a cake, but I refuse to have candles. Too many of them! There, off you go. Good night.'

Emmanuel stopped to kiss his mother and murmur his excuses, then walked very slowly upstairs. So Viva had 'made up her mind', she was going to marry Carteret. As he undressed he knew that a flame of resentment flared in his heart. What a fool he had been, talking to Simeon as he had done, being almost confident that Viva would consent to marry him. Why on earth should she? Carteret had made the running, had danced attendance upon her. Emmanuel Gollantz had, as usual, allowed work and business worries to absorb him. It was inevitable that one day Simeon would mention the matter of his father's marriage, and Emmanuel would be forced to concoct some lie—that the lady had refused him, or that he had changed his mind! Carteret—that red-faced half-wit!

Then his sense of justice asserted itself, and he admitted that because Carteret was red faced, and heavy jowled, it did not of necessity prove that he was a half-wit. He'd been kindly enough when poor Tatten died. Anyway, Viva had a right to marry whom she wished, and her memories of what marriage had meant with Emmanuel Gollantz might not be so pleasant after all.

'A tedious young man,' he reflected as he lay staring into the darkness, 'a very tedious and far too serious young man I must have been. I expect that now I'm a tedious middle-aged man—people don't really change very much. I must find a birthday present for her. Confound it, it can't be what I wanted to give her! How attractive she looked to-night, and . . . Oh, damn everything!'

The following Monday Simeon drove him to Bond Street, where Hannah greeted him as someone risen from the dead. Strange to walk into the big rooms, to turn his eyes towards that little room where his own brother had so nearly killed him! It all seemed so remote, so long ago, almost like a dream, a dreadful nightmare. Back in his own office, at his own desk, with Reuben Davis bustling in, shaking his hand and wishing him welcome.

'Everything is clear and clean,' Davis said. 'I have seen Arbuthnot and the other important dealers, and—after consultation with Bill and Mr. Charles—I have laid the whole case before them. It was the only course open to us as a firm of distinction. We,' he used the word with some pride, 'can afford to speak plainly and make admissions of faults which were not ours, but merely laid at our door. The attitude of them all was—admirable. There will be no reproaches, there will be no repetition. The firm stands exactly where it has always stood.' He laughed. 'The dirty linen which never belonged to us has been properly laundered!'

Emmanuel said, 'Thank you, Reuben. I am gr-r-ateful.'

Emmanuel worked steadily, delighted to find how easy it all seemed. It was about half past eleven when Hannah telephoned through to him.

'Sir Emmanuel, Mrs. Tatten is here, by appointment.'

'Damn it, I've forgotten to find her present! All right, Hannah, bring her right along, will you?'

He rose, peered in the glass, settled his tie, and then turned to meet her. As she walked towards him, moving very easily, smiling and bending her head to speak to Hannah, Emmanuel felt a small painful contraction of his heart.

If only it could have been different! If only he had not been so self-confident. If only—— He went forward, and taking her hand said, 'Many Happy Returns of the Day, Viva my dear. Come in. Hannah, I think a bottle of wine and some dry biscuits, don't you?'

'Ah, like the old days,' Hannah beamed. 'This is the day I have waited for—your return, Sir Emmanuel.'

Back in his office, the stout Jewess bustled about, setting out the gilt-necked bottle and the elaborate biscuit-box, the fine glasses which were kept in the little old oak cupboard, and the fringed napkins embroidered with the Royal Arms of Austria which Old Emmanuel brought with him from Vienna.

'You'll drink Mrs. Tatten's health, Hannah?'

'I shall be glad to, and also to wish you long life, Emmanuel.'

Viva said, 'My birthday is completely eclipsed by your return to work, Emmanuel. Really, no one cares a damn about my birthday.'

Hannah, beaming, protested, 'Mrs. Tatten—such a tale! Both are reasons for gladness! There, I must go.'

As the door closed Emmanuel said, 'I have not the faintest idea what you want for a birthday present, Viva. Give me some idea. I am incr-redibly stupid about these things.'

She answered lightly, almost indifferently, 'Oh, I don't know —a ring. I like rings, y'know.'

Emmanuel began to speak, to make some protest that Carteret might not approve, but his words died away into silence and he sat watching her gravely and intently. She was nibbling one of the 'dry biscuits' instituted by old Emmanuel, and from time to time sipping the wine which still bubbled in its hollow-stemmed glass.

Emmanuel thought, 'She's lovely, and I'm in love with her. It's not only jealousy because she's going to marry another man. I'm realizing that we married when we were both immature. Both intolerant. She was almost greedy for amusement, and I was so dull and lacking in understanding. Now it's different. I could make her happy, and she—she could make life completely different, she could give me a reason for working, for being ambitious. Oh, why didn't I ask her months ago? Why was I such a blind fool! Now it's—too late. Viva darling, life with you could be such—such fun! I don't want to grow old, I want to laugh and enjoy everything, and I can't do that alone. I want to hold a lovely woman in my arms again—only, my sweet, that woman has to be you, or I'll go hungry. We've both known beauty, and content and the complete joy of love ; we've both lost, both suffered badly. We know each other's "pasts", know that you'd have no more reason to be jealous of my "lovely Juliet" than I should have to be jealous of poor "Toby" Tatten. And, poor fool that I am, I never even asked you to marry me!' Aloud he said 'Another glass, Viva?'

She nodded. 'You're very silent this morning, Emmanuel, and I felt particularly gay when I came in here.'

'I'm sorry.' He refilled her glass. 'When is your engagement to be announced?'

'In *The Times* I think, the day after to-morrow.'

'I'd better wait, then, to write and congratulate Carteret.'

She turned on him one of those cold, half-insolent stares which he remembered, and asked, 'What has Carteret to do with it?'

'My dear, you told me that you had come to a decision regarding him!'

'So I had—a decision that nothing on earth would persuade me to marry him.'

'But this engagement——' He laughed. 'Really, Viva, what are we playing? If it is "Twenty Questions" I warn you I am no good at it.'

She twisted round in her chair so that she faced him squarely.

'Listen to me, Emmanuel. Yes, light a cigarette and give one to me. I want to talk to you. I never said—except possibly by implication—that I was going to marry "Buster". He's a good fellow, and one of the most deadly bores I know——'

'I thought,' Emmanuel said, as he handed her the cigarette and lit it for her, 'that I was the most deadly. Don't tell me that my only claim to fame is in danger, Viva.'

'I told you to listen! I am going to be married, my engagement will be announced the day after to-morrow, and to-day—my birthday remember—I am lunching with the man I'm going to marry. Now I'll tell you his name! Do you want to hear it?'

'Not particularly,' Emmanuel said coldly. 'A little more wine?'

'Yes—half a glass. Well, you'll hear it, whether you like it or not. I'm going to marry Emmanuel Gollantz. He hasn't asked me yet, but—damn it, he's going to! Now, what have you to say?'

He stared at her, and she watched him, thinking how old he looked for his years, how haggard he had grown, how white his dark hair was turning at the temples. His eyes holding always something that was mournful, even in his happiest moments. She longed to hold out her hands and cry, 'Emmanuel, let me take care of you, let me teach you to laugh again! I can do it, I will do it. I'm in love with you. Offering myself to you—take me. Say something.'

She heard the long breath which he drew, saw his long, sensitive fingers close on the cigarette and crush it out into the malachite ashtray which stood at his hand.

He said, 'Viva—Viva—do you r-really mean that?'

'I've never meant anything more sincerely in all my life.'

'Did you r-realize that I was in love with you?'

She retorted, 'Realize! You didn't realize it yourself until I put it into your mind! I planted the idea and it's—grown beautifully.'

'Beautifully. You're so r-right, so dead r-right. Viva——'

'Now listen to me again,' she said. 'I don't want you to go on saying "Viva" in various emotional tones at intervals. I want you to gather together all that charm of which we've heard so much, and tell me that you love me, and want to marry me. It's quite simple.'

Emmanuel stood up, came towards her and took her in his arms. Bending his head he found her lips and kissed them, whispering softly, 'Viva, dearest love, will you marry me, and let me try to make you happy always?'

'Emmanuel, what fools we've been! Now send for your beloved Hannah. I want to dictate something to her—immediately.'

'Kiss me again first.'

He telephoned to Hannah, who came bustling in. 'Mrs. Tatten wants you, if you will be so good, to take down something at her dictation.'

Viva said, 'It's for *The Times*, the day after to-morrow, please. "A marriage has been arranged and will shortly——" '

Emmanuel interrupted, 'I think that "ver-ry shortly" is better.'

Viva nodded. '. . . "very shortly take place between Mrs. Tatten of"—you know all that part, don't you Hannah?—"and Sir Emmanuel Gollantz of Ordingly, Herts." '

Hannah closed her note-book, and with eyes that swam with tears, beamed on them both. 'The God of our fathers bless and keep you both.' she said.

Guido smiled and nodded. 'This will be the crowned moment of my career. I shall stand before all the nobility and aristocrats of the world as the acknowledged friend of the noble Gollantz. Before priests and bishops no doubt! It is too much! And your brother Beel, does he not feel that Guido usurps this splendid place?'

'My dear Guido, Bill is only too glad to slide out of it. And it won't be a—spectacle, you know, only a ver-ry quiet affair.'

'The glory,' Guido returned, 'will be in my 'eart.'

'Afterwards,' Emmanuel continued, 'we shall come to Milano. Not, I think, to the apartment, Guido.' For a second the little Italian fancied that he saw a shadow on Emmanuel's face; it passed and he smiled again. 'Perhaps not to stay in Milano—I leave the arrangements to you. No, not Milano and not Como, my friend. The rest of Italy—make what arr-rangements you wish. They will be perfect.'

Guido came over to where Emmanuel sat, and took both his hands.

'So I go away in the morning, but to return, no? To return very soon. My beloved master, togezzer we have travelled many roads, long, dusty, when our feet were cut and bleeding. We 'ave fought, we 'ave felt our 'earts breaking—indeed for that reason of which we do not speak now, they will always ache a little. Because we are 'appy to-day, this is not to say that we forget all the yesterdays. I eat with enjoyment your Eengleesh apples, but I do not forget the sun-warmed peaches of my own country. 'Tis life, my dear. We 'ave lived and loved and—yes—died; now we live again—not the same life, but one w'ich is good, full, rich—beautiful. For spring the beauty and perfume of violets, for summer the rich scent of roses. Simeon is taking me back to London to-night, for I leave early. Now I say—for a short time—good-bye. In a month I shall be here again. My beloved Emmanuel—my dear master—you 'ave all my 'eart.'

'Arrivederci, Guido mio. Thank you for everything. A safe journey.'

Guido held up his hand. 'Almost I forgot! I travel, as you know, by the airplane. Now what is correct? Shall I wear formal dress, or will "ploos fours" be better, with a cap to match and an overcoat of 'Arris? I fancy that "ploos fours" are no longer smiled upon, no?'

Emmanuel replied, 'Slacks, I think, Guido. Tweed slacks, and I don't know about the cap. Why not a hat—a soft hat?'

'That will be my apparelling. Again—God bless you.'

The house was very still and Emmanuel, making his way to his room, saw the gleam of light showing under his mother's door. He hesitated, then knocked gently, and heard her voice bidding him to 'come in'.

She was lying in bed reading; as he entered she looked up, smiled and said, 'My dear, how very nice. Has your Signor Moroni gone?'

'Simeon is driving him back to town for the night.'

'But he is coming back—for the wedding?'

Emmanuel smiled. 'To be my best man. He r-regards it as the crowning point of his career. He's been a ver-ry good friend to me, that Guido.'

Angela laid her hand on his. 'So has someone else, my dear,

242

and never lose sight of that fact. When Viva is your wife—and I'm so happy about this—don't forget that she has always been, will always be, your very good, staunch friend. Be wise, Emmanuel, don't run risks for the sake of money or ambition. We went through a rather difficult time, but Charles assures me that now the Galleries have never been more prosperous. You have enough; you'll never be a poor man. Put Viva first and she won't make too many demands; let her imagine that you put work, advancement, success first, and she will increase her demands in a kind of attempt to justify herself.

'Don't underrate her intelligence. She is very, very intelligent. Talk to her about your work; don't say, or even think, "It can't possibly interest you." It does interest women to know something of their men's work and interests. And, Emmanuel, don't hesitate to make love to her. Women like being made much of— they listen for inflections in their men's voices, they watch for those small, rather unimportant things which do loom so large on their horizons. No woman ever tired of being told she looked adorable, of being told that she *was* adorable. We're conceited creatures, and ready to believe it all—only the person who says it must believe it!

'They love—love, and there are a thousand ways of making love. Gilbert and Sullivan may seem out of date to you, but I remember those lines about—what was it?—"a man who would woo a fair maid must apprentice himself to the trade, and study all day, in the usual way, if he wants to make sure——" There! I've forgotten the rest. Courting, wooing, call it what you will, shouldn't end with the marriage service. I'm talking too much, being a bore! But, oh, I want your happiness so much. You're content, my dear, dear boy?'

'Incredibly. Thank you for talking to me. It's time you were asleep, you know.' He bent to kiss her. 'Sleep well.'

'And you?'

He smiled, and Angela thought that he looked younger than she had seen him look for years. 'I'm going to telephone to Viva—just to say "good night".'

Angela glanced at the little clock by her bedside. 'It's nearly good morning, Emmanuel.'

'Then I'll say "good night" and then—"good morning",' he said.

CHAPTER THREE

As the tall man with greying hair ran up the steps of the gloomy Registrar's office, followed by a smaller man—whose hair was also grey, and whose clothes were so immaculate as to be slightly theatrical—a woman in the little crowd which had gathered said, ' 'Oo is the tall chap anywai?'

The smaller man turned, and raised his hat, giving her a beaming smile as he did so. 'Allow me to give information,' he said. 'This is the wedding of the great Sir Gollantz, of London, Paris and Milano. If eet is of interest, let me inform that I, Guido Moroni, am 'ere to be his—foremost man to-day.' He bowed, and followed Emmanuel into the building.

The woman turned to her friend and said, 'Blimy, whatcher know abart thet! Lot o' perishin' foreigners—Poles, I'd not wonder!' The other replied, 'They mike money some 'ow, an' charnce it. That feller said 'e 'ad three 'ouses. 'Ere, an' luke at the nobs drivin' up. Bleck Market, I'd not wonder! Coo, luke at 'em!'

Guido, standing beside Emmanuel, stared somewhat blankly at the room where the ceremony was to be performed. He sighed gustily.

Emmanuel glanced down at him. 'Not too impressed, eh? Not even the flowers make it look—what's my aunt's favourite word?—cosy?'

Guido said, 'I don't know this—kozi. I am sorry that you did not wait to be married in Milano—ah, at the Duomo, or Santa Maria Secreta—zeese are places of refinement! Zees place— *puff!*'

Emmanuel said, speaking very softly, 'The penalty one pays for having been divorced, my friend.'

'But eet was from the same lady you was divorced! Now all is mended again. Ah, zere is your Ladyship Aunt!'

He darted about, bestowing smiles, making his small precise bows, while Emmanuel stood watching, a faint smile touching his lips. His first wedding, how clearly he remembered it. The crowd of people, the scent of the flowers, his own nervousness,

244

and that of his brother Bill, who was his best man. Bill had lost the ring three times and each time had announced the fact in a whisper which seemed to echo through the church. A second later he had declared in a voice hoarse with relief, 'All right, old man, I've found it!'

Simeon came to him and shook his hand. Emmanuel liked his son's firm grip, and the rather hard strong hand. Beside him stood the girl he was to marry so soon. A nice girl, pretty, able to smile readily and with sincerity. Simeon would be a happy enough fellow; he'd make a good husband.

His aunt edged nearer to him. 'Good luck, Manny dear. Can't tell you how pleased I shall be to be your mother-in-law again! Pity Walter can't give the girl away; he's failing, y'know. However, Charles is a fine figure of a man! They're late—that's Viva! Never on time, that girl. Did I ever tell you, Manny, how I was three quarters of an hour late for my own wedding? Shockin' business! Poor old Walter thought I'd eloped with my groom! By the time I got there——'

Guido said, 'Please excuse. Lady Gollantz what-will-be-in-a-short-time 'as just arrived. Now, my dear friend—get to the right spot. Oh, what a dirty-looking old man! Is 'e the one who cleans the place?'

'He's going to perform the ceremony, Guido.'

'*Dio mio!*'

Emmanuel turned to see Viva enter with Charles Wilmot. She gave him a brief smile; he fancied that she looked paler than usual. They stood side by side, while Guido, still breathing heavily, watched them intently. The ring was ready. Emmanuel saw with a kind of tender amusement how Guido's hand shook. The ceremony was over, except for the signing of the register.

Guido said, 'Eet is not over. *Mama mia!* To pay so much monie for five minutes—less, only four an' a 'alf! Now 'ad we been in——'

The cold eye of the Registrar met his. 'Please keep quiet, sir.'

Guido blushed deeply and examined his fingernails intently. He turned to take Viva's hand and raise it to his lips, to shake Emmanuel's and with such intensity that Emmanuel said, 'Bless you, my dear Guido, don't pull it off!' He whispered, 'Have you given the old boy the money—you remember?'

Guido scowled. 'If you insist—but eet is robbery! 'E 'as done nossing, nossing at all!'

Viva said, 'Guido, my angel, he has, you know—he's made me Lady Gollantz.'

Guido stared at her, frowning for a moment, then he broke

245

into one of his brilliant smiles which made him look like an elderly cherub.

'I had forgotten! I forgive heem wiz my 'ole 'eart.'

He turned back to the Registrar and, handing him the notes which he had rolled into a neat cylinder, he said, 'Allow me. Eef I could be paid so much for so leetle—what a ver' rich man I should be! Good-bye.'

Emmanuel took Viva's hand, and together they walked to the waiting car. Lady Heriot's chauffeur had decorated it with white ribbons.

Viva wrinkled her nose, and said to Emmanuel, 'Why must they make it all so vulgar!'

He smiled back at her. 'I'm afraid that I think it's rather—amusing.'

Seated beside her, driving back to Portland Place, he took her hand and held it in his own, then said, 'Viva dear, take off your glove.'

She stripped off the glove, and he felt her hand warm and soft lying in his own. He lifted it and pressed it to his lips.

Viva said, 'Emmanuel, people can see!'

'And if they can! Why not! At this moment I should like all the world to be watching!'

She looked at him, her brows puckered into a little frown. 'You've changed. I was the one who used to defy—public opinion. You were always keeping one eye on the censorious public! You'll assure me that you prefer the ballroom to the sale-room in a moment.'

He nodded. 'It is more than pr-robable, pr-rovided that I can choose my partner.'

'And you're really happy?'

'Indubitably—always with the proviso that you are also.'

She laughed and shrugged her shoulders. 'Of course, I've got what I wanted—your title, Ordingly, and Emmanuel Gollantz thrown in as a make-weight!'

Emmanuel laughed. 'When you consented to marry me, you must have filled me with conceit. I don't believe that the title, or Ordingly, really matters a great deal. . . .'

Her eyebrows were raised a little as she asked, 'You really think that you were the determining factor?' He nodded. 'How right you are,' Viva assured him.

He held her hand rather more tightly. 'Viva, we're going to make a success of it. You feel that, don't you? We've both learnt so much, both been through a great deal. One evening my mother was talking to me about you. She reminded me that whatever else you had been, whatever you might consent to be

246

in the future, you had always been my very staunch and loyal friend. Real, solid friendship isn't a bad foundation on which to build—other things, eh?'

'What—other things, Emmanuel?'

'Understanding, great love and—speaking for myself—complete devotion.'

She said, almost as if she spoke her thoughts aloud rather than asked a question, 'You give me—complete devotion——'

'I shall spend the r-rest of my life trying to pr-rove it, and to completely convince you. Oh, there is so much I want to say and we must face this interminable reception! Viva, I'm impatient. I want to get to Par-ris, and two days later to get to Lake Garda. Shall we r-run away now, and telegraph fr-rom Par-ris?'

Viva pulled on her glove. 'Darling, we're there. We can't disappoint them. We're going to be on show for the next two hours. There'll be headlines in the evening papers to-night, "Baronet Weds Wife for the Second Time." '

He picked up his hat, and as the door was opened gave her his hand. 'Poor fools, they don't understand; this is a real marriage, a marriage of "tr-rue minds". Now, come and be charming to everyone.'

Lady Heriot's immense rooms were crowded, and a little man, grey faced and not too well dressed, watched the crowds of people who filled them. His name was Ezriah Habbemma, a Dutch Jew. Simeon Gollantz saw him, and leaving Daphne Conroy, made his way to where the little man stood.

He said, 'I think we've met before, sir—where was it?'

The strange whispering voice replied, 'At the funeral of the good Max Gollantz. I am ver' distant cousin of heem. But figure to yourself my pride when a card arrived for me—I live in a small private hotel in Bloomsbury—bidding me to the wedding of the son of Max. I seem to remember that on the mournful occasion of the funeral ceremonies of Max—may his soul rest in peace—zat some person asket for my address. So' —he smiled, a rather wistful smile Simeon thought—'here I am, ver' conscious zat I hev no—vedding garment.'

Simeon smiled at him in return, and the little Jew felt his heart warm, felt some of his intense shyness and uncertainty leave him.

'Don't worry about things like that, sir,' Simeon said; 'we none of us have. My own kit has appeared at funerals, christenings, and now at the wedding of my father. No one has any clothes now—at least not new ones—in England. You know—

your relations, sir? No? Ah, that must be put right at once.' He turned and beckoned to Daphne. 'This wonderful girl has promised to marry me—Daphne, this is our cousin, Mr. Habbemma.' So it began, and Simeon escorted him round the big rooms, introducing him to everyone, with that prefix, 'Our cousin, Mr. Habbemma, from Holland.'

That night, the little, rather shabbily dressed Jew, who had obtained work in Hatton Garden, for his knowledge of precious stones was considerable. sat in the sitting-room of the two Scots women who kept the hotel where he lodged.

They watched him leaning forward, with clasped hands, and eyes which shone with pleasure and excitement.

'Emachin eet, first the arrival of the card bidding me to attend the ceremony. Then, as I stood—alone, a leetle nervous, for since that time of which we shall not now speak, when I was in the concentration camp, my nerves are no longer good—to me came a young man. The son of my distant cousin, Sir Emmanuel Gollantz, Baronet. He took me to meet everyone. Ah!' —he bunched his fingers and kissed them ecstatically—'what peoples! The br-ride of Emmanuel—who in some strange way hed been his bride once before—it was ver' confusing. How fine she was! The *mutter* of the bride and bridegroom— both wiz titles. A brudder—name of Beel. French people—the woman ver' stout but still elegant, the man—also elegant. Italian people—she also stout, he like an Eengleesh man.'

One of the listening women asked, 'Now, would that be the singer? Iva Alfano she was, but her husband is an Englishman. Yes, go on, Mr. Habbemma.'

'Several people called Hirsch, from Austria I t'ink, also two men of the name of Jaffe. Also Austrian, I could tell from their lisping voices. An Italian count—Bocc—Bocc—I don't remember, a man with sad eyes.' He paused and sighed. 'At last I was sent here in a splendid car. As I was r-ready to dr-rive away who speaks to me but the bridegr-room! He said, "Cousin Ezriah," he said, notice that form of address, "Cousin Ezriah—to-day I have great happiness. I esk you to do me a gr-reat favour. I hev taken a great liberty. The liberty is in the car," he laughed, and now—observe what he sent home wiz me. Last t'ing he whispered, leaning through the open window in a manner most affable, "Eet is all kosher!" '

He laughed and shrugged his thin shoulders. 'Zis I do not t'ink was complete truth! Is champagne kosher—well, maybe, but pâté, and caviare, chickens covered with aspic, and so on— well, may be some is kosher, but not alls! In one month I am to veesit'—he threw out his chest a little—'my cousin, Sir Gollantz,

248

at Bond Street, number seventy. He hes—he assures me—plans for my future. Now, what do you hev to say, if you please?'

One of the Scotswomen, with fair hair and smiling eyes, answered, 'I should say, Mr. Habbemma, that this has been your lucky day!' The other, her eyes dark and filled with kindliness, added, 'In my opinion, that Sir Emmanuel's a fine kin' o' man. We'll wish him luck when you open one of they gold-necked bottles! An' mean it!'

Little Habbemma trotted off to exchange his best old coat for a slightly less good and much older one. The women's eyes met.

'Puir wee soul. He's just set up wi' himself!'

The other nodded. 'Ay, he is that. Mind, May, it makes you think. All those people gathered together—friends—Austrians, this wee Dutchman, Italians, French, English—not quarrelling about frontiers, an' reparations, just enjoying being friendly. It's a pity that kind o' thing can't—well, can't spread to governments and diplomatic missions, eh?'

Her sister answered, ' 'Deed ay!'

Emmanuel sat on the terrace of the Bella Riva and watched the night descend and the stars come out over Lake Garda. The past few days had been a time of unrest, movement, and almost constant travelling. He and Viva had flown to Paris; they had stayed the night in Louis Lara's apartment, for the Laras were still in England. Viva had wished to see La Spero's latest play, and they had changed quickly and eaten in a restaurant which Emmanuel had known for many years, where the food was always admirable. It was still excellent; but even Emmanuel, who was not given to strict economy, raised his eyebrows when he saw the amount of the bill.

Viva said, 'I thought that it would be pretty stiff.'

'Stiff!' he returned. 'If I lived in Paris, darling, I should have to sell an old master every week in order to live.' He talked with the proprietor, and teased him regarding the size of his bill. The old man spread his hands wide, and made a gesture of deprecation.

'What will you, monsieur? If you will eat well, then you must pay enormously. How do I buy, tell me? With my heart's blood! I have shed tears many times when I have asked the price of a capon! *Mon Dieu!* I have asked, are these capons then made of gold with diamonds for stuffing! But,' with an ingratiating smile, 'you have enjoyed our meal—and you, madame?'

'Immensely, and now we go to see La Spero.'

He beamed at them impartially. 'Ah, this one! What a woman! Do you know that she has married again? Indeed, yes.

One François Pascal, a Frenchman, he is a dealer in pictures. It was a great romance. He was in the underground movement' —he leaned nearer to Emmanuel and whispered, 'it is said, La Spero also!'

Emmanuel said, 'Pictures, eh?'

'Remember,' Viva warned him, 'you are on your honeymoon, not on one of your business trips! Watch for that red light, Emmanuel!'

'Dearest, of course you're right. Force of habit!'

They were entranced with the play, the lightest of comedies, but played with such artistry that even its impossibilities became credible. The audience went wild with delight and La Spero was called and recalled before the curtain.

Viva said, 'If I thought that she might be in her husband's Gallery to-morrow I should encourage you to go, so that I might have the chance to meet her. She is entrancing.'

'If I had said that,' Emmanuel returned, 'you would have been furious—at least I hope so.'

The next morning Viva said, 'Listen, if you really want to look at this man's pictures—we'll go. I don't mind. It would be amusing.'

'Even if La Spero is not there?' He smiled.

They drove to the Gallery Pascal, a beautifully lit, exquisitely decorated place, where the pictures were few but very good. It amused Viva to watch the change in Emmanuel when they entered. His rather lazy good humour, his easy acceptance of everything for which she expressed a wish, vanished. He became intent, alert, and completely absorbed. A slim man, wearing a short, carefully trimmed beard, came to speak to him. Emmanuel discussed various pictures with him, and then said 'Excuse me, monsieur, have we met before—where could it have been? I am certain that I know you. I recognize your voice too. Am I wr-rong?'

The man replied in English tinged with a pronounced French accent, 'I r-regret that I have to admit that monsieur is wr-rong. I am a Frenchman. I have lived in Par-ris for many, many years.'

'I imagined that I had met you in London, somewhere in Bond Street.'

The man bowed. 'Possibly in your own very fine Galleries. Oh, I r-recognized you the moment you entered as one of the firm of Gollantz. I am delighted that you found time to visit my small exhibition. It is a gr-reat compliment.'

Emmanuel presented him to Viva. Pascal bowed over her hand, and murmured his delight at the meeting.

'Last night we saw your wife in her new play,' Viva said. 'I wish that I could have met her. I have so many things I wish to tell her; how utterly charming, how brilliant, how fascinating she is.'

'All t'ose t'ings, madame, and so many, many more. One time when you pass through Par-ris per'aps you will give my wife the felicity of meeting you. She will be chairmed.'

Now they had reached their destination. Guido had found for them what he described as the 'finest hotel on the most beautiful lake in Italy'. Viva, tired with the journey, had gone to bed, and Emmanuel, unable to tear himself away from the beauty which was spread before him, sat alone to smoke his last cigarette.

Before him stretched the vast expanse of Lake Garda. There, outlined against the dark blue sky with its powdering of stars, lay the Island of Garda. In the distance the lights at Gardone twinkled and flung their reflected shimmer into the quiet water. He could hear the sound of a sentimental Italian love song. Played in the open air, the music was softened, made more tender, filled with appeal. The dark shape of a rowing-boat, the fisherman standing at the oar, driving the little vessel forward with long, steady strokes, passed swiftly and silently. The man was singing in a high tenor voice, 'Come back to Sorento'.

Two little dogs, running in the garden, intent on their absorbing affairs, halted to stare at Emmanuel; one came forward and rubbed a smooth, dark head against his leg, then as if confused at her own boldness, sped away after her companion. Far out on the water a light dipped and swung, hanging, Emmanuel thought, on the mast of some fishing-boat.

Emmanuel felt that a great wave of tranquillity swept over him, not a fierce, overpowering torrent of water, but something so gentle and tender that it merely seemed to support him, to make it unnecessary for him to make any effort. He was completely at peace, his worries and problems seemed to have been washed away and completely solved. That when he returned to England, possibly even to Milan, there would be matters both difficult and involved with which he must deal he did not doubt, but—for the time at least—they had no place in his life.

Julian, who had for so many years planned and schemed, contrived that the blame for his own misdoings should be laid at his brother's door, was on the other side of the Atlantic. Emmanuel did not feel that Julian was likely to trouble them again. A short visit to his mother, always provided that he made money and could carefully flaunt his success before her, would be the most they need fear.

Simeon was doing well, working hard and proving his knowledge and ability every day. He was deeply in love with Dahpne, he had sufficient—and more than sufficient—to keep her in comfort ; life for Simeon would present no great difficulties. Bill—well, Bill would always be what he had always been—capable, dependable and reliable. A most satisfactory fellow, Bill Gollantz.

And himself? He rose and leaned his arms on the stone balustrade, staring out over the water, and at the twinkling lights which marked Gardone. He was happy—and even as the thought came to him, he wondered how often in his life he had been able to say that with perfect truth? For the one miraculous year spent with Juliet—yes ; before that time and after—when it had ended—very, very rarely. Now, he knew that he had found love and content with Viva, not perhaps the gold and the glory, the brilliant hues, but colours which were clear, bright and essentially beautiful. They had talked earlier in the evening, as they sat smoking after dinner, drinking their coffee.

He had said, 'Have we really changed, Viva?'

'No, I don't think so,' she answered. 'We've grown more tolerant of each other ; we've grown less violent in our likes and dislikes, our tastes and amusements ; we can adjust ourselves more readily. Years ago we were both painted in such completely primary colours! We were like actors in a new play, we hadn't grown to "fit our parts". I think we were in love—for a time at least, until you bored me and I distressed and worried you—but I don't know how much we really loved each other.

'Now'—she turned and smiled at him—'it's different. We may really have learnt a little sense—particularly regarding ourselves. Anyway, whatever has happened, I'm completely happy, and I have a feeling—you can correct me if I'm wrong—that you are not altogether dissatisfied, eh?'

Emmanuel flung his cigarette out over the dark water, and watched the tiny light fall and disappear. He stood upright, and turning, saw that the light in Viva's room was still burning. As he watched, he saw the long windows open and she stepped out on to the balcony. She stood there, tall and slim, her figure outlined by the thin gown which she wore. He turned and walked quickly into the hotel and ran lightly up the stairs. She did not turn as he opened the door of their room, and making his way to the balcony where she stood, he said softly, 'I was looking at the night, then you came out on to your balcony. You're even more lovely than the night—you drew me away from the lake and the stars, away from the music and a fisherman who was singing—yes, even from a friendly little dog who came to speak to me.'

She slipped her arm through his. 'What did it say, this little dog?'

'It spoke Italian, darling.'

'Then translate what it said for me—you know what my Italian is.'

'It said, "Good evening, Emmanuel. How do you find yourself this evening?" I replied, "Signorina, I find myself that rarest of all things—a completely happy man." She laughed, and ran away to tell her friend. I heard them crying, "Oh, la! la!" '

Viva leaned towards him. 'And you told the truth, my Emmanuel?'

He said, 'Look at me and you will see the answer.' He took her face in his hands and looked down at her very tenderly. She drew a deep breath, then nodded.

'Yes, I believe that you spoke the truth. I won't fail you, my dear. It may not always be like this—we shan't find this beauty everywhere—but you'll always have me, and—well, I shall never let you go again.' Her lips curved into a smile. 'I'll never let you want to go away, my dear. The past—yours and mine—belongs to us individually. We may look back individually—but we'll look forward together.'

He drew her close, she felt his kisses on her hair, and heard him say very softly, 'Viva—be wise for both of us. You're wise, you're clear-sighted—and you're very, very wonderful.'

Fasamo,
Lago di Garda.
    September 1948.

All Futura Books are available at your bookshop or newsagent, or can be ordered from the following address:
Futura Books, Cash Sales Department,
P.O. Box 11, Falmouth, Cornwall

Please send cheque or postal order (no currency), and allow 55p for postage and packing for the first book plus 22p for the second book and 14p for each additional book ordered up to a maximum charge of £1.75 in U.K.

Customers in Eire and B.F.P.O. please allow 55p for the first book, 22p for the second book plus 14p per copy for the next 7 books, thereafter 8p per book.

Overseas customers please allow £1.00 for postage and packing for the first book and 25p per copy for each additional book.